Everything You Wanted to Know About Your Body But, So Far, Nobody's Been Able to Tell You

Chris Thomas and Diane Baker

Everything You Always Wanted to Know About Your Body But, So Far, Nobody's Been Able to Tell You

ISBN 186163 098 0

Cover design by Paul Mason
Internal illustrations by Chris Thomas

Published by:

Capall Bann Publishing
Auton Farm
Milverton
Somerset
TA4 1NE

About the Authors

Chris has been working as a healer and, more recently, as a psychic surgeon, for almost twenty years.

Diane has been a healer and reflexologist for nearly ten years.

Their first joint book, *The Healing Book*, is a teaching course on how to bring out the natural healing abilities inherent in everyone. It also goes on to detail some very advanced healing techniques for practising healers who wish to learn some of the methods of "Psychic Surgery".

Chris' other three books, *The Journey Home*, *The Fool's First Steps* and *Planet Earth - The Universe's Experiment,* are about the current human and planetary changes. These put the current and future world situation into the context of the real human history from Atlantis to the present.

There is a companion volume to this book:- *The Sequel To Everything*, which details case histories to help people understand how the symptoms can be read and how to make more sense of the body and soul's messages.

All these books are published by Capall Bann.

Chris and Di live and work in Wales where they have their psychic surgery practice.

Acknowledgements

We would like to thank the following people for their help and encouragement in the production of this book.

Ann Gedye BSc, MAR for the section on alternative treatments for HRT. Also for being an amazing source of information.

Pili Goss LCCH for her help and advice on homeopathic remedies.

Fiona Crosskill, Herbalist, for the many hours she spent to provide us with invaluable advice and help with the herbal remedies.

and to Tim and Linda Davis of Cleveland, Ohio for the original suggestion to write the book.

Contents

i

Please note:

The law currently is such that the authors and publishers must publish a disclaimer for any of the advice given in this book. As complementary practitioners, the authors are not allowed to make any claims as to the effectiveness of any treatment or natural remedy.

The laws governing complementary treatments and remedies are becoming more and more stringent as the medical lobby becomes more aware of the effectiveness of such approaches to health. It is the right of the individual to choose the form of health care they wish, but this freedom is being rapidly eroded by the actions of governments, globally, in response to pressure from the medical profession and pharmaceutical companies.

Therefore the suggestions made in this book are intended as a guideline only. Neither the authors nor the publisher can accept responsibility for any effects resulting from any treatment included in this book. Any and all health conditions should be referred to a health care professional at all times and none of the recommendations included in this book should be seen as a substitute for seeking medical attention.

THE FIRST HALF

The Body's Systems
and
Chakra Diagnosis

Introduction

Who are we really?

We have taken on board the orthodox scientific and medical view that our bodies are no more than a collection of random cells and chemicals which somehow has a life independent of everyone else.

Nowhere, within this orthodox view, is there space to consider the mind, the consciousness or the soul. As far as most medical doctors are concerned, we are no more than a collection of disconnected body parts which can only be treated by harsh chemicals, that might be considered to do more to harm than to heal, or by intrusive surgery.

All of our orthodox medicine techniques and practices fall under the name of allopathic medicine. This is a term which has been given by the doctors themselves to describe their view and their work. This word, allopathic, actually means prescribing drugs which act *against* the body.

With this kind of approach and philosophy, what chance do we have of truly understanding the body and the way in which it really works? Surely, now is the time when we should be finding ways of treating our illnesses with ways which work *with* the body and do everything possible to prevent the need for intrusive surgery or poisonous chemicals.

Our current approach to our bodies and our health is to ignore our core being, our soul, which is crying out for some attention and understanding. The reasons for illnesses and diseases can be simply understood and steps taken, by ourselves, to prevent them from occurring or to cure them once they have begun. No condition is excluded from this approach. Whether it is the common cold, a broken finger or a stroke, by understanding the mechanisms which brought about the problem in the first place, we can all diagnose and treat ourselves without the need for prescribed drugs.

We are able to take control of our lives and our health. All that we need to do is to recognise that we have the power and the ability to do so.

This is what this book is about - the way in which you can regain control of your own lives and your own health. Just think of it - no more doctors' bills, no more drugs, no more surgery. We are not talking about miracle cures, but very real and practical ways in which you can start to understand and work with your body and soul to keep both working together and in full harmony.

This book deals with the body in ways which comfort and heal the soul and provides the real reasons why ill health occurs. Once the root causes of illness and disease are understood, then true healing can be achieved. For the first time, a detailed explanation is provided of the mechanisms the "soul" uses to influence the physical body.

This book is divided into two halves. The first half explains the workings of the body's energy structures and links each "energy centre" to the body's organs and systems. Each organ and system is then described, and its' workings explained, in detail. This half of the book helps to explain why we have an illness and gives details of how to understand and eliminate the root causes. The second half helps you to understand and diagnose the symptoms and provides methods of treatment from a variety of different alternative therapies. These therapies have been chosen because they work, all without drugs and chemicals, in order to allow time for the root causes of the illness to be dealt with.

By using both approaches together, all illnesses and their symptoms can be totally eradicated and prevented from re-occurring. It sounds miraculous but, by understanding and

4

dealing with the root causes of disease, everyone can achieve their aims of a completely healthy body.

The authors are working healers. This means that we are people who work with energy to bring about a change of condition within a client's body in order to promote a change from illness to health. The work that we do has been called many things over the centuries, the most common being "spiritual healing" and "the laying on of hands".

By developing our abilities as far as we can we are now able to perform "psychic surgery" on our clients. This is made possible by manipulating energy in such a way that we are able to alter the way in which organs within the body function. Virtually any illness and disease can be treated using these techniques. This does not mean that we can produce miraculous "cures" every time, but what we can do is alter the way in which diseased or disfunctional organs or body parts work to bring them back to their proper function.

In order to achieve this, one of the authors has the ability to scan the body much in the way that an MRI scanner can (MRI stands for Magnetic Resonance Imager which is used by many hospitals to produce a three dimensional X-ray image of sections of the body). The difference between an MRI scanner and the author is that the author can psychically "see" inside the body to determine what is actually occurring as it actually happens. They can also "read" the body's energies. This is useful as they can track the healing work as it is being carried out to determine whether the healing is going to the right places and doing what it is supposed to do.

By using their ability to "see" in this way, it has been possible to follow the development of the human body, from early pregnancy to death, and arrive at the information presented in this book. There is no mystery or magic in this, just hard work and observation.

The explanations and methods presented in this book have been arrived at by using these observation techniques over many years and that which is collected here is the result of this work. What is contained within this book is not a "mystical" approach to health, in any sense of the word, but the result of many years of searching for the root causes of illness and the search for the most effective ways of dealing with illness.

There is no mystery to good health only sensible everyday solutions which all us of are capable of achieving. All that is required is the will to do so. By following the practical methods given here it is possible to remove all illnesses and prevent them from returning, allowing all of us to maintain our bodies in a state of good health.

Although "the soul" (or as the authors would prefer, our consciousness) is mentioned many times, it does not mean that this book has any particular religious connotations. The term "soul" or "consciousness" is used mainly because our vocabulary does not contain suitable alternatives. Our view is that religious beliefs and precepts belong to the individual alone. Religious views and ideologies are something which each of us chooses because it makes sense in particular aspects of our lives or because we accept the underlying beliefs inherent within that religion.

There are over two hundred recognised religions currently practised throughout the world and the views of some are totally contradictory to others, therefore, it is impossible to reconcile all of these doctrines, particularly within the scope of this book.

In order to explain the concepts raised within this book, we needed to find a suitable vocabulary and this is where the first difficulty arises. How can the idea of who we are be explained without resorting to words which have been in long term use and which mean different things to different people and which can be coloured by the reader's religious viewpoint? We have, therefore, attempted to express these concepts in language which does not imply any religious bias. Therefore, the words "soul" and "consciousness" are used in the context of being an integral but "higher" aspect of the self and does not take it's meaning from a particular religious belief or ideology.

The purpose of this book is to help us to fully understand the workings of the body and produce solutions which provide a permanent removal of symptoms by eliminating the underlying causes for disease and illness. This is a totally radical and holistic way of working. There is no need for gross chemical treatments nor for the surgical removal of any organs. By understanding ourselves we can at last fully heal our bodies and our souls.

Before going on to describe the mechanisms of illness and health, this would be a suitable point to lay to rest two very damaging prejudices and misconceptions. Illness and disability are not punishments by a deity. Neither are they a cause for guilt. These views and concepts belong to the middle of the last century when these conditions were not understood and could not be explained away by Darwin.

When Darwin produced his theory of evolution, he tried to put together an all encompassing explanation for the differences between the many species with which we share our planet. However, there were many things which the theory could not explain and one of these was illness. Illness and disability could not be a part of the theory as the theory depends upon evolution selecting useful character traits. As illness or disability are considered undesirable, there must be other reasons for these occurring. If illness or disability were not a part of the materialist view, they must come from God, and if they were undesirable, they must be a form of punishment.

This idea of punishment also fitted in well with many of the prejudices which existed at that time, especially the idea of human supremacy and bigoted viewpoints. If humans were the pinnacle of evolution, they must, therefore, be perfect. If a human was perceived as being less than perfect, they must somehow be cursed and therefore feared within society.

This underlying fear of the sick has been perpetuated and tangled together with other concepts and other values. It is long overdue for us to let go of these outdated and unrealistic views and consign them back to the nineteenth century where they belong. The real reasons for illness and disease are discussed throughout the rest of this book, what illness or disability are not, are a curse or punishment no curse or punishment of any kind from any source.

Chapter One

The Body and the Soul

In order to understand who we are, we must first begin with a fundamentally new look at ourselves and reverse many of the ways in which we think about our bodies.

We are used to using the idea that we are a body that has a soul. The soul is something which our religions mention but most of us do not usually have the time, or the inclination, to think beyond this concept. Nor do we, usually, need to see the world, and our place within it, in ways which take us beyond the physical dimensions. Our normal daily lives take us in directions where just feeding the physical body takes up all of our time. It is rare for us to find the time to properly feed the soul.

What we now need to do is to change this approach to who we are and how we are constructed. We are a soul, a vast created consciousness, which has decided to build for itself a physical body in order to experience a physical life. We have ignored this "higher" element of ourselves for far too long. It has been our ignorance of this aspect of ourselves which has led us into periods of ill health and, sometimes, death. By understanding the link between our "higher" element and our physical bodies, we can live longer and improve the quality of our lives.

So, how does the soul build a body?

To understand this process, we have to take a slightly different view of how the body is constructed. We are used to looking at the body as being physical tissues which have various functions. The medical profession's usual view is that the organs exist and have a function within the body, but at the same time the organs are also disconnected from each other. This is why we have ended up with doctors who specialise in particular regions or organs. Ear, nose and throat specialists, gynaecologists, heart specialists, etc. have all come about because of this view. Over the past few years most of us have begun to recognise that there is something fundamentally wrong with this view and have begun to seek out those who have a more holistic or "whole body" approach.

If we take a look at how scientists are beginning to look at the world, we start to see a slightly different picture. If you do not have a degree in physics, don't worry. We are not about to become technical. What the scientific research is starting to show is that everything is ultimately constructed of energy. What makes something solid or soft is the way in which the energies combine together to provide different densities of material. The best way to understand this idea is to look at water. Water in its normal state is a liquid. If we remove some of the energy contained within the water, it cools down and becomes a solid material we call ice. If we add energy to water, by heating it, it becomes a gas which we call steam. The make up of the water remains the same in all three instances, all that we have done is to change the amount of energy contained within it. To prove it, if we cool down steam it returns to being water. If we heat up ice, it returns to being water. What we have done is to remove some of the energy in the steam or to add some energy to the ice. In other words, we change the "frequency" of the energy contained within the molecules of the water.

The same is true for the body.

We have dense tissue such as bone and cartilage. We have pliable tissue such as muscle and organs and we have lighter tissues such as fluids. The only real difference between all of these is the frequency of energy that goes into making them up. So in the same way as ice, water and steam, the body is made up of different versions of the same basic material. All physical matter and tissue are constructed, essentially, in the same way. They are all energies of different frequencies which combine together to form different densities of bodily tissues.

This is the way in which the soul or consciousness builds for itself a body. It combines together different densities of energy to form all of the body's organs and structures around an energy "template" which is in the shape of the soul ie. human. In providing this description, we have not made reference to "a greater source" for the soul. As mentioned in the introduction, there are a huge diversity of beliefs as to the origins of the consciousness. We have no disagreement with any of them. What we are trying to describe here is the "mechanical" process by which the human body is developed. Whatever the ultimate source of the consciousness an individual believes there to be, there is a sequence of events which combine the energies of the consciousness into the energies of the physical body.

The Birth Process
There are many views as to how and when consciousness enters into the fetus in the womb. We are not about to enter into the debate on the rights and wrongs of abortion or to pass comment on the views held by either side. We hold our own views on the subject and it would be very wrong of us to present them here.

What we are about to describe is the way in which we have observed the conception and birth process and the way in which we have seen the consciousness form the developing baby. These observations have taken place over many years and our conclusions have been reached by working with and studying many pregnancies.

Everything begins with an agreement between the parents and the consciousness that is to form the new child. We are not usually aware of this agreement as it is made by the "higher element" of our consciousness which is not fully connected to our conscious mind (for more about our "higher selves" and the way in which it connects and works see chapter two). The soul, that is to form the child, and the souls that are the parents, agree that the pregnancy and birth is to occur.

There are very many reasons why some people can have children and why some people can't. There are also very many reasons why some pregnancies go to term and some do not. The reasons for these events can only be assessed on an individual level and, therefore, are not included here.

With the assumption that everything is as it should be, the next stage then begins. An agreement has been reached and an egg becomes fertilised. For the first few hours the cells that comprise the fertilised egg begin to multiply. This is a natural function of the egg cells, no elements of any consciousness is involved at this very early stage.

When the egg has expanded to about eight hundred cells, the incoming consciousness makes its first connection. This first connection takes the form of an energy link. What this energy link achieves is the beginnings of the incoming soul's formation of the physical body. We borrow genetic information from our parents, such as family characteristics etc., but the main proportion of our genetic information comes from our consciousness. The division is roughly twenty five percent from our parents and seventy five percent from ourselves. This first energy link is attached to the top of the head.

The second stage occurs in the region of twelve to fifteen weeks into the pregnancy. The exact time depends on the circumstances of the pregnancy and is decided by the parents and the incoming consciousness. The reason for this decision being made at this time is to ensure that the original agreement is still in place and that the early development of the fetus has proceeded properly. If the pregnancy is to proceed, the incoming consciousness makes a second energy link to the base of the spine. This second link connects the consciousness into the physical body and begins to form the fetus' body in detail ie. the skeleton and internal organs begin to properly form.

If everything is not as it should be, the pregnancy spontaneously terminates at this time, that is, the incoming consciousness removes the first energy link. This frees the incoming consciousness to begin the process again at some future date.

The third stage occurs in the region of twenty to twenty four weeks. Again, the exact timing is determined by the condition of the developing baby. At this stage the incoming consciousness begins to slowly enter the body and the mother begins to notice their presence. This is the time when the developing baby begins to move and kick. As the consciousness enters the body, it brings with it further energy links which provide the final details of the body's structures and organs.

The fourth stage occurs at about thirty nine weeks. This is when the incoming consciousness decides that the body has been sufficiently developed for birth to occur. At this time, the soul's energy links are strengthened and reinforced sufficiently to allow the child to exist outside of the mother's body.

From now on the incoming consciousness strengthens its connections with the developing child's body, drawing more and more of itself into the body as it continues to grow and develop. This continues to occur until the fifth and final stage of the soul's integration into its body. This final stage occurs at puberty where we change from the child into the adult. This is the time when our consciousness fully enters into the body and all of the soul's energy links become fully energised.

These energy links have become more generally known by a Hindu word :- the "chakras" (see illustration number one).

The word chakra is originally Sanskrit and has been inter-preted as "spinning wheel of light". This describes what the chakras look like when they are working properly, they spin, and from the front they look like a spinning wheel. From the side they look like a cone of spiralling energy with its point connected to the spine and opening out as it extends away from the body (*see illustration number two*).

There are seven chakras or energy centres contained within the body and they stay with us for the whole of our lives. They have very specific locations and specific colours.

The first is located at the base of the spine, right at the bottom of the coccyx. This is usually known as the first or root chakra and is coloured red. This is the second energy link that our incoming consciousness forms.

The second energy centre is located at the top of the pelvis, just below the junction with the spine. This is usually known as the second or the sacral chakra and is coloured orange.

The third energy centre is located in the abdomen, about one inch or twenty five millimetres above the tummy button. This is usually known as the third or solar plexus chakra and is coloured yellow.

The fourth is located in the chest, over the heart. This is usually known as the fourth or heart chakra and is coloured green.

The fifth is located in the throat, between the adams apple and the chin. This is usually known as the fifth or throat chakra and is coloured blue.

The next is located in the centre of the forehead, just above the bridge of the nose. It is usually known as the sixth or third eye chakra and is coloured indigo (a mixture of blue and purple).

The final one is located at the top of the head and is the first energy link to be connected by our incoming consciousness. It is usually known as the seventh or crown chakra and is coloured violet (sometimes in gold with some "advanced" souls).

Every single one of us has these energy centres or chakras. They are with us from birth and only leave as we leave the physical body. Every single one of us has these chakras. They are the soul made physical and are the means by which the soul communicates to us whilst we live out our physical lives.

If we can learn to "listen" to what our soul has to say to us, through the chakras, then we can learn to avoid ill health.

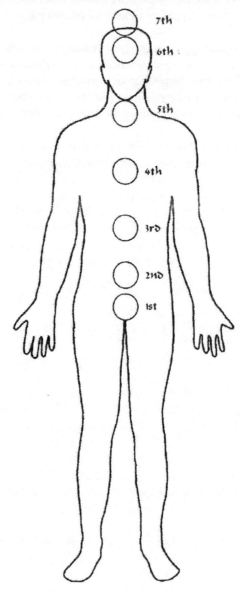

Illustration Number One - The Chakras

Chapter Two

The Body and The Chakras

For many people, the concepts and ideas discussed in chapter one will be very new. For those who are already aware of the chakras, the idea that they have specific functions will also probably be new. The chakras are so much more than most people give them credit for and they are certainly not just pretty colours on a wall chart. The chakras are the soul's messengers and can tell us a great deal about our state of health and how our lives have been affected.

The chakras are, literally, our consciousness made physical. They are elements of the self which have the role of reflecting the way in which we live our lives and how our bodies have responded to these life styles.

The chakras were first "mapped" and worked with by the ancient Sumerians. They began to look at the human body and how it worked over seven thousand years ago. They made observations and discoveries which formed the basis for their medical and scientific practices. These ways of working they called The Science of Life, or in Sanskrit (the name given to the ancient Sumerian language) "Ayurveda". Asian avatars and shaman have adopted many of these practices which form the basis for the Asian Indian traditions called Ayurvedic medicine. The Sumerian discoveries formed the basis for virtually all of the health traditions which are still practised today. They were the ones who began using herbs for healing which has led to both Eastern and Western herbalism and, ultimately, to all Western medicine.

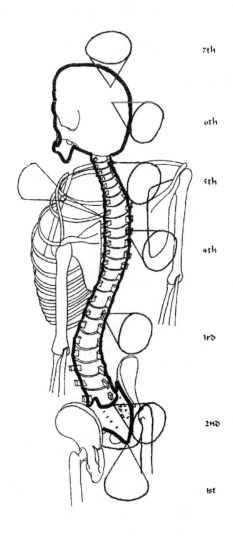

7th

6th

5th

4th

3rd

2nd

1st

Illustration Number Two - The Location and Form of The Chakras

Western medicine began by chemically synthesizing the active ingredients contained within plants and herbs. As modern drugs are becoming less and less effective in combating our illnesses, the drug companies are now searching the globe to find plants which contain new compounds that can produce a new generation of drugs. This is not the same as herbalism as herbalists use the whole plant, or a combination of plants, to produce a healing compound. What the drug companies do is to chemically produce an artificial version of what they consider to be the active ingredient and place it into other chemicals which we then swallow in tablet form.

The Sumerians also charted the body's meridians which are used in treatments such as acupuncture and kinesiology. The meridians are energy channels which distribute the energy of the chakras around the body and to the organs. The Sumerians also used plant extracts which they mixed with oils to provide healing in very subtle ways. These methods are usually called aromatherapy. So, as can be seen, the Sumerians brought about many of our orthodox and alternative healing techniques, many of which are still in use today all over the world.

In the West, our problem has been that we began to develop other forms of science and other medical practices which began to lead us away from the true workings of the body. These new traditions have totally replaced the old and we have created a reliance on chemically produced drugs instead of the older, much softer, but more effective, methods. Let's face it, nobody ever died of accidentally overdosing on aromatherapy massages.

Each chakra represents an element of our consciousness and each chakra relates very directly to organs or systems within the body which directly affects our state of health. We will be exploring these links in much greater detail throughout the rest of this book, so for now, we will begin with a general description. Although the basis for these descriptions comes from the Sumerian discoveries, the authors' have confirmed

19

these findings and extended their scope through their own observations and discoveries over many years of practice as healers.

The location and colour of the chakras was given in chapter one so now we will go on to relate them to specific regions of the body and elements of our personality (*see illustration number three*). The chakras are traditionally numbered from the root up to the crown so the first chakra is at the base of the spine and the seventh is at the top of the head. The chakras tend to have a primary and a secondary function. The primary function is the region of our consciousness which is most affected whilst the secondary function can be used to provide clues to the region of our life which has caused the hurt.

The First Chakra

The first, or root chakra, is at the base of the spine. The bones of the pelvis are divided where they meet the spine and so the very base of the spine is the bottom of the coccyx. This is the bone you can feel just where the buttocks divide.

This chakra has it's primary function of holding the soul in the physical world. This is the soul's energy link which is formed when a pregnancy has developed for about twelve to fifteen weeks. It confirms that the pregnancy is to continue and, therefore, literally "roots" us into our physical bodies. It's secondary function is how we deal with "fight or flight" situations, in other words, our sense of security.

The first chakra relates to the more physical aspects of the body such as the skin, the skeleton and muscles. It also controls the functions of the kidneys and the urinary system.

An example of how this chakra relates to the body would be where your boss has asked to see you. You do not feel very comfortable with their demand and feel a little insecure within yourself. The symptoms are that you feel slightly "panicky" and

20

feel the need to urinate. This might be a short term situation which can be quickly resolved but if you find yourself in situations where you are constantly feeling insecure, it can generate a more long term urinary problem.

The Second Chakra

The second chakra is located just about where the spine meets the pelvis, just at the top of the bone called the sacrum and this is why it is also called the sacral chakra. The chakra's primary function is to deal with our creativity. Its secondary function is with our sexual relationships.

The chakra relates directly to the reproductive organs. The ovaries and uterus (womb) in women and the testes in men. It will also affect associated organs such as the cervix and the prostate. It can also affect localised regions of the spine and pelvis.

An example of a second chakra problem would be where a woman is not happy in her relationship with her partner leading to irregular or painful periods. The same situation could lead to pains in the lower back or hips. On the other side, people who are very creative also tend to be highly sexual in their activities.

The Third Chakra

The third chakra is located about one inch or twenty five millimetres above the tummy button, but also located on the spine.

This chakra's primary function is to deal with personal power issues. These are to do with how your views and ideas are received by others or how you are treated as a person. It's secondary function is to deal with the emotions.

This chakra relates to all of the organs contained within the abdomen. These are: the stomach, the large and small intestines, the liver, the gall bladder, the pancreas and the spleen.

The best example of how these organs become affected is the gall bladder. Each of the organs in this region deal with aspects of the emotions, the gall bladder deals with anger. If we find ourselves in situations where we become angry but cannot express or release that anger, it becomes lodged in the gall bladder. The gall bladder is mainly involved with feeding bile into the intestines to help the body digest food. If it is not functioning correctly it can create constipation and particularly wind. If we go back to the example given for the first chakra, where your boss has demanded to see you, if they tell you that they are not going to accept your ideas and, in response, you become angry but cannot release that anger at your boss, you will probably end up with indigestion and wind in the short term. If these kinds of situations continue to happen you can end up with digestive problems or gall stones.

The Fourth Chakra

The fourth chakra is located in the chest, but attached to the spine, in a line with the heart. This is why it is also known as the heart chakra. Its primary function is the connecting point for the soul's physical energies and its higher energies. We will go on to investigate the soul's higher elements later on in this chapter.

The chakra's secondary function is how we express love, either for ourselves or for others.

The chakra relates directly to the heart, blood and circulatory system, the endocrine system and the immune system, particularly to the thymus gland.

An example of a fourth chakra problem would be in a situation where we are not able to pay attention to our own needs. Say you are constantly busy and under pressure at work, you go home and go to sleep but go to work early the following morning and go through the same routine every day for a prolonged period. In these situations we tend to forget about ourselves and just get caught up in our work. When we do take a break our immune system gives way and we come down with an illness such as a cold. If the situation continues over a long period we have a series of cold like illnesses which will eventually lead to a much more serious illness. A heart attack is another example of trying to work in this way.

The Fifth Chakra
The fifth chakra is located in the throat, on the spine, about mid way between the adams apple and the chin and is why it is also called the throat chakra. This chakra's primary function is to deal with self expression, how we express ourselves as individuals. Its secondary functions are communication and judgement.

The chakra relates directly to the lungs and bronchial channels; the vocal chords and to the metabolism, particularly to the thyroid gland. An example of a fifth chakra problem would be someone who is never allowed to express their own opinion. This leads to congestion in the chest and a persistent cough, as though they were always trying to clear their throat.

The Sixth Chakra
The sixth chakra is located in the centre of the forehead, just above the bridge of the nose, but also in a direct line with the spine. This region is commonly called the third eye and so this chakra is sometimes known as the third eye chakra.

This chakra's primary function is to deal with our "spirituality". This is how we acknowledge the existence of the consciousness.

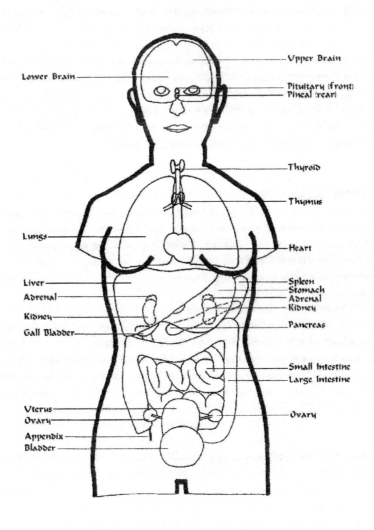

Upper Brain

Lower Brain

Pituitary (front)
Pineal (rear)

Thyroid

Thymus

Lungs

Heart

Liver

Spleen
Stomach
Adrenal
Kidney

Adrenal

Kidney

Gall Bladder

Pancreas

Small Intestine
Large Intestine

Uterus
Ovary

Ovary

Appendix
Bladder

Illustration Number Three - The Body's Organs

Its secondary function is our psychic vision. It relates directly to the ears, the nose, the left eye, the lower brain and sections of the central nervous system. It also relates to the pituitary gland. This is a gland in the middle of the brain that controls most of the body's hormone production.

An example of a sixth chakra problem would be someone who always denies the soul's existence, mainly to themselves. The topic rarely comes up in conversation so people's views are not usually aired in public. This constant denial can lead to eye sight or hearing problems.

The Seventh Chakra
The seventh chakra is located on the top of the head, which is also why it is known as the crown chakra. The chakra is located at the back of the skull, in a direct line with the spine. The seventh chakra's function is the entry point for the energy links between the "higher" elements of our consciousness and the "physical" elements of our consciousness. It relates directly to the upper brain and the right eye. It also relates to the pineal gland. This is a gland in the middle of the brain which controls the levels of a hormone called melatonin within the body. This is the first energy link to be formed between the soul and the fertilised egg in the womb. It is not possible to find an easy example of a seventh chakra problem so we will deal with these problems in detail in chapter nine.

The connections between the chakras and the health problems given in the examples might seem a little simplistic, but they are given to try to illustrate the links that exist within the body. We will go on to discuss more complex problems in later chapters.

As a note about the three illustrations given so far. They have been deliberately left in black and white. This is so you can colour them in for yourselves. We suggest this because it helps you to begin to understand the connections between the body and the consciousness. We suggest that you start with illustration numbers one and two and colour them in using the colours given in chapter one. Illustration number three is a little more difficult, but colouring it in would be a very useful way to understand how the body's organs and the chakras connect.

On a very simple level, this is how the soul "speaks" through the body. The body is very good at letting us know where we are going wrong in our lives, we have just forgotten how to listen. By adopting our western approach to health, we have effectively divorced ourselves from our bodies. Using the chakras in this way, as a diagnostic, we can begin to re-learn how to understand our bodies and the connections with our soul. The authors can state without any fear of contradiction that the chakras are the *only* one hundred percent accurate diagnostic tool. Nobody falls outside of this method of diagnosis. By practising this form of diagnosis for nearly twenty years, we have yet to find anybody or any illness that does not fit into this pattern.

As a simple exercise, think of someone you know quite well who has a health problem. Use the list given above to link the problem to a chakra. By using the description of primary and secondary functions, for the chakra, see how accurate it is to how the person lives their lives or the problems they have in their lives. We think you will find the answers you arrive at will be pretty accurate.

From the other side, remember the "old wives" expressions: "I was so angry, I could feel my gall rising!" (3rd Chakra - personal power and emotions), "Whatever you have to say, get it off your chest!" (5th chakra - self expression and communication). These expressions have been with us for a long time and show that at one time we understood the workings of the body and the soul much better than we do now. So, in order to understand the underlying causes for our illnesses, we need to start to understand that we are a consciousness, a soul, who has a body and that the body is a way of accessing and listening to the soul.

All illnesses and diseases can be avoided. All illnesses and diseases can be healed. There is no condition that cannot be corrected if we listen to what our soul is telling us through our bodies and correct the behaviour that brought about the problem in the first place. It is *never* too late to act.

We have often been told that the soul is a huge amount of energy. Although it was created, we still have total freedom of choice and can exercise what we consider to be good judgement. But where is it, this huge consciousness? Surely, it cannot all be contained within the body and the conscious mind? If this is all that we are, then somebody somewhere has got the sums wrong. In order to live out our lives, we have not needed to bring all of the soul into the body, most of it remains outside of the body but connected to it. The many reasons for this occurring are outside of the scope of this book (see *The Fool's First Steps* by the same author), but we do live our normal, everyday lives with only a percentage of our total conscious-ness. Individuals such as Jesus the Christ, Mohammed, Buddha, etc. are those who managed to fully integrate all of their consciousness into a human body.

So, if this is the case, where is the rest of us?

This is another region where we begin to have problems with our limited vocabulary. As most of us tend not to think too much about this element of our make up, we have not developed enough words to adequately describe the soul and consciousness. With the advent of the so called "New Age", we have begun to set about re-discovering more about ourselves and new words are beginning to enter into the dictionaries. The words most people have come to use to describe our " higher" elements is "The Higher Self". What the higher self is, is the other element of our soul or consciousness. It is connected to us, but at the same time disconnected. It can, sometimes, play a major role in our lives, usually without our knowing. More and more people are waking up to the fact that the higher self does actually exist and that consciously re-connecting with it can prove to be very enlightening. However, its role is very often misunderstood and misinterpreted.

The higher self is the keeper of all of our memories, the controller of our conscience. It is who we are, but very much larger and not constrained by a physical body. Many of the events that occur in our lives are actually decided by our higher selves and all we do is act out those decisions. It is the source of most of our inspiration and is, very often, mistaken for someone else (such as a spirit guide).

When we connect with the higher self, it is like we suddenly expand outwards and feel as though we have connected with the Universe. It is like a new birth, the beginnings of a new awareness. We do not miss it when we have not connected, but once we do, we could not conceive of going back to a world and a life where our greater connections were not present.

Through the higher self we can connect with the whole planet and all of its life or we can fly outwards and connect with the stars and the universe and meet some real Angels. Sounds good doesn't it? But, where is this higher self? The answer is again within the chakras.

So far we have looked at the seven chakras which provide the energies for the consciousness to form the "physical" body. The "total" consciousness, or soul, is actually comprised of thirteen chakras. Seven to form and to work with the body and six forming the residue of the soul or the higher self, a total of thirteen energy centres. The energy contained within the "total" consciousness is vast. We will not enter into the world of energy frequencies and dimensional capabilities at this point, but for those who are interested, a full description and energy range is given in our previous book, *The Fool's First Steps*.

The seven bodily chakras, if read correctly, can provide all of the answers as far as our health problems are concerned. However, learning to connect with and to work with the higher self can add a greater knowledge and understanding to these answers.

Obviously, the decision to connect with the higher self is a deeply personal one. If you decide to do so then there a number of meditations which are designed to do just that (see appendix one). But if this is not for you then just learning about, and making use of, the information that can be obtained from the bodily chakras can provide you with all of the answers for any health problems.

This book is all about human health, but it might come as a surprise to learn that animals also have chakras which perform in quite similar ways to those in humans. Animals do not have individual souls as is the case for people. They certainly have their own personalities, but their life energy, their consciousness, is derived from a form of "group soul" that belongs to each animal group. For example a dog group soul or a cat group soul. There are also group souls for cows, horses, wolves, alligators etc. The process for conception and energy linkages from the group soul into the physical body of the animal is very similar to the way in which it works for humans. The time scale is, obviously, very different, but the sequence of events is very much the same.

Domesticated animals, such as cats and dogs, tend to have only three chakras. Larger animals, such as cows and horses, will have four. Wild animals, such as wolves and bears, also tend to have four chakras.

Animal Chakras
The first, or root, chakra is located above the hip joint, a little way in front of the tail. It has a colour that is the same as the human first chakra, that is red, but tends to be not as vibrant a

colour as ours. So, it can be thought of as a "muddy" red. The first chakra has the same function as its human counterpart, to "root" the animal into the physical world. It also gives the animal it's fight or flight response, its sense of security. It relates to the skeleton and all of the lower body organs such as the stomach, intestines, reproductive system etc.

The second chakra is on the spine but located about the shoulder joint. It is coloured yellow but again a "muddier" version of the human yellow. It also usually has a blue colour around the edges. This chakra's function is how the animal relates to other animals or to the humans that share its life. It relates to the upper body organs such as the heart and lungs etc.

The third chakra is at the top of the head and is coloured green. The chakra's function is the animal's connection to its group soul. It relates directly to the central nervous system, eyesight, hearing and sense of smell.

Where the extra chakra exists, it is located in the centre of the back, mid way between the pelvis and the shoulders. It is usually coloured a dull orange with a green "cast" around the edges. Where present, this chakra shares some of the organ relationships with the first chakra.

Animal health is also chakra related. Any stresses within the animal's life, particularly those caused by events that are not part of the animal's normal behaviour, will create ripples and wobbles within the chakra in much the same way as our behaviour affects our chakras.

Legally, if your pet becomes unwell, you must take it to see a veterinary surgeon. However, alternative approaches are acceptable as long as the vet's instructions and treatment are not countermanded. In addition to the vet, consulting a spiritual healer, those who practice the "laying on of hands", will be the best people to help heal the chakra problems. Again, as with humans, all animal health problems can be diagnosed and healed by paying proper attention to the chakras.

The Chakra Vortex

There is a great deal of information about the chakras which is published in many books on the subject. Many of these books describe the chakras as being shaped like "flowers" and the best way of imagining them becoming energised is to imagine the petals of the flowers opening. Most of this imagery has arisen because most people cannot see the chakras directly. As a way of helping in visualisation exercises, teachers developed the concept of imagining a flower bud opening. In our experience, this imagery has led to many misconceptions, confusion and misunderstandings.

One of us is able to see energies. Over the eighteen or so years that he has been practising as a healer, he has treated many hundreds of clients. Each of these clients has had the same number of chakras in exactly the same positions and with exactly the same colours. It is also true that they have all taken exactly the same form, that of the vortex (see illustration number two). Whilst the concept of the chakras being formed like a blossoming lotus flower is romantic, it is misleading.

All energy, when given free reign to take it's natural shape, forms itself into the shape of a vortex. Think of the shape formed when you pull the plug on a sink full of water. Think of the shape of a tornado. They are all vortices. This is the shape that the chakras are. No chakras are ever any other shape. If you use visualisation exercises to help to energise and strengthen the chakras, this is the shape which needs to be visualised, it is the only shape that works effectively.

As you begin your visualisation exercise, try to imagine that the chakras are in the vortex shape with the point of the vortex directly on the spine. The first chakra points directly downwards with the open end of the vortex pointing away from

31

the body. The second, third, fourth, fifth and sixth chakras point equally in both directions, front and back of the spine. The point of the vortex is on the spine and the chakra opens as it extends further away from the body. The seventh chakra has its point located on the top of the head, in a direct line with the spine, with it opening directly upwards away from the top of the head. Each of the chakras should be worked on in turn each time that you carry out the visualisation exercise. Start with the first chakra, imagine that the chakra is spinning. As it spins faster, the colour becomes brighter and brighter until it becomes transparent. Once it has become transparent, move onto the next chakra and begin again, spinning faster, becoming brighter, etc.. Once you have finished with the crown (instead of becoming transparent, this should turn to gold), bring the gold all the way down the spine, connecting into all of the chakras, balancing each one until the root is connected and sparkling with gold. This exercise is the best way of energising and balancing the chakras. No other visualisation exercise has so powerful and so strong an effect.

Chapter Three
The First Chakra

The first chakra is the second energy link of the consciousness and the one that connects us with the planet. This link is only established when the incoming consciousness has determined that it is to continue with the birth process. This link arrives within the period of twelve to fifteen weeks into the pregnancy. The purpose of this link is to confirm that the pregnancy is to proceed and to provide the necessary information to form the developing fetus into the correct human form. If you look at photographs of a human fetus up until this stage in a pregnancy, then they could be of virtually any animal on the planet. It is the energy of the first chakra which activates the genetic coding sequences put in place by the seventh chakra link.

This link also confirms that the incoming consciousness is to be a part of the planet. It literally roots the incoming consciousness into the physical world. Because of this, it is the element of consciousness which provides us with our physical characteristics and our physical bodies. Therefore, everything connected into this chakra is to do with our most basic physical requirements.

This is the chakra that gives us our form and physical structures. It is therefore, in health terms, directly related to the skeleton, the muscles and the skin. It also relates to the kidneys and the urinary system. This is because the kidneys, and their removal of bodily toxins, represent the cleansing of the physical body.

The body is the physical manifestation of the consciousness, the soul, and all of the "physical" elements of the body relate to the first chakra. The physical body is the instrument by which the soul "speaks" to its more physical elements. In other words, whilst that element of the consciousness which is to experience a physical lifetime is actually physical, the higher self uses the body as a means of communication to let us know if we have "strayed" from our chosen path.

This chakra represents our "grounding" into the physical realms and provides us with our sense of security. Do I stand and fight or do I run away?

The Skeleton, Muscles and the Skin
The process of communication by the soul through the body has a number of stages. As this first chakra represents the more "structural" aspects of the body, then the first approach taken by our consciousness will be through the muscles, especially the muscles of the back. These "warning messages" usually take the form of soreness or stiffness within particular muscles. For example, if you find yourself in a stressful situation, which makes you feel a little unsure within yourself, then you will store the stresses in either the shoulder muscles or in the muscles of the lower back. If the stressful situation is a short term problem, then the muscles will relax. If the situation is of a more long term nature, then the stresses will build up and movement of the spinal bones can occur creating a more long term problem.

These short term types of problems can be dealt with by healing, a massotherapist, particularly an aromatherapy massage, an osteopath, or a Rolfing practitioner.

If the stressful situations we find ourselves in are of a more serious nature, then the next stage of the soul's "hinting" will occur. The spine is the route that all of the body's primary energies, the chakra energies, travel along and, therefore, is the most appropriate way to let us know that we have a problem. This level of "hinting" takes the form of small movements or "disruption" to a region of the spine. The disruption to the spine will occur in a region which corresponds to the other chakras and can provide us with a direct clue as to where the originating problem stems from.

If the pain is in the lower back then we are looking at an insecurity with the way in which we are being creative or there is a sense of insecurity within a sexual relationship (second chakra). If in the middle back, then it is connected with a personal power issue or an emotional insecurity (third chakra). If in the upper back, then we are looking at insecurities around how we express our feelings for our self or for others (fourth chakra). If the problem is with the bones of the neck then the problem will relate to an insecurity with how we express ourselves (fifth chakra). To illustrate this, we can give you a case history from one of our healing clients.

A young man came to see us who had quite a severe lower back problem. He had difficulty in moving properly and was in a great deal of pain. He told us that he had recently had a major argument with his long term girlfriend which resulted in their separating. By giving him healing to cleanse and re-energise the first and second chakras, the problem disappeared, we did not even have to work on the muscles. If these types of problems are not dealt with, they can result in long term pain and, ultimately, damage to the spine itself.

A very common problem amongst women is back pain following childbirth. The pelvis is designed to be a stable platform upon which the spine sits and all of the upper body's weight is taken through the spine, transferred through the pelvis and into the legs. During pregnancy, the pelvis expands to accommodate the growing child and "hinges" at the two points where the pelvis and the spine meet. There is a cartilage joint to either side of the sacrum bone that allows the pelvis to move in this way. At the time just following delivery, these bones should return to

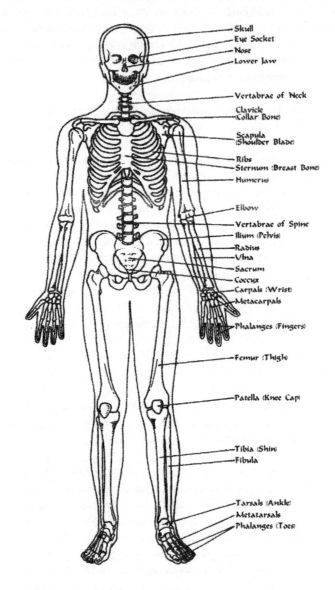

Illustration Number Four - The Skeleton

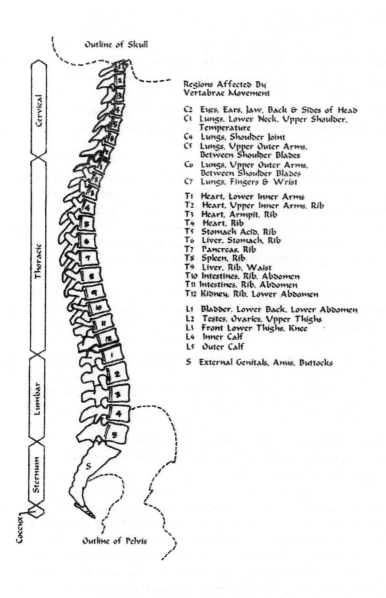

Outline of Skull

**Regions Affected By
Vertabrae Movement**

C2 Eyes, Ears, Jaw, Back & Sides of Head
C3 Lungs, Lower Neck, Upper Shoulder,
     Temperature
C4 Lungs, Shoulder Joint
C5 Lungs, Upper Outer Arms,
     Between Shoulder Blades
C6 Lungs, Upper Outer Arms,
     Between Shoulder Blades
C7 Lungs, Fingers & Wrist

T1 Heart, Lower Inner Arms
T2 Heart, Upper Inner Arms, Rib
T3 Heart, Armpit, Rib
T4 Heart, Rib
T5 Stomach Acid, Rib
T6 Liver, Stomach, Rib
T7 Pancreas, Rib
T8 Spleen, Rib
T9 Liver, Rib, Waist
T10 Intestines, Rib, Abdomen
T11 Intestines, Rib, Abdomen
T12 Kidney, Rib, Lower Abdomen

L1 Bladder, Lower Back, Lower Abdomen
L2 Testes, Ovaries, Upper Thighs
L3 Front Lower Thighs, Knee
L4 Inner Calf
L5 Outer Calf

S   External Genitals, Anus, Buttocks

Outline of Pelvis

Illustration Number Five - The Spine

37

their normal position. If the mother is feeling insecure during the birth, which many women are, then these bones do not fully return to the correct position. If these bones do not return properly, it sets up a condition where the connection between the spine and the pelvis is not level. This can result in the spine being forced into a position where it is pushed into a curve, resulting in back pain. This type of pain can vary from a localised dull ache to severe pain along the whole length of the back.

This kind of problem can also affect the skeleton and joints of the lower body. If the bones of the pelvis are not in their correct position, they can exert pressures within the hip joints or the knee joints. These can be considered to be secondary problems to the spine/pelvis problems, see below for more about this. The best way of dealing with the spine/pelvis problem is to treat it as soon as possible after childbirth has occurred. This can best be achieved by reinforcing and re-energising the first and second chakras. This is best achieved by visiting a healer or by meditation (see appendix one).

If it is not possible to take these steps, then there are several forms of treatment which can help. As psychic surgeons, we have developed simple, painless methods for dealing with this particular problem. A visit to a massotherapist as soon as possible after birth will help to relax the muscles and allow the bones to fall back into place. A visit to a craniosacral therapist or an osteopath as soon as possible after the birth should also help correct the problem.

If you suffer from this condition and it was not possible to take these steps at the time of birth, then you can help the situation with meditation to reinforce the lower two chakras (see appendix one). However, if it has been a long term problem, then you should consult someone who is able to correct bone positions and the muscles in addition to the meditations. Practitioners who carry out this type of work include craniosacral therapists and osteopaths.

The spine is not the only part of the skeleton that can be affected by first chakra problems. If we find ourselves in a situation where our sense of "security" is affected, then other body joints will begin to feel it. The way in which these problems occur is very much in the same way as spinal problems. It is the way in which the first chakra has been "wounded" which determines the area of the skeleton which is affected. If the wound corresponds to a region of our lives which is looked after by another chakra, then the wound will manifest itself in the region of that chakra. However, if the problem is not connected with another chakra then the wound to the first chakra can show up in the knees, the shoulder joint or the elbow joint etc. The way in which the consciousness shows that there is a problem is always manifested in a way which serves to illustrate the problem.

Knee joints will become affected if we are in a situation where our sense of "stability" is threatened. This could be as a result of situations within the workplace where we have assumed that we have a secure job or position, only to find that somebody else has been recruited to carry out a similar job to our own.

Another example would be where we are reasonably happy with our lives and have a close, happy relationship with our family. If one of those family members dies, especially a parent we were close to, then our sense of stability becomes affected and the knee joints start to have problems.

If we find ourselves in a situation where our first chakra becomes affected because we are taking on too much responsibility, then the shoulder joints can become affected. We feel that we are, literally, "shouldering" too much responsibility. If we become too inflexible within a situation of responsibility, then our elbows or ankles become affected, reflecting that lack of flexibility. The same applies to any situation where we are being too inflexible in our attitudes. If we try to, unreasonably, hold onto a situation of responsibility when we should really let go of it, the wrist and finger joints become affected. We are, literally, grasping it too tightly. Wrist and finger joints always become affected if we are trying to "grasp" onto something too much, in whatever region of our lives.

If we suffer from the spine/pelvis problem detailed above, then other problems can occur, particularly with the lower body joints. If the spine/pelvis problem arose because of a temporary sense of insecurity, such as childbirth, and no other factor is involved then the problem will remain localised to that joint and should, to a large extent, correct itself. However, if some of the factors which brought about the original problem still remain, then they can show up in other skeletal joints.

When the spine/pelvis joint problem occurs, it puts a "tilt" onto the line of the pelvis. When normal, the pelvic bones are in a straight line, where the joint has "slipped", the pelvic bones will sit at an angle. This misalignment will tend to put pressures onto the knee joints. If there is no sense of instability then the knees can usually carry on as normal. However, if you do have a sense of instability within your life, whether it is connected with the original problem or brought about by a further problem, then the knee will begin to "give way" and result in discomfort or pain.

On another level, if the pelvic tilt problem is present and you encounter problems within your sexual relationship (second chakra), then the hip joints will become affected. The hip joints are always affected by second chakra problems. These problems come about because of a sense of insecurity with regions of our lives connected with either the primary function (creativity) or the secondary function (sexual relationships) of the chakra. Again, the only effective way of curing these problems is to deal with the situations which brought about the imbalance within the chakra or chakras affected.

The symptoms can be dealt with by any of the practitioners given previously for structural type problems.

40

Another source of secondary type problems is with the spine itself. If there is a general sense of insecurity within your life then the spine becomes weakened. The "wobble" within the first chakra can transfer itself into the whole length of the spine. If you look at illustration number five, you will see a drawing of the spine and all of the vertebrae.

The central nervous system travels down the inside of the spinal column and carries information to and from the brain. This information is how we learn that something is too hot or too cold, painful or pleasurable, etc. Every sensation that we experience, throughout the whole body, has to travel through the main nerves carried within the spinal column. If any of the vertebrae, making up the spinal column, are displaced, then inappropriate pressures can be put on these nerves and the brain fooled into thinking that there is a problem with a particular region of the body. The most common example of this is where we experience pain and "pins and needles" in the legs. More often than not, the problem does not lie with the leg itself but with a back problem. The sciatic nerve carries signals between the legs and pelvis to the brain and enters the spinal column a little way above the pelvis. If there is pressure on this main nerve, whether by muscle pressure or a displacement of a vertebrae, the brain will tell us that we have a leg problem, whereas it is, in fact, a back problem.

If you look at illustration number five, you will see that each vertebrae has been labelled to give the part of the body which can be affected, through the nervous system, if that vertebrae is out of place. As an example of how this works, we can give you another case history. We were approached by a man who had a severe stomach problem. The symptoms were indigestion and bowel problems brought about by a severely acid stomach. His doctors gave him anti-acid treatments which worked for a day or two but then the problem returned. Eventually, they had diagnosed his problem as Irritable Bowel Syndrome (IBS) which is usually the name doctors give to any stomach or intestinal complaint which they do not have a clue about. After examining him, it was obvious to us that he had an upper back problem which had displaced the fourth and fifth vertebrae down from the neck junction. With these bones being out of place, pressure was put onto the nerves which connect with the stomach telling the brain that the stomach constantly needed to produce more digestive acid. This is what the brain did and all of the other problems resulted.

Acid stomach is frequently included in the list of IBS symptoms. In our experience, virtually all of these cases are due to this particular back problem. In the case of our client, we corrected the back problem and his stomach problem went away.

Again, the way in which these problems manifest themselves will fit into the pattern given by the chakras. These kinds of instances are a little more complex, but never the less, they will still fit. In our client's case, his problem stemmed from a basic insecurity within himself and especially his ability to carry out his job, creating a general weakness within the spine. This was aggravated by an inability to effectively express his emotions. So the situation needed to be read as: basic insecurity with himself and how he thought about himself (first chakra and fourth chakra) combining together to bring about a situation which reflected his emotional insecurity (third chakra).

When dealing with these kinds of problems, they can begin to become quite complex, but if you stick to the basic principles of reading the body's symptoms, then even these complex problems begin to make sense. All that you need is some experience and practice. As far as illustration number five is concerned, if you have a problem which is associated with a particular vertebrae, then it would be advisable to have your back checked as well as treating the other symptoms.

Osteoporosis

Another common problem is that of osteoporosis. This is where the physical structure of the bones, especially in the spine, begin to lose their density. In other words, instead of the bones being a very strong, virtually solid calcium, some of the calcium has been "lost" and the bone contains a higher proportion of air pockets. This is why this condition is also known as brittle bone syndrome.

The bones of the body are constantly being rebuilt. Over a period of twenty years, the skeleton is fully renewed. There are two specialised types of cells constantly at work within the body renewing bone. The first type of cells are called osteoclasts. These cells travel the body searching out "old" bones which they then dissolve, leaving behind a small hole. The second type of cells are called osteoblasts which follow behind the osteoclasts and fill in the excavation. This whole process is controlled by the hormone progesterone. When progesterone is plentiful, this rebuilding activity is constant. When progesterone levels begin to drop, such as after menopause, the activities of these two types of cells can be slowed making it more difficult for the bones to renew themselves so quickly.

The whole process can only be maintained by natural progesterone and oestrogen. The osteoclasts (the bone removers) have only oestrogen receptors, which stimulates their activity, and the osteoblasts have only progesterone receptors. Artificial versions of these hormones block the natural hormone receptors and bring the process to a virtual halt. If you are taking artificial hormones, such as HRT, stopping this treatment will stimulate the production of the body's own hormones but this will take a minimum of three months as it takes this time for the artificial hormones to fully leave the body. Another natural process which affects bone density is the level of calcium in the blood. Changes to bone density made in correcting blood calcium levels is controlled by the parathyroid and is detailed in chapter seven.

Osteoporosis is also a first chakra problem, but is caused by a lack of a sense of security that has occurred over a prolonged period. The condition occurs because the consciousness has been drained of its stability, a wearing away of its resolve, over a period of time. The spine has literally lost its rigidity, it is tired of fighting against the problems. This condition can occur to virtually anybody at virtually any age but it is most common in women who are past the menopause. The reason for this is because women are the ones who nurture the family. They are constantly expected to put away their own wants and needs and give to those around them. This situation will always cause women problems (see the second, third and fourth chakras in particular). With this constant drain on the women's consciousness, there will inevitably be a problem with their sense of identity as an individual. The questions: what am I here for? What is the purpose of my life if all I do is to do everything for everybody else? All questions that most women ask. A set of circumstances which inevitably leads to insecurity. These problems build up within the spine over a long period, but because the woman's will is to "serve" her family, the condition becomes masked. When she has passed menopause, the body's hormonal balance changes (see also chapters four and twenty one) making it less easy to hang onto the body's calcium. It is also a time when the family is more independent and the woman has more time to think about herself and what her needs actually are. Self realisation and especially regret can very often be the trigger.

The only real answer to this problem is to deal with it on a chakra level. Begin to regain control of your life and allow yourself to do the things that you want to do. Regain some control and the body will respond. Just because the bones have lost some of their density, it does not mean that the loss cannot be made good. We have treated a number of women for osteoporosis with very good results. The usual range of reduction in bone density is somewhere between 5% and 10%, with some women losing up to 20% of the bone density in localised patches. Following our treatment, we have received reports back from women who have told us that they have had their bone density re-measured and, much to the doctors' amazement, the density has risen by up to twelve percent.

Nothing is ever a lost cause. Even though there might be a serious reduction in bone density, it does not mean that it cannot be repaired. Once you understand the mechanisms for problems occurring, and do something about dealing with them, the body will repair itself. If you have osteoporosis and can find a way of dealing with your underlying insecurity, then by eating foods that are rich in calcium, the damage can be undone. It is no good taking calcium supplements, or even drinking large quantities of milk. The calcium in calcium tablets is not easily absorbed by the body and it is either flushed out, putting the kidneys at risk of stones, or it is stored within other body tissues, particularly the muscles of the middle back. If your doctor insists on giving you calcium injections it causes other problems. In our experience, injected calcium tends to stay close to the muscles it was injected into and only a very small proportion, about 2% - 5%, actually goes anywhere else in the body. This tends to lock these muscles up and cause further problems. Altering your diet to include calcium rich foods is the best and most natural way of dealing with this problem, see chapter fourteen for some suggestions and chapter twenty one for further comments.

Although the whole problem of osteoporosis relates to the first chakra and insecurity issues, the problem can be made worse by the surgical removal of the uterus and, especially, the ovaries as this will remove the organs which produce the necessary hormones (see chapter four).

The symptoms of osteoporosis can be generated and made worse by the use of steroid creams. When treating clients who have used steroid creams for skin problems, we have noticed that the bones can quite rapidly absorb the cream, reducing the chemical bonds within the bone calcium. Having checked through the medical literature on osteoporosis we discovered that this effect is well noted. Another, more surprising, cause of osteoporosis is to consume large daily quantities of protein (over 95 grammes), such as red meat, because it can drain the body of calcium.

For methods of dealing with osteoporosis, see chapter fourteen.

Arthritis

There are over one hundred forms of arthritis. All are caused by a break down in the cartilage and bone structure within a joint. The two most common forms are osteoarthritis and rheumatoid arthritis.

Osteoarthritis

Osteoarthritis is caused when the shock absorbing cartilage between the bones in a joint becomes worn, allowing the bones to rub together. The affects of this is to cause pain, sometimes severe pain, swelling and stiffness which can sometimes deform the joint. The joints most affected are the hips, knees, spine and hands.

To understand the reasons for osteoarthritis, we have to look at where the symptoms have arisen. As described above, particular joints will become affected due to the ways in which we deal, or do not deal, with particular situations. The joints are built into the skeleton to provide movement and flexibility and to absorb the shocks that can be put into the bone structures by movement or impact. The main form of shock absorption is within the cartilage between the bones of a joint. If this cartilage becomes worn, then there is excessive pressure on the joint. On a consciousness level, this means that we have become too flexible in our approach to our lives. We have not stood up for ourselves but always accepted the other person's view no matter what our feelings were.

The hips are affected by problems associated with the second chakra (insecurity with creativity or sexual relationships). The knees are affected by instability, in other words, by being too flexible, you have lost your stability (first chakra). The spine has become affected because you have not stood up for your wants in most areas of your life (first, second, third, fourth and fifth chakras). The hands become affected because you have held on to this position of giving way too tightly (first chakra).

Rheumatoid Arthritis
Rheumatoid arthritis is where the joints swell with stiffness and pain. The skin over the joint becomes red and shiny and there is a general feeling of stiffness and lack of movement. In some respects, the exact opposite of osteoarthritis. On a consciousness level, the problem is caused because we have been too inflexible in our approach to problems. We have taken our view and stuck rigidly to it despite there being other approaches and other ideas which were, probably, more sensible.

Again, as for osteoarthritis, the regions of the body affected will reflect the regions of your life where you have adopted this inflexible approach.

Suggested treatments for both of the main types of arthritis can be found in chapter fourteen.

Broken Bones
How can breaking a bone be diagnosed? Surely, they are the result of accidents! First of all, there is no such thing as coincidence. Everything happens for a very good reason and if you use the principles established so far, then even these kinds of injuries can be seen as a method employed by the consciousness to let us know that we are doing something wrong. The best way of illustrating this is to give you another case history.

We were approached by a young man in his mid twenties who was just recovering from a major injury. He asked us if we could help finish the mending process and give his energy system a major clean out. He had basically drifted throughout his life and never settled to any job or lived in one place for very long. Essentially he was always running away from situations and, really, away from himself. He was very artistic and quite psychic, so he knew that there were directions that he needed to go in his life but was trying hard to ignore them. He eventually ended up as a petrol pump attendant and worked a little as a car mechanic. He knew that he shouldn't be doing this job but couldn't be bothered to do anything more for himself (this is, basically, his description of himself).

One day, he was working on someone's car when a customer requiring petrol pulled in. He dropped everything and ran to the customer, he ran so fast that he didn't notice the car ramp and broke his skull in several places. During the six months that he was in hospital and convalescing, he had time to think about his life and what it was he should be doing. He found out about the courses on offer at the local college and enrolled himself on an art course.

On the face of it, it could be argued that the series of events were a complete coincidence. Another view would be that his soul had given him many hints and opportunities to sort himself out which he had deliberately ignored. The only way to "knock some sense" into him was to do that literally. Two years on and he is a very successful artist and musician and he is very happy. Again, the soul uses the body in very literal ways to let us know that we are going in the wrong direction. A broken arm or wrist means that we are stretching out for something which we cannot have. A broken leg or ankle means that we are stepping into regions where it is not feasible or desirable for us to go.

It sounds very simplistic, but if you have suffered a broken bone, think about the circumstances that you were in at the time and did the injury help you to let go of that situation or move you in a different direction? You will probably be surprised by the conclusion you reach.

If you do suffer a broken bone then it does need to be set properly by a doctor, alternative therapies are not the best for setting broken bones. However, they can help the break to mend more quickly and comfortably. Suggested remedies to aid the healing of bones are given in chapter fourteen.

The problems listed above for muscular and skeletal conditions is obviously not exhaustive. However, it can be used to provide a guide for deciphering what it is the body is trying to tell us. In using the body in this way, the soul is very literal. Why make something complicated when a simple approach can be so much more effective. Learn to read the body in this way and all health problems become a straight forward request for help from the soul. The soul tries to give us a gentle nudge to let us know that we need to correct our behaviour, if we ignore the nudge, it turns into a heavier tap. If the tap is ignored, it can result in a whack on the back of the head with a baseball bat.

The Skin

The skin is also connected very directly with the first chakra. Problems with the skin are the soul's way of alerting others that we have a problem. They are a very subtle way of saying to the outside world that we need some help. Effectively, what the soul is saying is that I find myself in a situation which I find uncomfortable and am feeling very insecure and I cannot deal with it on my own, please come and reassure me and give me some comfort. In this way, we are looking at more subtle messages of insecurity than with the muscles or the skeleton. So they are really minor manifestations of the same kind of problem, more a "I'm reasonably OK but could do with some reassurance" than "I'm really not very happy with this and my back is beginning to hurt".

Problems with the skin, although having their root in the sense of security of the first chakra, are usually brought about by a secondary cause. The world which we inhabit is ruled by chemicals. We have chemicals which can carry out very many functions. These functions vary from helping, such as making some environments bacteria free, to mildly harmful, to lethal, as with chemical weapons. In our daily lives we are bombarded with chemical residue which constantly irritate the skin. If we are in a vulnerable condition, as opposed to insecure, these chemical irritants can react with the skin and cause surface rashes. These are situations where skin conditions are brought about by an underlying unease with our environment.

Many skin conditions are caused by internal processes, especially in relation to our emotional well being and these will be dealt with in chapter five, the third chakra and chapter six, the fourth chakra. Many skin conditions are brought about by the way in which we deal with other people. Again, using a simple approach, there is the old saying where someone "has got under your skin". This applies to situations where the other people in question have failed to carry out their anticipated actions, whether it was something which you anticipated they would do or something they had promised they would do and didn't. These situations can bring about anger and frustration (third chakra) leading to a mild insecurity owing to your having to deal with yet another problem or situation.

The only way of determining the root causes behind a skin condition is to think back to when the condition first arose. Where were you? Who were you talking to? Did they do something which you were temporarily unhappy with? Is there an ongoing situation which is making you feel irritated and vaguely uneasy? Whatever the root cause, you need to deal with it as it can grow into greater feelings of anger, but particularly, insecurity, bringing about one of the other conditions discussed in this chapter.

For skin conditions, there are several forms of approach all of which can work very effectively. However, the use of steroid creams, whilst being very effective in the short term, will quite quickly cause potentially worse conditions to occur as they will thin the skin (see also osteoporosis). Reflexology can be used in this situation, but make sure that you check out the other organs such as the kidneys and the liver and also the lymphatic system (see chapter six).

Herbal remedies can be especially effective with these kinds of problems. The ones recommended in chapter fourteen work very well, but if you experience any problems then you should consult a qualified herbalist. Homeopathy also works very well for skin conditions. As the homeopathic approach is to treat each person individually, you should consult a qualified homeopath for all conditions.

Skin Cancer (melanoma)

The skin's colour is determined by the levels of the hormone melanin. Sunlight, for example, stimulates the production of melanin and turns white skin brown or black skin darker. Melanin stimulates receptors within certain skin cells, making them change colour. Over stimulation of melanin can produce melanomas (cancers) of the skin. But. Melanin receptors also have oestrogen receptors. A report written in 1968 and published in the *Journal of the American Medical Association* (by Drs JM Ellerbrook and JAH Lee - source *Hormone Heresy*) warned of the dangers of the contraceptive pill and potential skin cancers. Given the massive rise in skin cancers since the '60s, we think the link has been established. If you add to the pill the artificial oestrogens contained in HRT (hormone replacement therapy), the cause of the problem begins to become clear. Men are not exempt from skin cancers but their problem seems to stem from the environment becoming swamped by false oestrogens from a number of sources (see chapter twenty one).

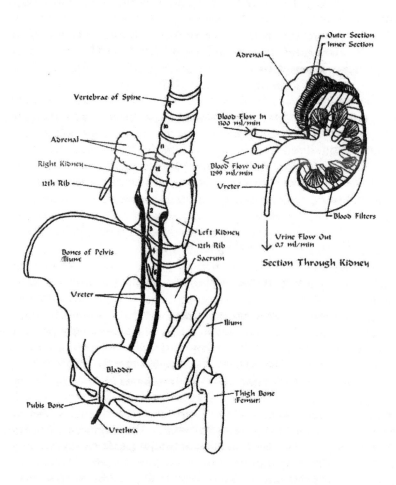

Illustration Number Six - The Kidneys and Adrenal Glands

There is a problem with sunlight intensity brought about by the chemical breakdown of the ozone layer, but, the biggest culprits by far, for the astronomical rise in melanomas, are artificial oestrogens.

The Kidneys and the Urinary System

We normally have two kidneys which are located in the back of the abdomen, on either side of the spine and just above the waist (see illustration number six). They filter the blood, removing waste material and adjusting the levels of various essential chemical substances so as to keep within necessary healthy limits. As they do this they produce a sterile liquid known as urine. As produced, the urine flows down the ureters to the bladder where it is stored until it can be conveniently disposed of. The bladder can store up to a litre of urine. Urine is discharged from the bladder through the urethra. The kidneys are largely responsible for controlling the amount of water in the body and controlling the acidity of the blood. Virtually all of the body's chemical waste products, including prescribed medication, are disposed of by the kidneys.

The function of the kidneys is controlled by a number of hormones which are secreted by several other glands and organs. The kidneys control fluid and chemical levels by both filtration and reabsorption. Essentially, the kidneys filter out harmful or unwanted elements within the blood and maintain a balance of essential minerals and vitamins by alternately retaining them and putting them back into the blood supply or eliminating them with the urine. The blood flow through the kidneys is about 1300 millilitres per minute. The kidneys also produce various hormones and enzymes which stimulate the production of blood cells in the bone marrow and help to control blood pressure levels (see chapter six - the fourth chakra). Attached to the top of the kidneys are the adrenal glands. These glands have inner and outer parts which have differing functions. The outer section (this is connected to the second and fourth chakras) produces various hormones which

53

include some of the sex hormones. The inner section produces adrenaline.

Adrenaline could be viewed as the hormone which epitomises the function of the first chakra. If we are faced with a situation where our security is threatened, the adrenal glands produce the hormone adrenaline which places the body in a state where we can choose to stand and fight or to run away. Adrenaline does this by speeding up the heart rate, increases the breathing rate and makes it easier to breath, raises blood pressure, takes blood out of the digestive system and puts it into the muscles, stimulates the rate at which bodily fuel, in the form of glucose, is burnt and creates a sense of alertness and excitement.

Adrenaline is produced every time that we feel insecure, this floods the body with all of the stimulants just mentioned. If we are in a position where the "fight or flight" response is inappropriate, the body has to dispose of the excess adrenaline. It does this in two ways, firstly by cleansing through the lymphatic system (this function is controlled by the third and fourth chakras and is covered in chapters five and six) and, secondly, the lymph system is drained into the blood which is cleansed by the kidneys. This stimulates the kidneys to function much faster, producing a greater volume of urine than is normal. This tends to overfill the bladder making us feel the need to urinate at much higher frequencies than would be normal.

The physical aspects of the first chakra, the skeleton, muscles and the skin, tend to store away the memories of situations where a wound has occurred to the chakra. The kidneys become affected when we are faced with situations where we wish to deal with the situation as it occurs. By forcing more blood flow through the kidneys and producing a greater quantity of urine, we are literally trying to flush the situation away by instantly cleansing the body. In situations where we feel under threat we feel insecure, this stimulates the body to produce adrenaline and we have to urinate. This is the main cause of incontinence in children and the elderly.

When we are young we are inexperienced in dealing with threatening situations. This could be from a school bully or an absent parent etc. and these situations produce an almost constant flow of adrenaline through the body making us want to urinate constantly. This process continues even when we are asleep and is the principle cause of childhood bed wetting. As we grow older, we learn to deal with these situations much more calmly and the adrenaline and, consequently, urine flow, reduces. The same problem arises in the elderly. As we grow older and become less confident, we lose our sense of security which increases the flow of adrenaline making us incontinent. In these instances, the only way of improving the situation is to increase their sense of security. This can be achieved in several ways and will be discussed at the end of the chapter.

Another problem associated with adrenaline is caused when we live highly stressed lives. If we are constantly under stress then the body will produce a virtually constant supply of adrenaline. This can have the affects detailed above but the problem can also manifest itself as a problem with blood sugar levels. Adrenaline stimulates the body into burning up the body's stock of glucose.

As the glucose is used up, our physical energy levels drop considerably and we find ourselves constantly tired and unable to function normally. Another problem that can arise is that we have constant headaches and, no matter what kind of pain-killers we take, the headache will not go away. This is a low sugar problem. This does not mean that we all must go out and eat huge quantities of chocolate, although that does make most of us feel better in other ways, adding sugars in this way to a low blood sugar level can actually make the condition worse, as can taking alcohol and fruits. We can, however, take in sugars in the form of soft drinks that contain high levels of glucose, especially drinks that are rapidly absorbed into the body such as isotonic types or high glucose content sweets etc. (avoid any containing aspartame as this sweetener can cause headaches). See chapters fourteen and twenty one.

Conditions such as kidney stones occur mainly because we feel in a constant or at least, a frequent state of feeling insecure and the kidneys are unable to deal with the high flow of chemicals and minerals that the blood is trying to flush through them. The situation is also made worse when we do not drink enough water. Kidney stones tend to form in two places, within the kidneys themselves or where the ureter joins the bladder. This condition can be helped by drinking low sodium mineral water, preferably from glass bottles, at the rate of at least two litres a day (plastic bottles contain a polymer which is very similar in it's chemical makeup to oestrogen. Water stored in plastic bottles will take up this polymer, and when we drink the water, we are taking in this artificial oestrogen*). We could also adopt a very low salt diet and urinate whenever we feel the need to, instead of holding on. Kidney stones can also be helped by the remedies suggested in chapter fourteen.

*A good source of drinking water is to boil tap water in an open saucepan or a kettle with its lid off. This removes most of the harmful substances contained within the water. Store the cooled water in glass bottles and drink from these. The water can also be further filtered, when cooled, by using a proprietary water filter.

Cystitis

Cystitis is an inflammation of the bladder that usually leads to a mild infection of the bladder and the urethra. Symptoms are usually a sense of discomfort within the bladder and severe pain and burning when urinating.

The bladder is the region of the body where we store unwanted toxins before they are finally eliminated from the body by urinating. The problem of cystitis is connected to an insecurity surrounding a very recent problem. It is the almost immediate symptom of trying to eliminate a problem but it is not quite able to be flushed away.

If you have cystitis then you are dealing with something which has made you feel "unsettled". You have virtually removed and dealt with the problem, but a small element of it is still present and you are hanging on to it. You need to look back over recent events and discover what problems or situations left you feeling uncomfortable and slightly insecure, probably a situation which you felt you had fully cleared. Ask yourself, have I fully dealt with this problem? Is there anything which I am still hanging onto?

If you have long term or recurring cystitis, then it is unlikely to be from the same originating cause. There will be a series of the events described above which manifest themselves in this way. Generally, long term cystitis means that you never fully deal with problems, you deal with a certain amount of it but usually leave a little piece of it unresolved.

Remedies that can help with cystitis will be found in chapter fourteen.

In Conclusion

The best way of dealing with all of the problems described in this chapter is to increase our feelings of security. This is usually something which is not easily achieved given the stresses and strains of normal, everyday life. However, the energies contained within the first chakra can be strengthened in several different ways. The first chakra's primary role is to link us into the physical, this role can be enhanced by carrying out physical tasks or exercises that can increase our sense of connection and well being.

Meditation (see also appendix one)

Meditation can help to increase the energies contained within the chakra. This is achieved by visualising the whole area being "flooded" with bright red light. This colour corresponds to some of the energy frequencies of the chakra and helps to stabilise and remove the chakra's "wobble". This can also be achieved, but much more subtly, by often wearing the colour red, either as underwear or as top wear.

Physical Exercise

Virtually any form of physical exercise can help to "ground" the energies of the first chakra. This can take the form of something as strenuous as a work out at the gym or as simple and gentle as washing the dishes by hand. These kinds of activities help by slowing us down and re-connecting with some of the physical aspects of our bodies and lives.

These exercises can also take the form of dance, whether formal, ballroom type dancing, or something a little more wild and free in form and expression. Dancing helps us to reconnect with the earth and to reinforce our physical nature.

Manual Work

This can range in form from building a house or piece of furniture, digging the garden or mending the fence, to taking up a hobby such as model making or dressmaking, needlepoint, knitting, beadwork etc., hiking or just walking more often. In other words, anything which involves us slowing down and being more aware of, and connected to, the physical world. All of these activities help to connect us to our physical selves and, therefore, help to reinforce the first chakra's energies.

The Bach Flower Remedies listed in appendix two are also intended to be used for root cause issues.

During the text of this chapter we have made references to several therapists beyond those detailed in chapter twelve. For those who are unfamiliar with these types of therapies, a description of appropriate types of practitioners is given in appendix six.

The remedies suggested in the second half of this book deal with the symptoms. The activities suggested in the course of this chapter begin to deal with the root cause of the problem and begin to heal the soul. Even if you decide to take the remedies, you will still need to sort out the root cause of the problem otherwise a cure will not be possible. The recommended activities are ones which *can* help to achieve a cure.

One point to remember about all of the kinds of problems discussed in this chapter. The body wants to heal itself. It is constantly adjusting the way in which it functions to compensate for the mistakes we make. As healers, we very often find that all we are really doing is working with the body to help it to heal itself, bringing about a balance of energies which promote self healing.

If the root causes of a health problem can be identified and dealt with or resolved, the body will undo virtually any damage done. This applies whatever the body's condition. Even conditions such as arthritis and osteoporosis can be undone by the body. What *has* to occur is that you fully deal with the underlying problem and the body will take care of itself.

Chapter Four

The Second Chakra

The second chakra is located at the back of the pelvis, just below the junction with the spine. This energy centre enters the developing fetus in the twenty to twenty four week period into the pregnancy. At this stage of our development, this energy link effectively remains dormant, all that it does is to partly energise the organs that are connected to, and controlled by it.

The second chakra's primary function, creativity, is active from the point of birth, but its secondary function, sexual relationships and sexual activity, remains dormant until puberty. Several elements of our sexuality become apparent before puberty but these are related to genetic and hormonal signals rather than the second chakra. The organs connected to the second chakra are:

In women. The vagina, the cervix, the uterus (womb) and the ovaries.

In men. The penis, the testicles and the prostate.

See illustrations 7a and 7b. All of these organs are to do with sexual reproduction and each has a particular function within this process.

Female Organs

Located in the lower abdomen, between the tops of the thighs is the entrance to the vagina. Surrounding the entrance are the labia. These are folds of fleshy skin which look a little like lips. Just above the vaginal entrance is the exit from the urethra which discharges urine from the bladder. Just above this is the clitoris. The clitoris is a small "pea" shaped protuberance which is highly sensitive to stimulation and which becomes enlarged, by filling with blood, when the woman is sexually aroused.

The vagina is a hollow tube about 8 to 10 cm (3 to 4 inches) long and made from strong fibrous muscles which allow it to stretch easily during sexual intercourse or when in use as the birth canal. The walls of the vagina secrete various levels of mucous. It constantly produces mucous to keep the vagina clean and free from infection. During intercourse the mucous production increases dramatically, which is also added to by secretions from the cervix, to lubricate the movement of the man's penis. The vagina leads to the cervix. The cervix is the entrance, or neck, of the uterus. In its normal condition, the cervix has a small diameter opening which connects the vagina to the uterus.

The uterus, or womb, is a "pear" shaped muscular organ which expands to accommodate the growing fetus during pregnancy. At the top of the uterus are two tubes, one to the left and one to the right, which lead to the ovaries. These tubes are called the fallopian tubes. The ovaries are also held in place by a ligament which attaches to the outside of the uterus. The uterus is lined with a soft glandular layer known as the endometrium. At the end of the fallopian tubes are the ovaries. These are small, oval sacs, about 3 cm (1 inch) long, which contain cells that will become the eggs.

From birth until puberty, the whole system remains dormant. With the final entry of the full consciousness, various hormonal systems are triggered within the body (particularly fourth and sixth chakras) and the woman begins a cycle of ovulation and menstruation which occurs every twenty eight days.

In medical terms, the first day of the cycle begins with the breaking down of the lining of the uterus (endometrium). The endometrium breaks down and is discharged from the body as blood (menstruation). On the fourth day, the ovaries begin to produce hormones which stimulate the re-growth of the endometrium and begins to prepare one of the egg cells for its exit from the ovary. As the egg cell changes, it begins to produce oestrogen. Several other hormones are produced from various other bodily sources during this period which, on the fourteenth day of the cycle, stimulate the ovary to release the now prepared egg (ovulation) into the fallopian tube. At about twenty one days, the body produces progesterone (the main female hormone) as well as oestrogen, which stimulates the endometrium to grow at an increased rate and is designed to implant and feed the egg if it becomes fertilised. If fertilization is to occur, it ideally happens on the sixteenth day of the cycle. From the sixteenth day to the twenty first, the egg travels down the fallopian tube towards the uterus. If the egg is fertilised, it implants itself into the endometrium. If it does not become fertilised, on the twenty sixth day the levels of oestrogen and progesterone drop to virtually nothing and the endometrium stops growing. On the twenty eighth day the endometrium begins to collapse and the cycle begins again with day one (menstruation), detailed above.

If the egg is fertilised a different set of sequences occur. Ideally, the egg should be fertilised on day sixteen of the menstrual cycle. This is so the egg is at its peak in terms of hormone receptors, this then becomes day one of the pregnancy. The egg is fertilised within the fallopian tube where it begins to slowly grow by dividing itself into two cells, four cells, eight cells etc. By the seventh day, following fertilization (twenty three days into the menstruation cycle), the fertilised egg implants itself into the endometrium (the lining of the uterus). By about day sixteen (of the pregnancy), the egg has developed enough cells for the first energy link to be connected to the top of the head by the incoming consciousness that is to be the new child. If all is well, the sequence of events detailed in chapter one begins.

The mother undergoes huge changes within the body which have a large number of hormonal and physical implications. It

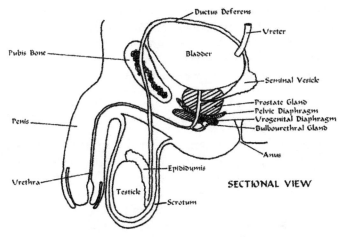

7a THE MALE REPRODUCTIVE ORGANS

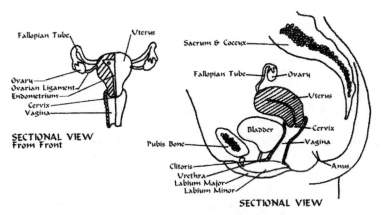

7b THE FEMALE REPRODUCTIVE ORGANS

Illustrations 7a and 7b - The Male and Female Reproductive Organs

is as though her life is put onto hold and her body puts all of its resources into feeding and developing the baby. This is where the sense of self and of security begin to become affected and can lead to the structural problems discussed in the last chapter. But her problems do not end there, of course, she still has to carry the baby to term and give birth to it. Then, it could be argued, is when her problems really begin.

Male Organs

The external male organs are made up of the penis and the scrotum. The penis is a longish muscle filled organ which varies in size from man to man. These muscles are unique within the body. When the man becomes sexually stimulated, these muscles become filled with blood and cause the penis to become erect. What makes these muscles unique is the fact that the blood remains in the muscles until the point of ejaculation. These muscles are known as the erectile tissue. Passing through these muscles is a hollow tube, the urethra, which discharges urine from the bladder. Underneath the penis is the scrotum. The scrotum is a sac of skin which consists of a number of muscles. Contained within the scrotum are the testicles. The testicles produce the male component in the fertilization process, namely the sperm. They are also responsible for producing the male hormone, testosterone.

The sperm are small, tadpole-like cells which are able to "swim" through fluids etc. by wriggling their tails. The sperm are produced within the testicles and then stored within a sac like protrusion at the back of the testes known as the epididymis. In order to produce the sperm, the testes need to be kept at a temperature that is slightly lower than normal body temperature (about 1^0 centigrade, 2^0 Fahrenheit lower than the rest of the body). This is the reason for the scrotum and testes being external to the body, to maintain the lower temperature. The temperature of the testes can be further adjusted by loosening or tightening the muscles of the scrotum. The sperm travel from the epididymis through a tube called the ductus deferens. These tubes, one per testicle, run in front of the pubis bone and over the top of the bladder. The sperm are stored in a small, walnut like sac at the back of the bladder called the seminal vesicle.

Also located under the bladder, and wrapped around the urethra, is the prostate. This gland adds a quantity of fluid to the sperm that is called the seminal fluid. From the seminal vesicle, the sperm travel through a tube that runs through the prostate and connects into the urethra. Further fluid is added by a gland located at the very back of the penis called the bulbourethral gland (sometimes known as Cowpers gland).

So, in order to produce a quantity of sperm to fertilise the women's egg, the sperm travels from the seminal vesicle, through the prostate, where seminal fluid is added, into the urethra, where further secretions are added by the bulbourethral gland, and is ejaculated through the end of the penis as semen.

Health problems, associated with both male and female organs, relate to the second chakra. This is the part of our consciousness that deals with our creative abilities. Our creativity does not only have to do with pursuits that are normally considered "artistic". We are creative in many regions of our lives. Virtually all of our day to day activities can be treated in two ways. They can either be as somebody else taught us or to try to be the same as everyone else (conventional), or we add a few of our own original thoughts, personalised touches etc. (creative). These creative ideas do not have to be particularly spectacular. They could be as simple as altering a cooking recipe, the way in which we decorate our homes, if you are a keen dancer, adding a few new steps of your own, adding little extra finishing touches to the clothes that we wear etc.. They do not have to be very much, it is just a question of putting a little thought into the things that you do.

On a secondary level, the second chakra looks after our sexual relationships. This is why the chakra does not become fully functional until after puberty, we are not sexually active until then and there would be little point in putting energy into something which we are incapable of using.

Health problems associated with this chakra will almost exclusively affect this part of the body. There can sometimes be problems created within other organs where there is a problem with the sex hormone levels. The second chakra can influence and affect all of the organs listed above and also some of the bone structures in this region of the body (see the previous chapter).

First of all, it would be fair to say that health problems connected with this chakra, and its associated organs, are not as easy to track down as they are for first chakra problems. During the whole of our healing experience, we have only come across two conditions which manifest themselves consistently in every individual for the same reasons. All other problems manifest themselves on a totally individual level. What this means is that it is not possible to be as precise about diagnosis for the second chakra as it is for the other chakras. Conditions can arise and organs can be affected but these conditions will manifest themselves in a way which is applicable to each individual. Therefore, if you have health problems that affect these organs, then you will need to look at the region of your life that is generating the chakra imbalance for yourself. This does not mean that we are abandoning you. We can point you in the right direction, but we are not able to give you a totally accurate diagnosis for the root cause of every single condition.

The key to problems with our reproductive systems is the second chakra's primary function, creativity. As mentioned above, our creative abilities do not have to be the primary concerns in our lives. After all, there isn't enough room in the world for all of us to be great painters, sculptors or musicians. But, what we do need to do is to find a way of making space in our lives for these kinds of pursuits. The soul is not a hard task master, all that it really requires is that we acknowledge that this aspect of ourselves does exist and that we learn to use it and express it. The biggest problem that most of us have is that we are afraid of making fools of ourselves. How can I go into an art class without looking stupid? The only experience that most of us have with artistic pursuits is when we were in school. Remember those classes? How to look and feel ridiculous in one easy lesson! These experiences tend to make us feel very insecure about picking up a paint brush or pencil or trying to create something that looks vaguely useful or attractive out of a lump of clay. You know what? - it doesn't matter.

All that we need to do is to try for ourselves when nobody else is looking. We can not all be Rembrandts or Henry Moores, but what we can do is little things for ourselves. Give it a try, it isn't going to hurt, you are not expected to give an exhibition of your work.

It would also be fair to say that a high percentage of the problems that are encountered with these organs relate to the chakra's secondary function, sexual relationships. We do tend to have very high sex drives. This is mainly due to an inherent need to pass on our genes. This is something that we do inherit from, and share with, our more animal ancestors. In physical terms, our genetic material is exactly the same as all other life on the planet, we just have more of it than any other form of life.

We also have a great need to share our lives with other human beings together with a great need to touch. We are, after all, inhabiting a physical body which allows the soul to be fed by our physical senses. As most of us have sexual urges and desires, forming close, loving relationships with others allow us to satisfy these needs. But, each one of us is an individual, with our own individual wants and needs. When we are in a relationship where the needs of one do not correspond to the needs of the other, conflicts of interest arise. It is these conflicts, between partners, which lead to a high percentage of second chakra problems.

This is an accurate way of discovering the root cause of the problems associated with these organs. If you are in a relationship which is, in some way, dysfunctional, then this is the most likely source of your problem. However, if you are in a close, loving relationship which satisfies your every need (or almost every need), then the problems that you have relate to the creative side of your life. Problems within these organs occur because one of these elements of ourselves is not being fully satisfied.

Before going on to look at the problems associated with these organs and determine their most likely root causes, we would like to make our position clear. We believe that we are all total individuals who have total free choice over our lives and the actions that we take in those lives. Therefore, on one level, whether we are male or female does not limit the free choices that are available to us. However, females are naturally nurturing and the choices made by most women lead them into situations where these natural, inbuilt, attributes are made use of. This is why many women opt to stay at home and bring up children. This is not a sexist situation, but a choice based upon a natural inclination. Therefore where reference is made to the roles of the sexes, these comments are made with the under-standing that women have made choices that reflect their natural bodily functions. This does not mean that men are excluded from these roles, it is just that women are more naturally equipped to be in these positions.

Female Problems

Women are naturally nurturing. This is a reflection of the fact that they are the sex that bear and nurture our children. This childbearing capability also means that in their turn, women also require a more caring, nurturing relationship and environment than men do. Therefore, women's requirements vary considerably, in this respect, from those of men. This variation in wants and needs is very often the cause behind many female problems. It is only when women feel nurtured and supported by their partners that they are able to easily fulfil their biological function of producing children. This does not mean to say that women cannot become pregnant in adverse conditions, it is just that the pregnancy is likely to be much easier and less complications arise if they feel safe and secure in their home environment.

Even if you do not wish to become pregnant, the way in which you feel supported by your partner can have an enormous influence on the health of these organs. Again, as mentioned previously, there is no entirely accurate way of relating symptoms to aspects of your life. All of these symptoms come about because of the way in which you live your life and the way in which you react and respond to the problems that you encounter within your life. However, we have come across a certain degree of consistency where women in similar situations produce similar symptoms. Therefore, we can begin to provide some clues as to where to begin looking for the root causes.

Women tend to be more creative than men. Most women will have had any of a number of creative pursuits in their teens. However, women are also more nurturing than men and when women find a partner they will tend to put aside their creative pursuits in order to look after their partner, especially if their partner is not positively supportive of her creative pursuits. This denial of their creative nature will tend to put wounds into the second chakra which can manifest itself in any of the organs. However, the organ that *can* be most affected by this denial is the cervix. Where we have been asked to heal cervical problems, a high percentage of these women have given up a creative career or a creative hobby in order to look after their partners.

In the same way, we have found that vaginal problems can be caused by a problem within a sexual relationship. The woman is not happy with the relationship, either permanently or temporarily and wants to distance herself from her partner. To most women, this distancing is represented by a reduction in lovemaking. This manifests itself as a withdrawal of the energy that makes up this part of her body, resulting in a weakening of the vagina's structure, leading to infection.

Ovarian problems can be brought about by a removal of the wish to produce fertile eggs. This can be either a temporary wish or a permanent one. If temporary, the symptoms will be something like a cyst. If permanent, the symptoms can be more serious such as a collapse of the ovary or even, in extreme cases, ovarian cancer. One of the conditions which does have a consistent link between symptoms and root cause is irregular periods. The uterus (womb) is the centre of a woman's body and represents everything that is nurturing and giving. It is the place where new life is created and the place from which new life is born. If a woman arrives at a point where she no longer wishes to provide a form of nurturing, then she will "shut down" this part of herself.

This shutting down can be because she is tired of constantly giving of herself to others. It can be because she is in a relationship where she does not want to give any more to keep it alive. It can also be because she is trying to be successful in her career and does not want to be seen as a "soft", giving woman but as a tough business executive. Whatever the reason, and these are the three most common, she removes the energy from the organ which epitomises her nurturing. As this energy is removed, it starts to break down or to prevent the proper formation of the lining of the uterus, the endometrium. This will result in her periods (menstruation) stopping altogether or the pattern of her periods changing. This pattern change can range from having periods only every couple of months to having periods every few days.

The other consistent problem and root cause is that of a prolapsed uterus. This is where the uterus begins to collapse and pass through the cervix into the vagina. This situation is usually brought about by the continuation of the situation which brought about the irregular periods or the continuation of the situation which brought about the vaginal problems. To best illustrate this we can give you a case history.

We were approached by a woman with a prolapsed uterus. This was not her only symptom but the reasons behind the prolapse gave a clue to all of her other symptoms which are covered in other chapters. Basically, she was someone in a loveless marriage. Her husband was someone who only had time for his business, he never devoted any time to her or her needs. Despite her efforts to help him, he refused to even think that his behaviour could have an affect upon her or her wellbeing. She felt that she could not leave the marriage as she had deeply held religious beliefs that would not let her even consider divorce. So, gradually, she had stopped their love-making and she had withdrawn any part of herself which would give him comfort. Literally, a complete shutdown of all giving within the relationship from her. Over the years she had major problems with vaginal infections and her periods had stopped many years ago. She had totally withdrawn herself out of any aspects of caring, nurturing and sex, at least as far as her husband was concerned. This does not mean that she took a lover, she would not even contemplate the thought of that, but cared for other people as a complementary therapist. However, by withdrawing herself in this way, it meant that her body responded in ways which reflected her wishes. A total denial and withdrawal of her caring nature towards her husband.

We think that most women would agree that she took the right course of action, and we would agree with that. Except. By this total withdrawal, she created major problems within her body. What the soul wants of us is to be ourselves, no more and no less than that. By this denial of herself, this lady created problems which hurt her more than her husband. Her religious beliefs would not allow her to divorce her husband. Therefore, once we had worked on the prolapse, the only way in which she could help prevent the problem from occurring again was to take up a creative hobby.

If the second chakra is affected by its secondary function and the situation cannot be resolved in any satisfactory way on this level then the only recourse is to deal with it on its primary level, creativity.

The Menopause

As with all regions of our lives, even the naturally occurring ones can be fraught with problems. The menopause is the time in a woman's life where all of the hormonal and physical awakenings that took place as part of puberty are reversed. The hormonal balance within the body changes, particularly in terms of progesterone and oestrogen production. By reducing the levels of these hormones within the body, it stops the lining of the uterus from renewing itself and the ovaries stop preparing eggs for fertilization.

The timing of the menopause is, again, something which is determined on an individual basis. With some women, the menopause can occur almost immediately after puberty, reflecting the soul's decision that it would be inappropriate to bear children in this lifetime. Whilst for some women, they remain fertile well into their sixties. There are no hard and fast rules for the range of ages that a woman remains able to bear children, only the individual's own consciousness can determine that.

Most tribal cultures have a tradition where a women who is past the menopause becomes the "crone". This is not a derogatory term in any way. The crone is the wise woman, the keeper of tribal knowledge and the dispenser of wisdom. In this way, decisions made within the tribe were made by the male tribal elders and the tribal grandmothers. A balance.

In our western traditions, which mainly arose due to our religions being male dominated, women have mainly been viewed as baby factories who look after their man. Fortunately, this totally invalid view is beginning to rapidly change. Unfortunately, many women are still held within this kind of view and many of the problems encountered during menopause are due to women's attitudes towards themselves. If I can no longer bear children, then I must be useless. This is the kind of comment we have heard many times from menopausal women. With this kind of brain washing going on, is it surprising that many women have problems at this time. On the good side, society's views are beginning to change and, gradually, older women are starting to regain their position of the holders of wisdom and knowledge, a crone revival.

As this change of status is gradually being accepted by society as a whole, it has a knock on affect on attitudes towards women. Many more women are now starting to understand that they can regain their own power and are taking much more control of their lives. As women begin their route back to themselves, men are also having to change their views and their ways. To most men, a strong woman who stands within herself and her own power is a frightening thing. But men, especially younger men, are starting to work with women and a balance is returning to life. As more and more women regain control of their lives, their health problems, especially ones related to the second chakra, are diminishing.

The same applies to menopausal problems. Women who are aware of their worth tend to have a, comparatively, straight forward menopause. What actually occurs, during this period of a women's life, is that she experiences a range of symptoms. These are normally hot flushes, night sweats, insomnia, headaches and general irritability. Some women also experience a thinning and drying of the vaginal walls making sex uncomfortable.

The general medical view is that the menopause is some kind of illness which requires treatment to "cure" it. This attitude arose from the pharmaceutical companies trying to re-market their oestrogen products into HRT (it is a huge money making industry for these companies) and is a severe distortion of the reality of the menopause.

In consciousness terms, the menopause is the time when the woman can stop being the mother and regain control of her own life. The processes involved within the body to bring about the menopause are quite amazing. The pituitary gland (sixth chakra, see chapter eight) begins to send a new set of hormonal signals through the body and the ovaries and uterus begin to change. The first change is that progesterone levels begin to fall and oestrogen production alters and its levels drop sufficiently (about 50%) to prevent egg cells from being prepared for fertilization. The adrenal glands (see chapter three) begin to alter and to produce progesterone as the ovarian levels begin to fall, keeping this hormone's level sufficient to manufacture the oestrogen. Progesterone is the primary female hormone and all other female hormones, the group of hormones known as oestrogen, testosterone etc., are produced by the body from progesterone. The lining of the uterus alters and begins to produce a hormone known as prostacyclin which helps protect the body against blood clotting and heart disease.

As a note about female hormones. The body is designed to function as it passes through its various stages and hormones are produced in varying quantities to suit each stage. With the rise in the number of hysterectomies carried out at the insistence of the medical profession, this subtle balance is being increasingly disrupted. All illnesses and problems encountered within the body are brought about by imbalances within the chakras caused by the lives that we lead. The body is capable of adjusting itself to virtually any situation it has to cope with, but, it cannot re-balance itself if vital organs are missing. Is it only coincidence that the number of women dying from heart disease is rising directly in line with the number of

74

hysterectomies being performed? - it would seem unlikely. If you are faced with the decision of whether you need a hysterectomy or not, then it would be a good idea to seek a second opinion from a qualified herbalist or qualified homeopath before agreeing to surgery as there are a number of alternative approaches which can relieve many of the symptoms that prompt doctors into recommending hysterectomy.

At the onset of menopause, the whole of a woman's body readjusts itself to a changed set of circumstances, a new freer phase of life. Traditional tribal cultures celebrate menopause as it is a transition into wisdom.

To assist with the symptoms of menopause, some women take oestrogen and progesterone supplements. These supplements take several forms, but most women opt for Hormone Replacement Therapy (HRT) which is supplied, on prescription, by their medical practitioner. We are amazed by the number of doctors who are, apparantly, unaware of the dangers and side effects of HRT. Even if HRT is taken, once you stop the treatment, you will still have to go through the menopausal bodily re-adjustments (see chapters fifteen and twenty one).

One major, and very serious, side effect which we have noticed with long term use of HRT is that the eyesight can suffer. Most of our clients report that they have difficulty focusing and they are noticeably more short sighted. This eye problem is caused by the artificial progesterone (progestin) contained within these drugs. This particular artificial hormone tends to coat the optic nerves creating pressures which can affect the eyesight. Virtually all of our women clients who are taking HRT have experienced this problem.

With the rise of interest in alternative approaches to health problems, a large number of treatments are available which help with progesterone and oestrogen but which do not involve taking artificial hormones. Several of these alternatives are listed in chapter fifteen. If progesterone levels can be stabilised within the body, many of the menopausal symptoms do not occur, or at least their affects minimised and the length of time that the symptoms persist can be greatly reduced. So many of these symptoms are actually produced by oestrogen dominance created by the pill or HRT and compounded by artificial oestrogens in the environment.

If you are taking HRT, especially for a long time, then coming off the drugs can have side effects, most of which are more akin to withdrawal symptoms than anything to do with the menopause. All of the alternative suggestions listed in chapter fifteen do work, but if on HRT, they should, initially, be taken alongside the HRT whilst you gradually reduce the levels of HRT you are taking. See also chapter twenty one.

The menopause is a natural part of life. Whilst the body is undergoing this level of change there will inevitably be symptoms generated by this change. If you have your life in control and are adequately expressing your soul's wishes in regards to the function of the second chakra, then the symptoms will not be too severe or persist for very long. If you have had a hysterectomy, or are experiencing excessive menopausal symptoms, there are a number of alternative remedies available which can help the body to regain some of it's natural balance. Some suggestions will be found in chapter fifteen or you can consult with a qualified practitioner, such as an expert on natural hormone alternatives.

As we said at the beginning of this section, only you can determine the root cause, or causes, of your particular problem. How you deal with these problems can only be determined by the way in which you live your life. If your problems are brought about by your relationship, then you have two choices. Either resolve your relationship situation in a way which suits you or walk away. If this is not possible, then you have to turn to an activity which allows you to express the chakra's primary function and take up a creative way of expressing your feelings. Creativity is the second chakra's primary function and energy put into this side of your life can override any dysfunctions in the secondary function. The problems listed here and the suggestions to help heal them sound very harsh, but the only real way forward out of these particular problems is to regain control of your life and to express your wishes, particularly in creative terms.

There are complementary approaches which can help to relieve the symptoms of these particular problems and these are listed in chapter fifteen.

Male Problems

Male second chakra problems are, obviously, not as extensive as female problems, mainly because men have less bits to go wrong. Male problems tend to be: inability to achieve an erection, testicular discomfort and prostate problems.

Virtually all of the problems experienced by men, in these organs, are for the same reasons for women having problems in their corresponding organs - lack of creativity. Having said that, another source of men's problems is also related to social conditioning. We seem to have laid down very rigid stereotypical roles for the sexes, mainly due to religious conditioning, which are only now beginning to change. Women are the home makers and men are the providers. The conditioning can be so strong that any deviation from these roles can have major affects on the way in which we think about ourselves. Stop a man from being the provider and he ends up with all kinds of health problems. However, as "maleness" is usually defined as a man's ability to achieve an erection, this is the region of his body which can be the first to suffer. So, in a lot of ways, the second chakra functions relate to our sense of identity as a sexual being, particularly in the case of men.

Men are seen as being the strong silent types who go out and kill the sabre toothed pig in order to bring home the bacon. Men who have a more sensitive, caring and creative side are not seen as "real men". Any threat to this way of thinking results in the man's second chakra becoming drained of all energy. On the other hand, men who are artists, painters, musicians etc. also tend to have very active sex lives. So, we have complete conflict and deeply held misconceptions. Most male problems arise because they become locked into the provider role and totally forget about and, quite often, deliberately suppress their creative side. A well turned clay pot can be as effective as the drug "Viagra".

As with female problems, it is impossible to define male problems in terms of specific situations. They occur on a purely individual basis and can only be fully diagnosed by taking a close look at each individual's life. However, there are particular circumstances which will produce similar affects.

If we start with the organ which holds the greatest sway in a man's affections, the penis. The penis has two functions, to eliminate body waste from the bladder and, secondly, to become erect in order to have sex. Most men do not have too many problems with the first function, except as a secondary condition (see below and the previous chapter). So, when men say that they have penis problems, they are talking about their ability to have and maintain an erection. Most erection problems come about because the man is locked too much into the provider role and does not put enough energy into his creativity or into his relationship. Alternatively, problems can arise because the man is in a new relationship and is insecure about his place or his role (in this situation the man can also have lower back pain - see the first chakra). As with the first chakra, the first indications that there is a problem with the man's attitudes is in the muscles. So, in many respects, an inability to achieve or maintain an erection is a warning sign that there is a problem with the way in which the man is dealing with this element of his consciousness and problems with the other organs can arise, especially with the prostate, if this first indicator is not paid attention to.

Testicular problems tend to first manifest themselves as a low sperm count. There are many reasons for this occurring, however it is usually due to the man not wanting to father a child. This could be a very temporary situation such as in "yes I want a child, but not just at the moment" to a more long term problem as in "I probably do want children, but I am not ready for that yet", or even "I'm not sure if I want children, but I know that I do not want you to be the mother" and any other variation you can think of between the extremes given here. If the situation continues, this can lead to the testicles becoming swollen, sometimes even shrivelled. In extreme cases, it can even lead to testicular cancer, something which is increasingly common.

Testicular problems, such as a low sperm count, are brought about by the attitudes given above, reducing the energy available from the chakra. However, the problems can be made worse by external factors. Our environment is now filled with hormones, especially artificial oestrogens. This situation has arisen for several reasons. Firstly, the increase in plastic usage. Most of the types of plastics used to bottle water and fizzy drinks are made from a type of plastic which contains a polymer very similar to oestrogen. When these bottles are filled with liquid, some of the polymer leaks into the fluid. If the bottles are warmed, such as by being stored in a warm place or exposed to the sun, the liquid contained within the bottle can become saturated with the artificial oestrogen. Secondly, as meat is sold by the kilo, artificial oestrogen is injected into food animals at an alarming rate to boost fat production and encourage water retention to make the animals larger and more valuable. Thirdly, the usage of artificial oestrogen contained within the Pill and HRT. All of these factors are then combined as these artificial hormones are not easily removed from sewage and our rivers are becoming saturated with artificial oestrogen which enters into our water supplies.

So, men are increasingly taking in artificial versions of the female hormone and problems with sperm counts are rising because of it. Even though this is an external factor, if the chakra can be brought back to its full function, then even these problems can be overcome (for the effects of these artificial hormones on women, see chapters fifteen and twenty one).

If the situations which led to erection or testicle problems continue unchecked or unresolved, they can lead on to problems with the prostate. The prostate is the organ which produces semen. Semen is the white, sticky fluid which forms the bulk of an ejaculation and is a carrier for the sperm. The prostate begins to produce semen as soon as a man is through puberty. In healthy situations, semen production is virtually non stop. It is the main reason for pubescent boys having wet dreams and spontaneous ejaculations.

If the prostate becomes dysfunctional, it tends to swell and disrupt the flow of urine through the urethra. When emptying the bladder, the flow of urine should be constant. A good indicator of a potential prostate problem is when the flow becomes intermittent or stops and restarts when urinating. If the swelling remains unchecked, it can result in pain just under the scrotum and even localised sweating. Ultimately, the prostate can become irritated and even cancerous.

We have been consulted by several men with prostate cancer and have usually found the same underlying causes and the same methods of dealing with the problem. Most of these men have been in their fifties and sixties and have led lives which meant that they always saw themselves as responsible providers for their families. This meant them working extremely hard and usually very long hours. As healers, part of our healing work we try to identify the root causes for a health problem and give our clients "homework" to help them deal with the root causes of their problems for themselves (we can take away the symptoms, but we cannot take responsibility for our clients' lives). In these cases, the homework has been to take up some kind of creative hobby. When we have seen these clients again, the ones who did their homework have clear prostates, those who have not started to look at their problem and take responsibility for it, have still had some kind of problem with their prostate. If they take up a creative pursuit, the symptoms usually disappear, if they do not, the problem ultimately returns and we have increasing difficulty in putting any energy into the region.

All of these problems can only be cured by dealing with the issues which brought about the problems in the first place. Treatment of the symptoms can help to provide additional time whilst you find a way to resolve your problems. Listed in chapter fifteen are suggested alternative approaches which avoid using drugs.

In Conclusion

Second chakra problems boil down to two very straight forward choices. If you have problems with these organs then you are either not being creative, or not creative enough, or, you have relationship problems.

The easiest way of diagnosing where it is you need to look in your life is to ask yourself one simple question: Does the relationship I am in satisfy my needs on every level? If the answer to that is yes, then your health problems lie in a lack of creative activity. If the answer is no, then you either need to find yourself a new partner or you need to take up a creative hobby. The same applies if you are not in a relationship. If you have problems with these organs then the only cure is to take up a creative pursuit.

If you answer yes to the question and are being fully creative, but still have these types of problems then either you are not being strictly honest with yourself or you need to come and see us for a free consultation as you are totally unique.

Also take a close look at the description of the Bach Flower Remedies given in appendix two. These can help to deal with issues on a root cause level in terms of personality characteristics and attitudes. Be totally honest with yourself in assessing your character!

Chapter Five

The Third Chakra

The third chakra is located on the spine in a position that corresponds to about one inch (25mm) above the tummy button. This chakra is formed within the developing fetus in the twenty to twenty four week period into the pregnancy. Its primary function is to deal with issues of personal power, effectively how seriously we are taken by the people around us. Its secondary function is to deal with the emotions. Both functions are active from birth but slowly develop as the child develops and begins to deal with it's life.

The organs connected with the third chakra are: the liver, the gall bladder, the spleen, the pancreas, the stomach, the large and small intestines (see illustration number eight).

All of these organs deal with digestion and blood cleansing. They are also totally linked in terms of organ function, each organ depends upon the other to function correctly. However, in terms of chakra function, each organ is responsible for one element of our emotional well being. In this way, a problem with one of these organs relates very specifically with a particular emotion. Personal power issues can affect the whole region but will most affect the organ that relates to the emotion we express to respond to the situation we find ourselves in.

The Liver
The liver is the largest organ in the abdomen. It is located in the right side of the abdomen and is wedge shaped with the thinner end to the left side of the body. It is high up within the abdominal cavity and sits behind the lower ribs, just under the

diaphragm. It is reddish brown in colour and of a "spongy" consistency.

Like the kidneys (see chapter three), the main function of the liver is to filter the blood. Most of the blood received by the liver comes from the intestines and is, therefore, very rich in essential vitamins and minerals. This mixture includes substances such as glucose, amino acids, fats, minerals and vitamins. The liver processes these according to the needs of the body and either converts them into useful nutrients or disposes of the waste through the blood into the kidneys. It also cleanses the blood of old blood cells and converts them into bile. The bile is stored in the gall bladder (see below) and added into the intestines to aid digestion.

The liver also breaks down toxic substances into safer chemicals and either re-uses them within the body or passes them onto the kidneys. For example, digested proteins produce ammonia which is highly poisonous to the body, this is chemically altered into urea which is the greatest bulk of urine. It also breaks down alcohol into substances which are not so harmful to the body. The liver is able to regenerate itself after disease, toxic damage or injury to a remarkable degree. Other bodily organs could not take the kind of abuse we give to the liver and continue their functions. However, there comes a point where even the liver cannot deal with the amount of rubbish we sometimes put into it. When this happens, sections of liver cells die off and form into nodules, this is a condition known as cirrhosis of the liver and can have a "knock-on" affect on many of the body's organs and systems.

The liver could be described as the body's central processor, everything that we put into the body eventually ends up passing through the liver. This is also how the liver functions as far as the chakra is concerned. All of our emotional issues pass through the liver and are distributed into the other, associated, organs. The liver itself deals with the two most powerful of emotions, fear and jealousy.

Both of these emotions are ones which, if we experience them at all, are usually only short term. We can experience them in all kinds of situations, especially fear, and they will temporarily cause a mild variation in the liver's function. If the emotions persist for any length of time, they can result in some of the organ's filtering functions breaking down, producing a slightly jaundiced appearance to the skin and the whites of the eyes ie. slightly yellow.

These emotions can cause long term damage. However, most damage occurs when we have been experiencing the emotion over a long period and then take other actions which put the slightly weakened liver under greater stress. With most people, these other actions usually take the form of excessive amounts of alcohol or heavy, addictive drugs such as heroin. With substances such as these, the body is normally strong enough to deal with them in the short term, however long term use, especially when there are strong emotions present, can cause damage. The main reason for people turning to these substances is to try to hide the emotional fear they have been experiencing over a prolonged period. Most addicts and alcoholics are calling for help, they need help and reassurance that they no longer need to be afraid. Once these people recognise that the problem stems from their emotions, then they can begin to recover. Go and speak to some reformed addicts, and they will tell you that their addiction originally stemmed from a constant sense of fear and they used the drugs to try and deal with it, to switch it off.

In recent years, there has been a large increase in liver problems. These kinds of problems are usually generated without the sufferer being an alcoholic or a drug user. The way in which we currently live our lives promotes a climate of fear and jealousy. The workplace is now an environment where we are expected to perform at levels far in excess of those of only a few years ago. Many companies force their employees to strive for ever increasing targets for sales, performance, etc.. This constant pressure puts the workforce into a situation where

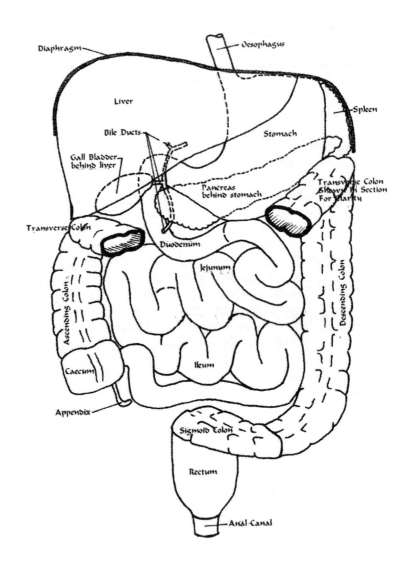

Illustration Number Eight - The Third Chakra Organs

they are forced into being made jealous of the high rewards for those who do meet their targets and in constant fear of losing their jobs if they fail to meet their own. There is nothing wrong in being ambitious, it is taking it to excess that causes the problems.

These kinds of situations can also lead to skin problems such as psoriasis and excema. As these are skin problems they also relate to the first chakra (see chapter three). The way in which these two situations link together is where we become insecure in relation to situations where we are also under threat in some way, such as the workplace example given above. These situations can lead to the liver's blood cleansing functions being affected causing skin eruptions (see also the lymphatic system covered by the spleen below).

Liver problems can only really be dealt with on a root cause basis. What is it that is making you afraid? Fear comes from a sense of lack of self assurance. Learn to recognise that. Take self defence or self assurance classes to help build up your self image.

Jealousy also stems from the same root cause. If you are jealous of somebody then you are comparing yourself to them and, because you do not think much of yourself, you think that you are somehow less than them - comparisons such as these are totally invalid.

The remedies suggested in chapter sixteen deal with the symptoms of liver problems, but there is no substitute for reclaiming your self worth.

The Gall Bladder

The gall bladder is a small, fig shaped, hollow sac that sits inside a small depression in the back of the liver. When the liver produces bile it is stored within the gall bladder. When produced, bile is about 97% water, the gall bladder absorbs and discharges most of this water, concentrating the bile, which it stores until ready for use.

When we eat fatty foods, the gall bladder releases the bile into a duct which enters the exit from the stomach (the duodenum). The bile breaks down the fatty food which makes it water soluble and, therefore, easier to digest. The bile, from the liver, also contains salts and other substances which help to make up the concentrated bile from the gall bladder. If the gall bladder doesn't function fully, the salts can become lodged within the gall bladder and duct which blocks the flow of bile. If this blockage is not dealt with, gallstones can form. Gallstones can be anything from smaller than one millimetre to anything up to two centimetres (one inch) in diameter.

Gallstones used to be surgically removed but are now usually broken down into smaller pieces by ultrasound treatment (lithotripsy). Blocked gall bladders are still, usually, surgically removed. If the gall bladder is removed, the bile from the liver is discharged directly into the duodenum in it's original, watery, state. This makes the breaking down of fatty foods very difficult and can result in other digestive problems. Many more women have gall bladder problems than men, when you work out why gall bladder problems occur, it is not difficult to see why.

The gall bladder stores anger. This is anger which we have felt but have been unable, or unwilling, to express. Every time we feel anger but do not let it out, it goes into the gall bladder.

As healers, virtually every woman we see has some form of gall bladder problem. This can range from intermittent blockages to small stones. When we work on the gall bladder, we always warn our clients that there will be some reaction as the stored anger clears.

This reaction will vary from client to client and can vary from a couple of days of severe flatulence to a sense of extreme anger. This second condition was so bad with one client, having never expressed her anger at anything - including being abused as a child, that she went home and totally trashed her apartment.

There are several ways of dealing with this problem, all of which are to do with letting go of the stored anger. First of all, the best way of dealing with your anger is to express it to the person who made you angry in the first place. This clears the air between you, allows you to make your point and prevents any residual resentment (especially gall bladder problems). However, this is not always possible or desirable, especially if the person making you angry is your boss, your best friend, or a child, so you must find other ways of releasing the suppressed anger.

We have a homeopath friend who recommends her clients go to a junk shop and buy as many old and cracked plates as they can afford and go out and smash them - very effective and it also provides you with a large quantity of raw material for making mosaics (very good for the first and second chakras). If this approach isn't for you, then try the old tribal method of "giveaway". Giveaways are an extremely effective and useful way of dealing with this problem and it can be carried out in either of two ways, both of which involve writing down your anger. The first is to write all of your feelings, angers and hurts in the sand at the low tide mark, then stand back and watch the incoming tide wash all of your angers away. Don't worry about the sea, it's big enough to take them. If it isn't possible to make it to the beach or there isn't enough beach to write all of your grievances down, you can write it on paper. It doesn't matter how much you write or even what you write. This is for your eyes only, nobody else will see it. So, get everything onto that paper, all of your hurts, your angers etc. etc., everything. Once you have begun to write, you will be surprised just how much emotion you have stored away. Start at any point you like in your life and just write down what comes to mind. This is not meant to be a novel so it does not need to be grammatically correct, all that matters is that you express your feelings.

Once you have written everything down, dispose of it, don't read it back to yourself as it will put all of the emotions back into your system. Burning is the best way as it totally disposes of the evidence, and, if burnt with dried sage, it can also help cleanse any emotional residue. This is best done out of doors as it could set off the smoke alarms, especially if you use dried sage as it produces a large amount of smoke. If you do use dried sage, fresh sage doesn't burn very easily, then try to stand within the smoke as this will also help to cleanse your aura of any negative thoughts.

Another way of using the giveaway is to paint your feelings. Again, it does not matter what these paintings look like, just as long as you are expressing what your feelings are. They can be just blobs of colour, abstract shapes, anything, as long as, to you, they mean your anger, frustration etc.. These paintings can be disposed of in the same manner as the written form.

Expressing your anger is the best approach, giveaways are the next best thing, but in the meantime there are some suggested remedies which can help with the symptoms and these are listed in chapter sixteen.

The Spleen
The spleen is located high on the left side of the abdomen, between the stomach and the left kidney, just below the diaphragm and is about the size of a clenched fist. The spleen is the body's main blood filter, clearing the blood of the residue from the breakdown of red blood cells and other unwanted semi-solid material. The spleen contains the largest collection of lymph tissues within the body (for details of the lymphatic system, see chapter six). It is also one of the major producers of antibodies. Antibodies are part of the body's immune system, the primary fighter of illness and disease.

Basically, the spleen works by taking the blood supply from the heart and filters it by passing it through various structures and specialised cells. It chemically codes each blood component as being useful or not useful, the blood then passes to the liver which processes the information provided by the spleen. As viruses etc. enter the spleen's filters they are identified and antibodies produced to kill the virus etc., keeping us as fit and healthy as possible.

The upper body lymphatic system is controlled by the fourth chakra, but the lower body lymphs are controlled by the third chakra through the spleen. So, although the spleen is controlled by the third chakra, it is also influenced by the fourth chakra.

As a point of interest, blockages to the lymph glands in the legs and groin are the main cause of cellulite. If the spleen is kept in good condition, then cellulite can be reduced. The lower body lymphs can also be a major contributor to psoriasis in the lower body (see illustrations eleven and twelve).

Another function of the spleen is to provide a substance called intrinsic factor into the stomach. This substance affects several digestive functions and is described below.

On a third chakra level, the spleen stores our unexpressed frustrations, particularly where those frustrations are connected with anger.

There is no easy answer as to how to deal with these frustrations, other than to not let them get into the spleen in the first place. Express yourself is the key phrase of the third chakra. Always say what you want and what you feel and all of the organs remain free and clear. Given that in most people's lives this course of action is not always available, the second best solution is the giveaway. If you do have frustrations in your life which are difficult to deal with then use the giveaway process to help to clear them. Problems with the spleen can lead to some very serious illnesses and it is better to look after it as much as possible, so the remedies suggested in chapter sixteen are intended more for a preventative approach before real symptoms appear. If you have been medically diagnosed as suffering from any of the illnesses connected with a dysfunctional spleen, then we suggest that you consult with a qualified herbalist or a qualified homeopath.

The Pancreas

The pancreas is a longish (16cm - 7inches), thin organ which fits between the spleen and the duodenum (the exit from the stomach). It has two very specific functions, both of which are vital to our wellbeing. The pancreas' first function is to secrete digestive enzymes. Enzymes are chemical "messengers" which help to accelerate the way in which other bodily chemicals act and react. Almost everything that happens in the body, on a chemical level, is controlled by the action of one or more enzymes. This is a similar, but different, messenger system to hormones. From this it can be seen that the body contains many thousands of different enzymes. In the case of pancreatic enzymes, they are secreted into the bile duct from the gall bladder which help to increase the action of the bile in breaking down fatty foods etc..

The second function of the pancreas is to monitor the amount of glucose contained within the blood and muscles. It does this by measuring glucose levels and secreting particular hormones which stimulate cells within the liver to produce more, or less, glucose. The pancreatic hormone which will be best known by most people is Insulin. Insulin helps to accelerate the way in which body cells take up glucose, giving us our physical energy levels.

If insulin levels reduce, it can result in the condition known as diabetes mellitus (known to most people as diabetes). This is a condition where the muscles do not get enough fuel, in the form of glucose, and the body begins to feed off itself to keep us moving around. This is a very serious condition which can have many very serious side effects.

The pancreas also secrets three other hormones, in addition to insulin, the functions of two of them are known. Located at the back of the pancreas are four small glands, known as the islets of Langerhans, and it is these glands which secrete these hormones. One stimulates particular types of glucose producing cells in the liver, different ones from insulin. The second inhibits the action of the growth hormones, it stops the body producing too many cells, it also inhibits some of the function of neural transmitter cells.

As a point of interest, we did come across one seven year old client who found it difficult to concentrate and was, usually, considered to be hyperactive. When we checked through his system, we found that the pituitary gland was not fully formed, reducing the amount of growth hormone in his system. The pituitary gland is covered by the sixth chakra, see chapter eight. As a result of this problem, the neural transmitter hormone mentioned above, somatostatin, was overactive. This reduced the brain's functions sufficiently to inhibit his ability to concentrate. By correcting the pituitary function and balancing the pancreas, we were able to correct the problem. So, problems with the pancreas fall into two groups, digestive and blood sugars (glucose).

From a chakra point of view, the function of the pancreas is a little more difficult to describe. We all have emotions and we deal with those emotions in a way in which we see fit at the time, suiting the circumstances that we find ourselves in. However, this is not necessarily the way in which the soul wants us to deal with them. Essentially, we have a suitable reaction and an unsuitable reaction. A suitable reaction would be where we deal with the situation, fully, as it arises. This involves using a certain amount of force to express our reaction and emotion connected with that particular situation. If we do not use sufficient force in our response, the residue of the correct amount of force becomes lodged in the pancreas. See, we said it was difficult to describe. It is a little abstract, but what it means is that if we should have dealt with a situation by shouting and screaming and all we did was mutter under our breath when we were away from the situation, then all of the shouting and screaming that we didn't do gets lodged in the pancreas.

Where the lack of reaction was due to our being afraid to respond, the blood sugar aspect becomes affected (the hormones that promote glucose production in the liver become suppressed). The digestive response is covered below.

Where the blood sugar response is triggered, it usually leads to diabetes mellitus (it is important to call it by it's full name as there is another form of diabetes. This is called diabetes insipidus which is an extremely rare disorder of the pituitary gland which can affect the kidneys). Diabetes mellitus has two forms. Type 1 diabetes mellitus is caused by a break down in the insulin producing cells. Type 2 diabetes mellitus begins with the onset of age and is also linked to obesity. Whether type 1 or type 2, the root cause is the same. With type 1 the pancreas is responding to current or recent problems and situations. Type 2 occurs where the problems have been buried away over many years and only manifest themselves as the body begins to age.

Again, the only way of dealing with these problems is to respond appropriately to the situations we find ourselves in at the time that they occur. If it is not possible to respond in this way, then the only other course of action is with the giveaway. Whatever, the problems have to be dealt with and released out of the body otherwise a full cure will not be possible.

If you have diabetes and wish to change from your insulin injections, you will need to consult a qualified herbalist or a qualified homeopath. The remedies suggested in chapter sixteen can help some mild conditions.

The Stomach

The stomach is located in the upper left part of the abdomen and is immediately below the diaphragm. It is in front of the spleen, above the pancreas and partially behind the liver. Essentially, it is an open ended sac like organ. The stomach is the receiver of the food that we eat and the fluids that we drink. It is connected to the mouth by the oesophagus, which passes through the chest cavity and the diaphragm, it is also connected to the small intestines by the duodenum.

The stomach's function is to break down the food that we eat in order for it to be digested by the intestines. It does this by secreting stomach acid, a modified form of hydrochloric acid, and secreting an enzyme called pepsin. Pepsin breaks down proteins into a form that is easier to digest. The lining of the stomach looks like a "squidged" together wet paper bag, full of troughs and ridges. As the stomach fills with food, it expands and the ridges become smoothed out. The lining is made up of a huge collection of finely ridged cell structures (if you ironed out the stomach lining it would look like a sheet of needlechord fabric) which produce mucous, to keep the stomach moist, the acid and the pepsin.

As food enters the stomach it is turned into a paste by the actions of the acid, pepsin and the muscles of the stomach. This paste is then slowly passed into the duodenum where the bile from the gall bladder and the enzymes from the pancreas are added before it passes into the small intestine for digestion. The stomach lining also contains a large number of cells that belong to the lymphatic system and are controlled by the function of the spleen. These lymph cells secrete a substance known as intrinsic factor which binds together with vitamin B12 which allows the absorption of the intrinsic factor into the lining of the small intestine to aid digestion. If the intrinsic factor is not properly absorbed, then it can lead to a vitamin B12 deficiency which is known as pernicious anaemia.

Stomach disorders include a dry stomach, which comes from a lack of pepsin and mucous. This allows the stomach acid to irritate the stomach lining. Too much stomach acid is usually caused by a back problem, see chapter three, the first chakra. A dry stomach brings about a set of conditions where a particular form of bacteria can breed and multiply. Stomach and duodenal ulcers are caused by this bacteria. The bacteria is called helicobacter pylori.

To understand the chakra's affects on the stomach, we have to become very literal. These are situations which we were so unhappy with that we could not "stomach" them. The way in which the stomach becomes affected will depend on the other emotions involved in the situation. Sometimes, the response can be immediate. If we come across an unpleasant scene, such as an accident, where we do not have a suitable emotional response, we can vomit. Sometimes the problems can be more long term where we are forced to "swallow" our frustration which affects the spleen, resulting in a dry stomach and acid irritation (the mucous and acid production are largely controlled by the action of the spleen), etc.. So you can begin to see how these things work together to create particular problems.

For short term problems, we obviously need to get ourselves out of the situation. For long term problems, we need to look at how the functions of the associated organs have been affected and deal with the underlying causes of the problems that we have.

As an example of how these situations can link together, we can give you a case history. We were approached by a lady in her seventies who had terminal stomach cancer. The cancerous tissues were very extensive and she had been told that she had no more than six months to live. She was a victim of her time. Women of this generation were brought up in a climate where their sole purpose in life was seen as being a good wife and mother. These kinds of social pressures meant that this highly intelligent, ambitious woman had to swallow all of her hopes and aspirations and settle down to the role of wife and mother. She hadn't really resented the situation as she had done her job extremely well and ensured that her children had as many opportunities as possible, at whatever cost to herself. Eventually, this constant act of "swallowing" her self manifested itself as stomach cancer.

Stomach cancer usually occurs in women when they are in their sixties and seventies (in the same way as osteoporosis - see chapter three). This is the time when their children are independent and they can take an honest look back on their lives and begin to grieve for their lost life. It would be easy for us to say that they should have been more forceful in their earlier life and to have done the things that they wanted to do, but we are standing and looking from the perspective of the nineteen nineties where many more freedoms exist. Women who were born in the nineteen twenties and thirties did not have our freedoms. Social and religious pressures meant that women were not allowed to do the things that they wanted to do. The few women, from this time, who were brave enough to fight these pressures and opinions, were the ones who changed the world and gave us our freedoms.

So we have a lady who had done what was considered to be the right thing and ended up with stomach cancer. We spent a long time with her and explained how her illness had originated and how she could help herself deal with the illness. Some time later, she returned to the hospital for a further set of tests. The new x-rays showed that the stomach cancer had gone and the stomach tissue was now normal. Unfortunately, what the x-rays also showed was that her pancreas was now cancerous and the doctors' diagnosis was that this new cancer was terminal and medically untreatable.

From a chakra viewpoint, this new condition does make sense. The reasons for the stomach cancer are detailed above. By healing the stomach, the body disruption caused by the unresolved issues in this lady's life transferred themselves into the next weakest organ, in this case, this was the pancreas (the emotional force used in responding to a situation) and a further cancer was the result. However, by our explaining to her how the soul works through the body, this lady now understood how to deal with the problem and set about dealing with it herself. Two years later, she is doing well and the pancreatic cancer is in remission, she has no further health problems and neither the stomach nor the pancreatic cancer has returned. This lady went back to college and is now doing what she always wanted to do. Whatever age you are, it is never too late to do your own thing! Re-take control of your life and you can even cure your own cancer.

What this case illustrates very well are two points. First, whatever problem you have and no matter how much tissue damage has occurred, the body can be returned to full health. Secondly, by understanding the problem and the mechanisms involved, this lady was able to regain control of her own life and deal with a life threatening illness without assistance from anybody else.

As healers, this lady's case is the perfect example of how healing should work. Our healing appointments usually last about an hour and a half. This time is made up of providing healing to the affected area, or areas, and helping the client to understand the underlying mechanisms and root cause issues that brought about their problems. The clients who go away from us and begin to take control of their lives are the ones who don't get their symptoms back.

Try not to wait until you have a near death experience before you take control of your life!

Suggestions for relieving the symptoms of stomach problems are listed in chapter sixteen.

The Intestines

There are two different types of intestine, the small and the large. Collectively, we know them more commonly as the bowel. The small intestine is immediately below the stomach and once through the stomach, the small intestine begins to digest our food. The small intestine has three sections, each of which perform different functions. The first section is called the duodenum, although we have described it as being the outlet for the stomach, it is actually the beginning of the intestine. At the duodenum, bile and digestive enzymes are added to the food, these help to break the food down so that the rest of the system can remove necessary ingredients to keep the body working. The next section is called the jejunum. This section contains millions of tiny fibre like cells (called villi) which perform virtually all of the digestion and absorption functions. The next section is the ileum. This is the last section of small intestine before it changes into the large intestine. This is, basically, a holding section as most of the nutrients and vitamins etc. have been absorbed as the contents passed through the jejunum.

The large intestine (the colon) starts at the lower right corner of the abdomen where the ileum connects into a section known as the caecum. Attached to the bottom of the caecum is the appendix. The appendix is connected to the first chakra. The caecum is really just a right angle bend in the plumbing which leads into the ascending colon, this extends up to the top of the abdomen, just under the liver. There is another right angle bend which leads into the transverse colon. This runs across the whole width of the abdomen on a line just below the stomach. With another right angle bend, it drops downwards and becomes the descending colon. There is another right angled bend in the bottom left hand corner of the abdomen where it turns into the sigmoid colon. In the middle of the body, in a line with the spine, the sigmoid colon bends again and forms the rectum which leads into the anal canal.

The main function of the colon is to reabsorb water from the bowel contents (this is why you become dehydrated if you have diarrhoea and why faeces is semi-solid). It also secretes mucous to allow for the free flow of the contents, especially around the many bends. As plumbing design goes, the colon (large intestine) could not be worse, too many right angled bends. From the stomach to the rectum, the total length of the intestines (the bowel) is about 7m (about 22 feet).

Problems with the intestines range from the mild, as in diarrhoea and constipation, to the major, as in acute Crohn's disease. Then there is a large variety of symptoms covered by the blanket term Irritable Bowel Syndrome (IBS).

What all of them amount to in the end is that we are hanging onto our emotional "rubbish" (there is a four letter word, in very common usage, which is used to describe the contents of the intestines and would describe what we mean much more graphically, however, we didn't want to use rude words). Intestinal problems begin because we are refusing to let go of an emotion or a point of view which is not doing us any good. What we mean by a point of view is how we think about ourselves in terms of how others think about us, are we strong are we weak, are others better than us or are we better than them etc.. In other words, personal power. Once we let go of these views and begin to reach a balance in how we think about ourselves, we begin to relax and let go of the rubbish we are hanging onto.

To give you an example of how the process works, here is another case history. We were asked to deal with a case of constipation. The lady in question would spend three or four days without a bowel movement. When she did go to the toilet, she described it as being like "rabbit droppings". The problem stemmed from the fact that she dealt with emotional situations by not expressing her side of the argument. It was easier to be non-confrontational and accept the other person's viewpoint than to express her own. Because she almost always responded to these kinds of situations in this way, she did not use any kind of force in expressing her feelings. This lack of force lodged in the pancreas, slowing down the production of digestive enzymes. This slowed down the ability of the small intestines to digest her food. Also, by never expressing her feelings, by hanging onto her "rubbish", the intestines were also prevented from functioning correctly.

Again, the giveaway is probably the easiest approach to these kinds of problems. What is it you do not want to let go of? Whatever it is, it is blocking up your digestive system. This is why most diets do not have a long term benefit. Unless you have let go of the underlying emotion, you will always put weight back on. If you are free of emotional debris, then the body can deal with just about anything that we put into it without harm and without changing our natural body weight or shape.

The remedies listed in chapter sixteen can help with the symptoms of many bowel disorders but until you learn to let go, you will keep going around in circles.

Reflexology can be very helpful in dealing with all of the organs and disorders listed above. Identify the region of the feet which correspond to the region or organ and let somebody massage them for you. The initial pressure should be *very* gentle as the sensation of pressure on these points can be quite sharp. As the intensity of discomfort begins to reduce, the pressure of the massage should be gradually increased until the reflex point feels clear and comfortable.

Working on the corresponding reflex points on the hands can be almost as effective and you can do this for yourself (see illustrations numbered seventeen and eighteen).

In Conclusion

The soul, the consciousness, uses the body to try to talk to us and let us know when we are going in the wrong direction.

With the third chakra, it is personal power issues which manifest themselves as emotions. If we are not expressing our wants and our feelings in a way which maintains our sense of who we are, they become lodged in an appropriate organ.

If we do not clear these emotions the organs become dysfunctional leading to many different health problems. Remember the "old wives" sayings, I was so angry, I felt my gall rising; I just had to vent my spleen etc., they totally fit the situation and recognise the organs where we store particular emotions. As always, listen to what the body is saying by linking your ailment to the chakra. What is your soul trying to say to you and why aren't you listening?

> • Learn to express your emotions fully and clearly. If it is not possible to do so directly to the person who has caused you a problem, use the giveaway as soon as possible.

> • Take self-assurance or assertiveness classes to help you build up your own self image - this will help with problems with other chakras as well.

> • Very carefully and thoroughly read the list of Bach Flower Remedies given in appendix two and use them to help release some of the character traits which can cause some of your problems. Be totally honest with yourself or ask your best friend/partner to choose one or more for you.

Chapter Six

The Fourth Chakra

The fourth chakra is located on the spine at the level of the heart and is the reason why it is sometimes called the heart chakra. Like all of the middle chakras, the fourth chakra enters the fetus' body during the twenty to twenty four week period of pregnancy.

The chakra's primary function is to link the higher, non-physical energies of the consciousness to the lower frequencies of the energies of the physical body. The chakra's secondary function deals with the way in which we express love. This expression can be how we feel for others or how we feel about ourselves. The organs and systems which the fourth chakra controls are: the heart, the blood and circulation; the endocrine system; the immune system.

The Heart, Blood and Circulation

The heart is an extremely muscular organ located in the lower section of the chest, behind the sternum bone. The main bulk of the heart is slightly to the left of the centre line of the sternum. The heart comprises four chambers, these are the right and left atrium and the right and left ventricle. The heart is the pump that keeps blood circulating around the whole body. Blood supplies oxygen, nutrients and innumerable chemicals, hormones and enzymes to every part of the body (through the arteries). All of these various components inform the organs and muscles etc. what to do and when to do it.

The blood also removes carbon dioxide (used oxygen), toxins and other harmful material from all of the body's tissues and organs and delivers it into the cleansing organs (through the veins) and back to the heart.

The heart has two sides, one side deals with blood without oxygen, this is called the systemic circulation, and the other side deals with blood with oxygen and is called the pulmonary circulation.

The used blood, the systemic, de-oxygenated blood, arrives in the right atrium. It is then pumped at low pressure into the right ventricle. From here, it is pumped at high pressure into the lungs. Whilst in the lungs, the blood takes on oxygen (the lungs are controlled by the fifth chakra, see chapter seven). From the lungs, the now oxygenated, pulmonary, blood is returned into the left atrium. It is then pumped at low pressure into the left ventricle. The left ventricle then pumps the oxygen rich blood at high pressure into the rest of the body. Both of these pumping sequences happen simultaneously, the left and right atriums and the left and right ventricles pump at the same time. When we feel our heart beat, it is the high pressure pump of the ventricles that we are feeling.

The heart is made from particular types of muscles which generate their own "electricity" to keep it pumping. In this way, it does not need any stimulus from the brain, like all other muscles do, to keep pumping. The oxygen rich, pulmonary, blood is pushed around the body and into every single organ, muscle and out to the skin. It deposits its oxygen into all of the body's cells and collects used oxygen, in the form of carbon dioxide, and circulates it back to the heart for pumping into the lungs for a new oxygen supply. (See illustrations numbered nine and ten).

The blood is made up of red corpuscles (erythrocytes), platelets, (thrombocytes) and white cells (leukocytes). The percentages of each ingredient is, roughly, 98.5 - 99% red corpuscles, 0.6 - 1.0% platelets and 0.2% white blood cells. All of these constituents are manufactured by the bone marrow.

The red corpuscles are modified body cells which are specifically designed to take in and discharge oxygen. These are the cells that give blood it's distinctive colour. They are a form of protein called haemoglobin. To give some idea of how many there are, each litre (about $1^3/4$ pints) of blood contains between 4,000 million and 6,000 million red corpuscles. These cells collect oxygen from the lungs and transfer it into every other cell in the body. They swap the oxygen for carbon dioxide from the cells, and carry it back to the lungs where they swap it for oxygen. Red corpuscles live for about 120 days and when they die they are cleared out of the blood stream by the spleen (see chapter five).

Platelets are small pieces of cell which help the blood to form clots when we damage the skin. If these were not present in the blood, we would bleed to death every time we cut ourselves. When people are described as haemophiliacs, their blood lacks the right amount of platelets. Platelets live for about 10 days.

White blood cells are part of our immune system and their production and usage is determined by the organs that are part of that system, see below. Essentially they bind with organisms that are attacking our bodies, such as bacteria and viruses, and destroy them.

To help the blood to circulate, the veins and arteries contain "valves" which help prevent the blood from going backwards. They help to pump the blood around the regions which are furthest from the heart, especially in the legs. These valves are located at intervals along the blood vessels. They open and close periodically to allow the free flow of blood in one direction only. If the valves become deficient, the section of blood vessel immediately below it becomes expanded because it now has to take the weight of two sections of blood. We call these expansions varicose veins.

The blood is an immensely complex biochemical soup. Everything that happens within the body, apart from the nerves, is given its instructions through the blood.

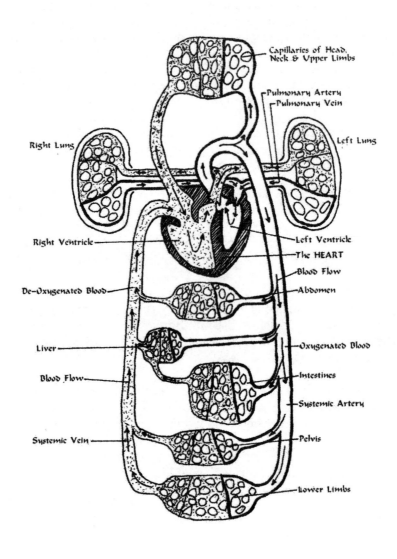

*Illustration Number Nine - Schematic Illustration of the
Circulation System*

Virtually all blood disorders are caused by external sources, but they have their root in how we respond to our own needs. If we are happy and comfortable with ourselves then the body is, generally, able to fight off any outside "attack". If we have doubts about what we think about ourselves, then other systems, throughout the body, combine together to weaken our immunity, see below. Conditions such as leukaemia occur when we take this lack of self love to extremes. Leukaemia is a condition where the bone marrow stops producing red blood cells and produces mainly white blood cells. This literally stops feeding the heart and the rest of the body with oxygen and we eat ourselves from the inside out. We love ourselves so little we feel that we ought to disappear.

Heart conditions, such as angina and heart attacks, occur because we have extreme difficulty expressing our love for others. We keep our love so tightly enclosed within ourselves that it virtually stops the fourth chakra from functioning, taking all of the energy out of the heart. Like all of our health symptoms, heart attacks come in stages. It starts with a gentle tap on the shoulder by the soul, a heart murmur. If we ignore it, we receive a harder nudge with a minor stroke or angina. If we ignore this we have the baseball bat, a heart attack. Heart attacks and strokes are not always fatal the first time that one occurs. However, if we ignore the first one, by not changing our attitudes to others and expressing our love more freely, the second one is usually fatal.

Angina, or more correctly, angina pectoris is a condition where one of the arteries supplying the muscles of the heart with blood (coronary artery) becomes slightly blocked and the muscles do not receive sufficient blood to function correctly. Symptoms of angina pectoris are a feeling of a tight band around the chest and a sharp pain within the chest and the feelings of pain and pressure in one of the limbs, usually the left arm. A heart attack occurs when one of these arteries becomes fully blocked and the heart stops beating all together, either temporarily or permanently.

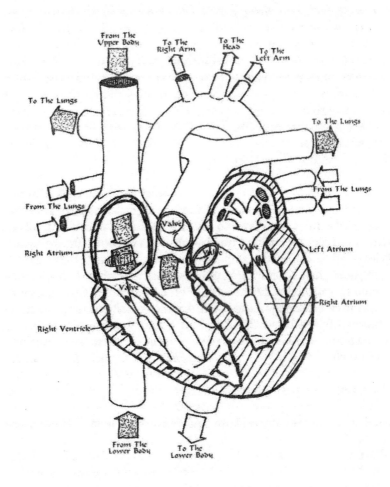

Illustration Number Ten - The Chambers of the Heart

A stroke is where the arteries feeding the brain partially collapse or become partially blocked (thrombosis), reducing the supply of blood to the brain. The affects of this loss of blood supply will vary considerably depending on the region of the brain affected and will vary from a mild discomfort to the loss of movement of one side of the body, either temporarily or permanently. Severe strokes can be fatal.

Many blood conditions also relate to other organs. As an example: a modified form of cholesterol known as LDL can cause a fatty deposit to form on the inside of the arteries, a condition known as hardening of the arteries, or athero-sclerosis. This condition only occurs when we go against the desires of the soul. See chapter twenty one for more details of cholesterol and the role it plays in the body and the popular misconceptions associated with this substance.

For example, there are several tribal peoples who have, by western standards, extremely high cholesterol levels (such as the Masai peoples of Africa) and yet the incidence of heart conditions amongst these peoples is exceptionally low. Cholesterol is an essential part of healthy cell production and is, therefore, produced by the body itself. The organ that produces cholesterol is the liver. If you look at chapter five, you will see that the liver deals with fear. If you put the two together, you have someone who is too afraid to express their love. Literally hardening their heart.

So, the heart and blood are all about love. How we express it for ourselves, but not in a selfish, egotistical sense, and how we express love for those around us. If we are free, honest and open with our expressions of love, our hearts remain free and open. If we close ourselves down, by not expressing our love, the heart will let us know, in no uncertain terms, what it thinks about it.

The only real way of dealing with heart problems is to re-learn how to love.

Men, in particular have heart problems. This is mainly to do with social conditioning rather than their wishes and wants. Society expects men to work as hard as possible, and very long hours, in order to provide for their families. Many men become obsessional about their responsibilities and see their provider role as a way of expressing their love. Hard work becomes a substitute for a cuddle. Maintaining this situation over a prolonged period, most of their working life, leads to a situation where they can only express their love for their families through financial means. When such men suffer a heart attack, it gives them the opportunity to change their lives, by slowing them down, and to reassess their priorities. Those who learn to let go and re-learn how to express their love usually describe themselves as being re-born and given a new chance at life. These are the people who go on to live more fulfilling lives. Those who ignore the warning signs and revert to their old patterns of behaviour will usually undergo a second heart attack which is frequently fatal.

With women, the situation is usually one where they have either fallen into the same trap as men or they have withdrawn their love for those around them and turned their expressions of love too far inwards.

All that the soul requires of us is balance. Move the point of balance too far in either direction and we have problems, see the thymus below.

Circulation problems usually manifest themselves as cold fingers and toes, as in Raynaud's disease. This is a condition brought about by not wanting to "step" into areas where you are uncertain about how your love will be accepted. Remember the old expression "having cold feet" about a situation. In reality, you are closing yourself off from a region of your life where this withdrawal is undesirable.

Take a look at the situation you are faced with. It probably has many attractions but you do not have enough confidence in

110

your self to express your love in this way. Ask yourself "what is it I am afraid of? If I am offering an open and honest love, how can it be refused?" If you approach the situation with an open and unconditional love, it will be accepted and the circulation will return.

If you have heart or blood problems, then you should consult a qualified practitioner. Herbalism, in particular, can be extremely effective as can homeopathy.

The suggested remedies given in chapter seventeen are to help keep the blood clean and flowing as well as your love will allow it.

The Endocrine System

The endocrine system is comprised of a series of glands whose functions are controlled by chakras other than the fourth. These glands are the pineal, seventh chakra; the pituitary, sixth chakra; the thyroid and parathyroid, fifth chakra; the thymus, fourth chakra; the adrenals, fourth and first chakras; the pancreas, third chakra; the ovaries and the testes, second chakra. The thymus is also part of the immune system and this is covered below. The linking factor that all of these glands have is the blood and this is why, physically, the system is controlled by the fourth chakra.

Glands are cells, or a collection of cells, which are capable of selectively removing substances out of the blood stream and altering their chemical make up. These altered substances are then put back into the blood supply to perform a different function somewhere else in the body. Substances produced in this way include digestive enzymes, hormones, tears, sweat, milk etc..

Essentially, the endocrine system performs the extremely complex function of keeping the body in balance and functioning correctly.

The endocrine system is the embodiment of the fourth chakra's primary function of connecting the higher, spiritual energies, with the lower, physical energies. It is the body's regulatory system and maintains every organ, every cell, in a condition where it can perform its function correctly. Everything, within the physical body, is monitored and its efficiency is adjusted by the endocrine system.

This is the way in which the soul speaks to us, and how all of our incorrect responses are transferred into the appropriate organs. This system is the key to how imbalances within the chakras become transferred to their connected organs.

Traditionally, the fourth chakra's primary function has been stated as how we express love and the energy merging function is listed as the secondary function. This is a view which we have also expressed in the past. Really, it stems from a lack of understanding of the magnitude of the importance of the endocrine system.

Ask most people, including many doctors, what the endocrine system does and, at best you will receive the answer that it has something to do with the glands, at worst you will get a totally blank look - what's the endocrine system? It has only been through the research work that we have carried out for this book that we have finally understood the magnitude of our error. The description given above sums it up very nicely, this is the physical mechanism that the soul uses to speak to us, how could anything be more important than that?

For health problems connected to the endocrine system, see the whole of this book.

The Immune System

The immune system is the name given to the way in which the body deals with infections and disease. The organs and nodes that make up this system are the "lymphoids". When people speak of the lymphatic system, it is the immune functions of the body that they are talking about (see illustrations numbered eleven and twelve).

The lymphatic system is made up of a collection of organs and nodes which add special cells into the blood stream to fight and destroy anything that is not a necessary part of the body. These can include, viruses, bacteria, old blood cells, etc. (see illustration number eleven). Lymph nodes are collections of lymph cells (usually incorrectly called lymph glands by just about everybody) which manufacture and distribute antibodies to fight infections.

The body has a network of lymph tissues that is nearly as extensive as the circulation system (see illustration number twelve). These lymph tissues, similar in shape to blood vessels, drain unwanted material out of the body and into the lymph nodes. From the lymph nodes, the lymph fluid is drained into the blood vessels where it is dealt with by the appropriate organ such as the spleen or the liver.

The lymph tissues are the ones that take the brunt of too much adrenaline (see chapter three). When in the "fight or flight" mode, the muscles become filled with blood and adrenaline, if we do not react in a physical way, the adrenaline turns to a substance similar to salts.

If these salts were left in place, the muscles would seize up and become very tender. This is why after carrying out unaccustomed exercise, the muscles are usually stiff the following morning - you have overloaded the lymphs and they cannot cope with all of the extra adrenaline salts.

The main organs associated with the lymphatic system are the red bone marrow and the thymus. The bone marrow is the site where most of the body's cells are manufactured. As far as the lymphatic system is concerned, the cells manufactured by the marrow are B cells. B cells are called lymphocytes. Some of these cells migrate to the lymph nodes and other lymph organs. Many migrate to the thymus and become T cells. T cells are lymphocytes which perform slightly different functions to the other lymphocytes formed by other lymphatic organs.

This is starting to become complicated, so let's try and explain it a little more simply. The lymphatic system works like this. The bone marrow produces B cells which travel to the lymph nodes and the lymph organs where they are changed into lymphocyte cells. When something enters the lymph organs that should not be there (these unwanted things can be bacteria, viruses, dead blood cells, etc. and are called antigens), the lymphocyte cells are activated and produce antibodies. The antibodies surround and attack the unwanted material. The antigen is identified, by its chemical signature, and further lymphocyte cells are manufactured, by the bone marrow, that correspond to the particular antigen. This is, essentially, how homeopathy works. By introducing a small quantity of an illness (an antigen), that you want to guard the body against, it stimulates the body to produce particular lymphocyte cells. If you then contract that illness at some future date, the body's defence mechanism has the ammunition ready to fight it.

The antibodies can fight the illness by themselves or they will stimulate the thymus to produce T cells which then "kill" off the antigen. There are several types of T cells, all of which essentially perform the same function. Contained within both the B cells and the T cells are particular cells which have a memory. These cells remember the antigens that the immune system has had to fight. If those particular antigens are encountered at a future date, the memory cells are activated and they stimulate the production of the correct antibodies and T cells. Quite amazing really!

All of the organs and nodes shown in illustration number eleven are able to produce antibodies but only the thymus can produce T cells. The thymus is located in the chest, just above the heart and is wrapped around the tube that passes our breath into the lungs, the trachea (see illustration number thirteen).

The thymus is the main gland of the immune system and of the lymphatic system. All of the T cells are produced by the thymus and all of the upper body lymphs drain into the thymus. The upper body lymphs play a major role in our well being and can have a major effect on our health. At birth, the thymus is, proportionately, a very large organ. This is because it is the body's main defence mechanism. When we are children, the immune system is only beginning to become functional. Any illnesses (antigens) which we encounter are new to it and so the thymus has to work particularly hard to stave off illness and infections. As we encounter each childhood illness, the system builds up its memory banks and we are more able to fight off bacteria and viruses. In a strange way, the more illnesses we have as a child, the better, as we are then better equipped to fight off illnesses as adults as the immune system cells have built up a greater level of memory. This early work carried out by the thymus is extremely important and once past puberty, the thymus actually begins to shrink as our immune system becomes more able to deal with illness from the memory cells. The thymus has another function and, after puberty, this second function begins to play a larger part in our lives. This is to do with the lymph tissues and is the mechanism used by the fourth chakra to alert us to particular types of problems.

As can be seen from illustration number twelve, the lymph system is extremely extensive. It reaches into every part of our bodies and performs an invaluable function, the removal of toxins from physical tissue. All of the chakras have an influence, in one way or another, on the amount of toxins contained within the body. Our primary way of dealing with these toxins is through the lymphatic system and, conse-quently, the thymus. In the same way as the soul uses the endocrine system to talk to and influence the physical body, the physical body uses the lymphatic system to talk to "us". Us

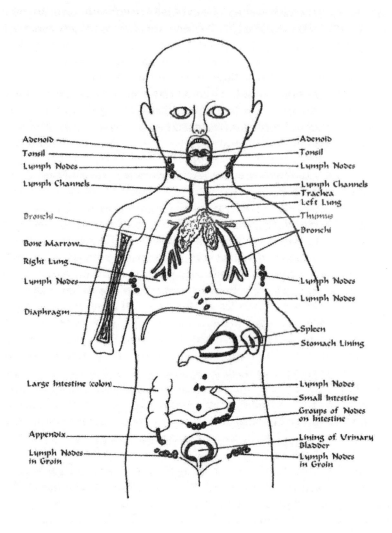

Adenoid
Tonsil
Lymph Nodes
Lymph Channels
Bronchi
Bone Marrow
Right Lung
Lymph Nodes
Diaphragm
Large Intestine (colon)
Appendix
Lymph Nodes
in Groin

Adenoid
Tonsil
Lymph Nodes
Lymph Channels
Trachea
Left Lung
Thymus
Bronchi
Lymph Nodes
Lymph Nodes
Spleen
Stomach Lining
Lymph Nodes
Small Intestine
Groups of Nodes
on Intestine
Lining of Urinary
Bladder
Lymph Nodes
in Groin

Illustration Number Eleven - The Organs and Nodes of the
Immune System

116

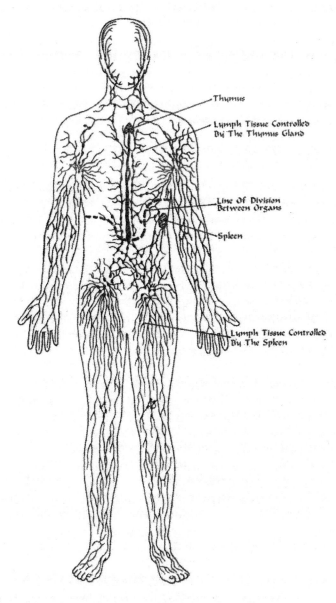

Thymus

Lymph Tissue Controlled
By The Thymus Gland

Line Of Division
Between Organs

Spleen

Lymph Tissue Controlled
By The Spleen

Illustration Number Twelve - The Lymph Network

being the physical element of our total consciousness, the conscious mind. The conscious mind can be thought of as the bit of the mind that we think and understand with, it is the part of you that is reading the words of this book. If the liver is the central processor of what is going on within the physical body, in terms of physical functions, the thymus can be thought of as being the central processor that is the interface between the soul and the physical body.

But.

We are also talking about the fourth chakra, how we express love, and the thymus plays a major role in how the body responds to those messages and expressions. Every single part of our body is served by a part of the lymph system.

Think about this for a moment. How we express, experience or give love has an affect upon the lymphatic system. If we fall in love with someone, our "spirits" lift, our physical body feels like we are indestructible and can move mountains without any effort. Physical, emotional and spiritual harmony. If we fall out of love, zilch. Everything collapses.

So in terms of expressing our love, whether for ourselves or for others, the thymus plays a major role. The example given in chapter two for the fourth chakra is a good one and serves to explain how the thymus works, at least as far as self love is concerned. If we are *in* love, then the body can cope with just about anything as we draw upon our partner's energies as well as our own. But, if we experience problems, especially with how we see ourselves (how we love ourselves), then problems will begin. This is not a question of can, but will. We are not talking about sex, second chakra, but about our image of ourselves, how we see who we are in our loving relationships.

The old expression is very true, if we do not love ourselves, how can we love anybody else? If we do not love ourselves then we expect the person we love to compensate for us and this is where so many second chakra problems stem from. This attitude also has a devastating affect upon the thymus.

The thymus controls the functions of the lymphatic system. It primarily deals with the upper body, but it can also affect the lower body. All of the body's regions where fat collects, for example, is controlled by the lymph system. Although these regions are controlled by other chakras and their well being is controlled by those chakras, if we do not love ourselves then any problems we have in these areas will be compounded by the influence of the fourth chakra through the lymphatic system.

For example, most women have a low self esteem. This is due to many reasons, their image of themselves, the unrealistic image of women presented by the media, the image imposed by their partner, the image imposed by other women, etc.. This all adds up to women being brainwashed into believing that they are less than they are on all levels and fat accumulates. As we said in chapter five, unless the emotion underlying the problem is dealt with then diets will never work. This is true for both men and women, it is just more of an issue as far as women are concerned for the reasons stated above. (Incidentally, this is being written by a man so it is being discussed from a health viewpoint and not a feminist one).

The thymus has so many implications within the body. For example, the lymph nodes within the neck are also controlled by issues of how we love. If these nodes are "up", we can experience very many uncomfortable symptoms. Headaches, including migraines, are primarily caused by blocked lymph nodes. Sinus problems, many ear problems, including tinnitus, can be caused by blocked lymph tissue. Tinnitus, in our experience, is very often caused by the lymph tissues being blocked and putting pressure on one or more of the main blood vessels that run behind the ear. The sounds described by tinnitus sufferers are no more than the sound of the blood rushing through the blood vessels, amplified by the blocked lymphs pushing the vessels against the back of the ear. These lymph tissues become blocked because the thymus is blocked causing the lymph fluid to back up within the lymph tissues. The thymus becomes blocked because we are not expressing our love fully, especially love towards ourselves. Our expressions of love towards others is dealt with by the heart, but the way in which we express love for ourselves is dealt with by the thymus.

Women, in particular, have problems with self love. Even with our new freedoms, women are still considered to be somebody's daughter, somebody's girlfriend, somebody's wife, somebody's mother, etc., they are never allowed to be themselves (this is still being written by a man) and so many problems arise because of this view. As healers, 90% of the women we treat have lymph tissue problems associated directly with the thymus, particularly lymph tissue within the breasts and with the thymus itself. We almost always have to unblock our female client's thymus and underarm lymph nodes. Very often, the whole of the body's lymph tissues are blocked. This situation can be remedied in one of two ways, you can learn to love yourself or you can have a full body lymph massage. Believe us when we say that it is far easier to begin to love yourself than it is to endure a lymph massage. But, so often this is the only course of action open. So many women see the idea of loving themselves as being selfish - "I can't spend any time on myself as I have my husband, my children, my dog, my next door neighbour's pet worm to look after" and just about any other excuse that they can think of.

Try to look at it in this way, the thymus becomes blocked because you do not love yourself. The lymph tissues across the chest become blocked because the thymus is blocked. The underarm lymphs become blocked because the thymus is blocked. Because the thymus is blocked, part of it's immune functions become blocked and you end up with breast cancer.

The thymus produces T cells to fight infection. Part of the T cells' job is to fight cancer cells. With the thymus blocked, it does not fight cancer cells. With the lymph tissues blocked, it provides conditions where cancerous cells can grow. By not loving yourself, accepting yourself as a person worthy of your love, the thymus becomes blocked, the lymph tissue becomes blocked and the thymus' ability to fight cancer cells becomes blocked, with inevitable results. Breast cancer is caused because women do not accept themselves as a person in their own right.

It does not take very much to begin to love yourself. Start to give yourself little treats, a small box of chocolates, a glass of your favourite wine, a couple of chapters of your favourite book instead of doing something for somebody else, a small bunch of flowers that are for you and only you etc.. Start taking the time for yourself and start to say no to other people, especially your family. Lay down a few new rules in your household that begins with "I want". Start to say NO. You do not have to be rude in this, just things like - I am more than happy to help you, but not just at the moment. Understand the meaning of the expression - learn to say no more often because, then, your yesses will have more impact.

This all begins to sound a little bit heavy and that we are trying to lay down the law. But it really isn't that way. So many of the women we treat have breast lymph and thymus problems and this is because they have allowed themselves to be trodden on by everybody else. You do not have to stop being a slave to your family or your friends, if that is what you really want, but what you can do is to create some time for you during your day by saying no to your husband, your children, your best friend, anybody, this allows you to find that small space for you. Try it and you will be surprised by the response. Once you say no, and mean it, your family will understand that they have to stop asking and they will do whatever it is for themselves. Learn to understand that doing everything for every body else does them no favours, and certainly doesn't do anything for you.

Think of how the thymus begins its life. When we are born, it is huge because it does a vast amount of work in protecting the body. As the body grows and remembers how to do things for itself, the thymus shrinks and doesn't have to work so hard. The same applies to your family, when it is young, you have to do everything for it because it cannot do it for itself. Once they begin to grow and the more they do for themselves, the stronger and more able to fight for themselves they become. By making them do as much as possible for themselves you are helping them to face life and all of its challenges. The more that you do for them, the less that they learn and the more unable they will be to cope with life.

Men get heart attacks, women get breast cancer. Two different sides of the same coin. Both sides express their love in ways which are harmful to themselves. Both sides express their love in ways which will ultimately cause the greatest harm to the other (if you are not in the world, how can there be a love shared?).

This is, obviously, not always the case. Women also have heart attacks and men also have lymph, even breast, cancer. If we love in one way only, we end up with problems.

Women are also experiencing a very large rise in deaths from heart disease. It has now taken over from breast cancer as the most common cause of death in older women, especially post-menopausal women. This does not mean that women are becoming increasingly hard hearted. What it does mean is that the sequence of events that can lead to death occurring is changing. When illness forms within the body it is because somewhere along the line we have neglected a region of our personalities or made inappropriate emotional responses. This neglect leads to an organ or system becoming stressed in a way which reflects the chakra wound. Several organs or systems might actually be affected by our neglect, but the illness will manifest itself in the organ most wounded.

When women do not find a way to love themselves, the thymus and lymph tissues will be most affected, sometimes leading to breast cancer. But, the heart will also be affected as they are "hardening their hearts" towards themselves. In cases such as these, where more than one region is affected, the one most affected will be the one which first causes a problem, however, if there are other factors involved, the secondary organ might show up as the weakest.

This is the reason for heart disease becoming more prevalent. Traditionally, the lymph tissue would be the primary problem, however, with the increase in uterus removals (hysterectomy) the body is robbed of an essential hormone (prostacyclin) which protects against heart disease and the heart is now coming under severe stress (see also chapter four). The other factors involved have switched the order in which these health problems manifest themselves with a consequential rise in deaths as, medically, heart disease is much more difficult to diagnose than breast cancer.

In Conclusion

We have to learn to find the balance. This is what the soul wants and what we need most of all. This is the essence of love, how to express it in ways which do the most good. Good can not be done if love is only expressed in one direction, there has to be balance in all aspects of the soul.

  • Learn to express love for your self. Take time off during your day that is just for you (especially women).

  • Learn to express your love for others (men, especially, need to learn this lesson).

  • Read appendix two and discover the right Bach Flower Remedy to help you to let go of some of your unhelpful character traits.

Chapter Seven
The Fifth Chakra

The fifth chakra is located on the spine, on a line that is about mid way between the adams apple and the chin and is often referred to as the throat chakra. This chakra also enters the body in the twenty to twenty four week period into pregnancy.

As we arrive at the chakras that are located above the heart, we enter into regions of our consciousness which begin to move away from purely physical connections. As was stated in chapter six, the fourth chakra is the meeting point for the higher energies and the lower, physical energies. Although the fifth, sixth and seventh chakras have a direct influence on the physical body, their primary and secondary functions become a little less physical and begin to move into the more abstract elements of our lives.

The fifth chakra's primary function is self expression. This is not the same as the second chakra, which deals with expressions of creativity, nor the third chakra, which deals with expressions of our emotions, but deals with expressions of ourselves as a unique individual. This is where we say who we are and what we think. Its secondary functions are connected to communication and judgement.

The organs this chakra controls are the lungs, the bronchial channels and the vocal chords; the thyroid gland, which is largely responsible for the body's metabolism.

The Lungs and the Bronchial Channels

The lungs are spongy, air filled organs one on each side of the chest cavity. They are made up of an outer layer of very elastic, muscle like fibres containing a sponge like "matrix" of branches and tubes that are the bronchials. The function of the lungs is to take in oxygen from the outside air, and transfer it into the blood. As it transfers oxygen to the blood cells it takes carbon dioxide, and other unwanted gasses, out of the blood cells and expels them out of the body as we breath out.

Breathing is carried out by an automatic process, we don't have to think about it, we just do it. Breathing in is carried out by the chest muscles, the ones linking the ribs together, expanding. This enlarges the chest cavity and air is pushed into the lungs by outside air pressure. The diaphragm at the bottom of the chest adds to this pressure by stretching downwards into the abdomen. As the diaphragm stretches downwards, it squashes the organs in the abdomen, see chapter five, especially the stomach, and this movement helps us to digest our food and move it around the digestive system. As we breath in, it stretches the elastic outer layers of the lung. Breathing out is carried out by these outer layers returning to their normal position. So, to breath in, we have to move several muscles, but to breath out, the lungs do it for us.

It's a little like blowing up a balloon. We blow into the balloon's nozzle to inflate it, but if we let go of the nozzle, the elastic skin of the balloon pushes the air back out. The right lung is made up of three "lobes", or sub-divisions and the left lung has two lobes. The left lung is smaller because it has a recess which fits over the heart, called the cardiac notch.

As we breath in through the nose, any large, unwanted, contents of the air, such as dust, is filtered out by the hairs that are at the entrance of the nostrils. The air then fills the nasal cavity which is lined with mucous producing cells which extract smaller pieces of debris out of the air. The air is cleansed by these smaller pieces sticking to the mucous. Smaller particles are air born pollutants such as the muck that comes out of car exhausts and other small particles, such as pollen, are filtered out here. At the back of the nasal cavity, the air enters into the pharynx. This is a muscular tube which is made up of three sections. The first is called the nasopharynx and contains a gland called the pharyngeal tonsil (this is not the same tonsils that are removed with tonsilitis, those are located either side of the back of the mouth and are called the palatine tonsils). It also contains two short tubes, one on either side called the eustachian tubes, which connect into the middle ear and help to balance air pressure within the ear. The pharyngeal tonsil adds water vapour into the air to make it moist. The pharyngeal tonsil also contains a large amount of lymph tissue (see chapter six) which helps to clear any bacteria out of the air before they enter the lungs.

The second section of the pharynx is called the oropharynx and is where the back of the mouth connects to the back of the nose. Beneath the oropharynx is the laryngopharinx. This is the point where the throat divides into two separate "tubes". One tube continues down in a line with the pharynx and forms the oesophagus, which leads to the stomach. The airway goes through a bend at this point and forms the second tube, which is called the trachea, and leads to the lungs. This means that when we breath, air enters the stomach as well as the lungs. Food is prevented from entering into the lungs by a "flap" of skin attached to the back of the tongue called the epiglottis. As we swallow food or liquid, the tongue tilts backwards and the epiglottis covers over the entrance to the trachea directing what we are swallowing into the oesophagus. If food entered into the lungs, it would quickly block the tubes of the lungs and we would die of asphyxiation (lack of oxygen).

As the laryngopharynx turns into a bend and forms the trachea, there is a region known as the larynx. The larynx contains the vocal chords. These are two pieces of strong muscle, or sinew, and each have a "flap" of softer muscle attached. The sounds that we make, speech, singing, grunts, etc., are made by the sinews and flaps opening, closing and vibrating in the larynx as air from the lungs passes through the larynx. Supporting the larynx is a piece of cartilage which is suspended from one of the bones of the jaw. As we speak, sing, swallow, etc., the larynx and cartilage move up and down. This is the movement we see in the throat as we swallow etc., and is more commonly called the adams apple.

The trachea is wrapped in bands of cartilage which help to strengthen it and keep the tube open. The trachea is also wrapped in a large number of large blood vessels. These blood vessels are quite hot and some of the heat is transferred through the walls of the trachea to warm up the air to prevent the lungs from freezing up on a cold day. The trachea continues down through the chest until, just above the heart, it divides into two. Where it divides it forms two smaller tubes which are called the primary bronchi. One tube goes to the right lung and one to the left. Once into the lungs, the tube divides again into the bronchial tree. A branch of the tree goes into each lobe of the lungs.

Each of these branches divides into smaller and smaller tubes which carry the air to every single part of the lungs. Eventually, these bronchial tubes, or bronchiole when they are this small, reduce down to less than one millimetre in diameter. Attached along the length of the bronchiole are small round sacs called the alveolar sacs which contain cells called the alveolus. The alveoli are the gas exchanging cells.

As the primary bronchi pass into the lungs they are joined by the systemic and pulmonary arteries from the heart (see chapter six). As the bronchial trees divide into smaller and smaller bronchi, so to do the arteries. These divide into smaller and smaller sections until they are about the same diameter as the bronchiole and are known as capillaries. The capillaries and the bronchiole join up with each other at the alveoli cells and this is where the gas exchange takes place.

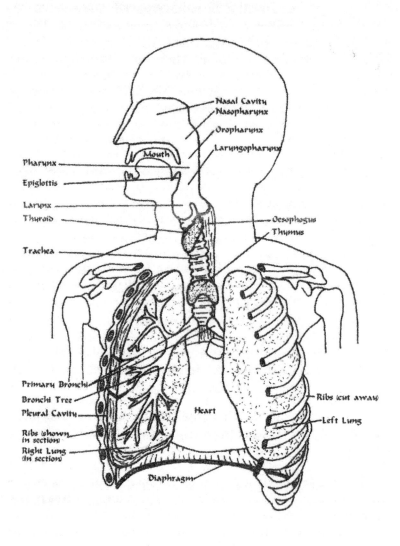

Illustration Number Thirteen - The Throat and The Lungs

The systemic capillaries discharge their load of carbon dioxide and other unwanted gasses into the alveoli cells. The blood cells then take on oxygen out of other alveoli cells and change into the pulmonary capillaries and go back to the heart.

So, as we breath in, we take in oxygen through the air, this is then distributed throughout the lungs and into the blood. Unwanted gasses from the blood are transferred into the lungs and pushed out into the atmosphere as we breath out.

Lining the inside of the ribs, throughout the chest cavity, is a thin membrane called the pleural. This membrane helps prevent the outside of the lungs rubbing up against the ribs, causing friction etc.. There is a small gap between the lungs and the inside of the ribs when we breath normally so that the lungs do not actually touch the ribs. When we breath heavily, however, they do touch and this is when the pleural membrane helps to prevent damage to the outer cover of the lungs. The air gap is known as the pleural cavity.

The Thyroid and the Metabolism

Wrapped around the trachea, just below the larynx, is a large gland called the thyroid. The thyroid is really made up of two glands, the thyroid and the parathyroid. Medically, the thyroid and parathyroid are seen as a part of the endocrine system (fourth chakra). In terms of overall functions, this is correct. But in terms of how the soul uses the body to talk to us, the fifth chakra covers the thyroid and parathyroid.

The Thyroid

The thyroid is a large, "bow tie" shaped, gland which produces the hormone thyroxin. Thyroxin is the main hormone which controls the body's metabolism. The metabolism is the name given to the way in which the body behaves chemically, especially in relation to the flow of energy and building materials in and out of the cells. The metabolism is divided into two processes, those that build up the body (anabolism) and those that break down the body (catabolism).

The way in which these processes work, in general terms, is with the amount of oxygen contained within the blood cells. Normal oxygen levels keep the body functioning correctly. High oxygen levels speed up the metabolic rate and the body functions at a higher level, burning up oxygen and bodily tissue, especially fats and muscles, very quickly. People with a high metabolism tend to be very skinny. Low oxygen levels slow down the metabolism and the body functions at a much slower rate. People with a slow metabolism have a tendency towards being overweight and are usually lethargic.

The Parathyroid

The parathyroid glands are four, bean shaped glands that are embedded in the back of the thyroid gland and are about half a centimetre (quarter of an inch) long. The parathyroid secretes a hormone called parathormone which controls the levels of calcium within the blood. Calcium within the blood and other fluids is extremely important. The calcium atoms carry electrical impulses from the brain and nervous system and keep the organs and muscles moving correctly.

Most brain impulses are carried from the brain, through the nerves and other tissues by a process similar to electricity (see chapter eight). If the level of calcium within the blood drops, the parathyroid produces parathormone which stimulates the release of calcium from the bone structures. The body sees the correct level of calcium within the blood as being far more important than calcium within the bones. This does not produce the same affect as osteoporosis (see chapter three). What parathormone does is to soften the bones and makes them "flexible" (in extreme cases), whereas osteoporosis makes the bones brittle.

Blood calcium also helps the blood to clot.

Health Problems and the Fifth Chakra

The Respiratory System

The respiratory system is all about communication and expression. In order to communicate, on any level, we have to speak to make ourselves understood. In people who are unable to speak or those unable to hear, the fifth chakra still controls these functions but they are expressed through hand gestures.

Lung, chest and throat problems occur in people who do not express their thoughts very well. This can be through lack of confidence or it can be through not wanting to contradict somebody else. As individuals, we do tend to defer to those who make the most noise and not say anything ourselves. Unfortunately, those who make the most noise usually have the least to say and are covering up their own insecurities.

A perfect example of this kind of situation was where we were approached by a lady with breathing problems. The doctors could not tie it down to anything specific and she had tried all of the drug remedies that they had to offer without any success. From talking with her, it became obvious that she totally gave herself over to other people in certain situations. Whilst at work, she was able to communicate well and express her thoughts and feelings, but at home she gave in totally to her partner. If her partner, who was domineering, said anything or expressed an opinion, this lady would accept it without question. Her partner realised this and took full advantage of the situation.

We cleared out the lung problems for her and tried to help her to understand what the underlying cause was. She did understand us but refused to say anything to her partner about what her problem was. Some time after seeing us she was rushed into hospital with her lungs filling with liquid, she was literally drowning herself. We went to visit her in hospital and talked with her again about the underlying causes and gave her the idea of the giveaway. She understood but didn't want to do anything about it. The medical opinion was that she was terminally ill with no more than several weeks left to live. The medical profession had written her off and her partner had written her off. Her partner had arranged for her to be taken into a hospice within days of the diagnosis, where she could die, and had probably made arrangements for the funeral.

But she didn't die. It took several months, but she finally realised that she didn't want to die and that her only course of action was to take back some control. She is still not fully recovered, but at least she is beginning to deal with the situation and starting to reject her partner's domination. So, although this was an extreme case, it does serve to illustrate that no matter how serious an illness, nor how much tissue damage has been caused, nor how long the symptoms have been in place, it is never too late to change. Once that change begins, the body will repair itself.

If you have chest/lung problems, even just a persistent cough, then it will be because there is something that you are not getting off your chest, and that is you. Your thoughts are not being shared. Look at it another way - what right have you to deny the world of your thoughts. It will be a much better place if you let the world know who you are.

Lung problems are currently thought to be as a result of car pollution or of smoking. Whilst these can aggravate a problem, they are not the root cause. If we express our thoughts fully, the chakra spins correctly and it will, literally, throw off any polluting elements. Asthma, lung cancer, etc., are not caused by smoking or air born pollution but by a lack of expression, all that the pollutants do is to make an existing weakness worse.

Thyroid Problems

The best way of understanding the problems associated with the thyroid is to say that men rarely get them. They are not unknown in men, but very common in women.

As we are in the fifth chakra, how we express ourselves and how we communicate those expressions of self and how we judge ourselves, then we are looking at issues surrounding these concepts. Do I express myself and perhaps make myself look foolish? If I express myself a lot will others notice that what I am saying is based on what I want others to think of me instead of what I think of myself? If I don't express my opinion, maybe I can disappear into the corner and nobody will notice me.

Problems with the thyroid fall into two groups, overactive and underactive.

Overactive Thyroid

Symptoms associated with thyroid hyperactivity are to do with many of the body's systems speeding up. There is steady and sustained weight loss to the point of appearing anorexic. Loss of appetite. There is a sense of nervousness, sometimes severe, leading to a form of paranoia in extreme cases. Hot flushes, sometimes feeling constantly too hot and a dislike of hot weather. A sense of everything being too slow for the sufferer, "I'm operating at this speed, why isn't everyone else?" Leading to irritability and impatience. Excessive bowel movements. Shakiness and the eyes can bulge.

People in this situation are trying to make themselves look smaller. If nobody can see me because I'm being very small and moving too fast, then they won't ask me for my opinion.

Underactive Thyroid

Symptoms associated with an underactive thyroid are, in many ways, the opposite of hyperactive. There is steady and sustained weight gain. Increase of appetite. Yellowing and scaling of the skin with the skin looking puffy. Slowing down of the body and the mind. Lethargy. Loss of menstrual periods. Hair loss. People in this situation are trying to make themselves look bigger, more important than they feel about themselves. If I puff myself up to look important, maybe nobody will notice the little mouse inside.

Another condition associated with the thyroid is a goitre. Goitres are large, fleshy growths in the middle of the throat. In this instance, the body is saying, I think that I have a lot to say but I am being blocked from saying it.

In all of these instances, the soul is expressing itself through the mind. The mind is using the body to express the person's inner thoughts. If you are not prepared to use words to say what you think, then the soul is going to use the body to let the world know that you have something to say, but you are not saying it. There really is no escaping from the soul. Somehow or other, it will let its wishes be known no matter how much we try to block it or run away and hide. The truth of the inner person will always find a way to let us know that we are not paying it enough attention.

The Parathyroid

Parathyroid problems are associated with how good we are at expressing our thoughts. Especially in how well we are sticking to our thoughts and not modifying them to suit someone else's view. If we keep avoiding them, become too flexible in the way in which we express our own thoughts, the bone structure becomes affected.

When we express our opinions, especially publicly, two parts of the endocrine system come into play. The adrenals flood our system with adrenaline to help us decide if we run away or give our talk. How we react to that depends upon how secure we feel within our thoughts. Secondly, the parathyroid releases parathormone which stimulates the muscles to accept a greater amount of nerve impulses from the brain.

If we run away, we use up the adrenaline and the parathormone. If we stand and talk, we can often begin to shake and sweat. It is the combination of these two hormones within the muscles that make us respond in this way. If we are secure in what we are saying, the symptoms stop. Actors, for example, have stage fright before they go onto the stage, once they realise that they have remembered their lines, they calm down.

In Conclusion

So, really the fifth chakra is all about saying what we think. If we do so, we do not have any problems. If we "swallow" our thoughts, all sorts of problems can manifest themselves. We have to learn to express ourselves, there is no other real answer.

- Learn to express your thoughts and how to communicate those thoughts.

- If necessary, take self assertiveness classes in order to help you be more expressive.

- Take art classes to help you find a new way of expressing your thoughts and ideas - it will also help with any problems you may have with the second and third chakras.

- Take up singing, toning or chanting classes. These help with self assurance, it takes a lot to overcome our fears of our voice, and helps to clear the lungs and airways.

Read the descriptions of the Bach Flower Remedies given in appendix two to help clear any undesirable character traits that are holding you back. However, until we live in a society that begins to allow us to be honest and forthright, see chapter eighteen for remedies that can help the symptoms.

Chapter Eight
The Sixth Chakra

The sixth chakra is located in the centre of the forehead, just above the bridge of the nose, on a line with the spine. This is the last of the "physical" chakras that are formed within the body in the twenty to twenty four week period during pregnancy.

This chakra deals with our sense of self within a more "spiritual" aspect. Who we are within the "universal" community as much as within the physical. Really speaking, we are looking at our sense of identity in terms of "The Creator Spirit". The secondary function of the sixth chakra is our "psychic" vision, our ability to see beyond the physical and break away from the constraints of the physical senses.

Both of these elements of ourselves are extremely contentious as far as the medical and scientific communities are concerned. As far as they are concerned, if something cannot be weighed, measured or dissected, it cannot exist. The closest that they come to an acceptance of these elements of self is to accept that, somewhere, we have a mind. What could be seen as the leading edge of science, Quantum Physics, has, in recent years, come to the conclusion that everything exists because someone, something, somewhere thinks that it does. It is a view which is not easily acceptable to most of those in the scientific community as it begins to enter into the world of religious beliefs, a region of life which these people avoid like the plague for the reason given above.

The realisation arose because the physicists noticed that the outcome of their quantum experiments is largely determined by what the experimenter "thought" the likely outcome would be. The idea that the universe exists because someone thinks that it does begins to approach the concept of a Creator and this unnerves them.

As far as the rest of us are concerned, we each have our own views and beliefs as to whether a "Creator Spirit" exists or not and the role that "Spirit" plays in our lives.

From our viewpoint, that of healers, we have to work within realms that take us away from the purely physical on a daily basis. From our researches, the body exists as a group of energies that resonate at particular frequencies which our brains are tuned into accepting as being solid, physical matter. Everything that we see on the planet is comprised of collections of atoms. These atoms are themselves comprised of energies. By blending all of these various energies together, we arrive at the physical. This is the way in which all of the energy therapies work. They work with the fundamental building material of the body and bring back a balance to the regions which have become depleted of energy during our day to day existence.

The chakras give us our physical form and physical material. The energy "conduits", that keep that body functioning, are the body's meridians. They distribute the chakra, life giving energies, to the organs and to every region of the body. Illness occurs for the reasons that have been discussed in this book, but, mechanically, the organ or region is deprived of some of the frequencies of energy that maintain its structure because we have set up "wobbles" within the chakra. These wobbles generate breaks and imbalances within the meridians and the body becomes affected.

As far as the sixth chakra is concerned, the physical bits that can be affected are the ears; nose; the left eye; the lower brain and the central nervous system and the pituitary gland. Don't ask us why it is only the left eye, its just the way in which the wiring works. What these organs amount to, collectively, are the physical senses. The pituitary is a little different and we will discuss that particular gland later on in this chapter.

The body has five physical senses: hearing, sight, smell, taste and touch. The scientific community is trying to add a sixth sense into this list, that of a sense of gravity, which way is up or down. Arguably, they are correct, as knowledge of our orientation does play a very important role in our lives. Collectively, we use these senses to understand the world around us. The information gathered by the senses provide us with the raw data that the mind processes to make decisions on the way in which we live our lives.

But the mind also works in other ways and on other levels. A further sense has to be added to this list and that is "psychic awareness". This sense draws in a huge variety of information from very many sources, but particularly from the other people around us. This can range from "reading" the way in which other people's bodies are "talking" to us, as with "body language", to other people's thoughts and emotions that are given form in the auras that surround us. The aura is the energy "field" that surrounds all living things and is an outward manifestation of the chakras' energies. Senses on these levels are controlled by the seventh chakra and are covered in the next chapter. For now, we can begin to look at the "physical" senses.

The Central Nervous System

The key to the way in which all of the physical senses work lies in the body's nerves. To begin to understand how the central nervous system works, it is probably easier to start at the edges and work inwards.

Throughout the whole of the body is a vast network of sensory systems. All of these systems link up together to keep the brain informed of what is happening both within and outside of the body. The system starts with microscopically sized fibres which are interwoven into the skin's surface layer (called sensory receptors). The ends of these fibres are shaped a little like spirals which vibrate on contact with outside influences. These outside influences can be in the air or on surfaces which we touch and register such things as texture, pain, etc.. As these spirals begin to vibrate, they set up a minute electrochemical reaction which travels back along the nerve fibre (neuron). The neurons then connect into the central nervous system which takes these electrical impulses to the brain through the spinal cord. Depending upon the type of stimulus being fed into the brain by the receptors, the brain responds by sending a similar signal down through the central nervous system and along a different set of neurons that are attached to effector nerves and the body makes a response.

An example of this kind of activity would be where we touched a saucepan of boiling water with a finger. The receptor cells send a signal to the brain telling it that we were touching something which was very hot and would harm the body. The brain receives these signals and decides that the body should not be harmed in this way and sends a signal back to the effector cells to tell the muscles to contract and move the finger away from the heat.

There are similar receptor and effector cells in every part of the skin and muscles. These kinds of nerves form the peripheral nervous system and are a part of the motor nervous system. This is the system that responds to outside stimulus and makes the body's muscles move.

A second part of the nervous system is responsible for performing certain functions within the body which are not subject to outside influence. These are the parts of the body that keep it functioning such as the beat of the heart or the impulse to breath etc.. These types of functions act regardless of any other stimulus and form the autonomic nervous system.

A further part of the autonomic system links the organs and glands to the brain. This part ties in with the endocrine system (see chapter six) and informs the brain of all of the hormone, enzyme, etc. activity that is occurring throughout the body and helps to keep the body running as smoothly as our various activities will let it.

All of these peripheral and autonomic nerves link together to form the spinal cord. This is a large bundle of nerve fibres that run inside the spine (see also chapter three). Each vertebrae has a recess to each side which allows the nerves to pass in and out of the spinal cord. Within the spinal column is a sac of fluid which protects the spinal cord from damage as the spine moves and flexes. It acts a little like the lubrication oil in a car engine, allowing the structure to move without causing damage to or affecting the nerves of the spinal cord.

The spinal cord enters the brain through the brain stem (see illustration number fourteen) where all of the nerves are collected together. From the brain stem, the nerves connect into the hypothalamus. The hypothalamus is really the brain's central processor. All of the nerve impulses enter into the hypothalamus and from there they are distributed to the regions of the brain that deal with specific functions.

This is, obviously, a very simplified version of the workings of the central nervous system, but it does give an idea of the complexities of the workings of the system and how it transfers the outside world into the body and how this is processed by the brain to arrive at an appropriate response to those outside influences.

The central nervous system gives us all of the information that we need to know about the world around us and our location within it. Therefore, health problems associated with the nervous system are to do with how we act with and respond to the world outside of us. By generating problems within the nervous system, we are shutting ourselves down so that the outside world cannot influence us. We have switched ourselves off in order not to receive the information that is being presented.

This switching off varies from the loss of sensation in the finger tips, not wanting to feel what is going on, to life threatening diseases like Parkinsons Disease where we lose all sense of the world and retreat into a world of our own. All of these kinds of illnesses are to do with a withdrawal of the self from everything around us. "I have had enough of the world, or a particular aspect of it, and I am going to retreat into my self in order to not face it again".

We have treated a number of people for these kinds of illnesses with a varying rate of success. Again, removal of even these kinds of symptoms is really not that difficult, but like all matters connected to our health, it is how we can help our clients to see what it is they are doing, and how they respond to their new understanding, that decides how long term our healing has been. If the person suffering these conditions can learn that it is within their own power to alter their outlook, then the symptoms can be permanently removed and any damage can be undone.

Even the most serious of these complaints can be healed. Parkinson's disease, Alzheimer's disease, multiple sclerosis, etc. are all treatable and reversible if the underlying reasons for the disease can be reversed by the person suffering them. As impossible as this sounds, it can be done.

The Eyes

The eyes are our windows onto the world around us. The light, that is all around us, bounces off the objects that are in front of us and is passed through the cornea. Behind the cornea, the light images are collected together by the eye's pupil and focused onto the back of the eye (the retina). The retina is covered in receptor cells which group together at the back of the retina to form the optic nerve. All of the information collected by the eye is passed along the optic nerve and into the back of the brain to an area called the occipital lobes. Here, all of the information from the optic nerve is decoded and the brain tells us the scene we are looking at.

The eye pupils are the small, black circles that are in the centre of the lens. The space between the cornea and the lens is filled with fluid which expands and contracts to allow us to focus on the object we are looking at. The lens is the round, coloured bit in the middle and gives us the colour of our eyes. The pupils will grow larger to allow in more light at night and smaller to stop us being blinded by bright light. The pupil will also grow larger if we are looking at something that we like such as a loved one or food etc. (see illustration number fifteen a).

The eyes are positioned at the front of the head to allow us to see forward and in a plane that is on a line with the front of the face. They are positioned here mainly because of our upright stance. Animals, for example, who walk on four legs, have their eyes at the side of the head. So, as a species, we only look forwards.

The eyes are kept clean by blinking the eye lids. This movement is lubricated by the tear ducts that are situated above the eye and on the side furthest from the nose. As we blink, the debris is pushed to the lower eyelid where it is washed, by the fluid of the tears, into the lower corner closest to the nose. This is why we appear to cry from this corner. The ducts closest to the nose drain the tears into the back of the nose. Because of this connection, we cry if we smell something that is too strong as the fumes travel up the back of the nose and directly onto the cornea.

Problems with the eyes and eyesight are to do with how we view the world. Short sightedness, myopia, is due to our shutting out the world beyond our immediate vicinity. "I like the world as it is immediately around me, I don't want to see

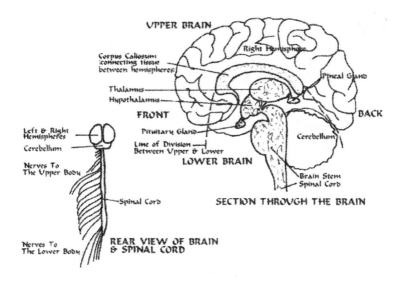

UPPER BRAIN

Corpus Caliosum
connecting tissue
between hemispheres

Right Hemisphere

Pineal Gland

Thalamus

Hypothalamus

FRONT

BACK

Left & Right
Hemispheres

Cerebellum

Nerves To
The Upper Body

Pituitary Gland

Line of Division
Between Upper & Lower

LOWER BRAIN

Cerebellum

Spinal Cord

Brain Stem
Spinal Cord

SECTION THROUGH THE BRAIN

Nerves To
The Lower Body

REAR VIEW OF BRAIN
& SPINAL CORD

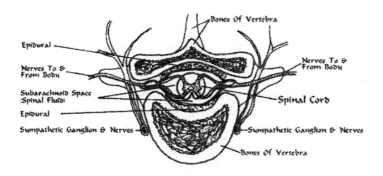

Bones Of Vertebra

Epidural

Nerves To &
From Body

Nerves To &
From Body

Subarachnoid Space
(Spinal Fluid)

Spinal Cord

Epidural

Sympathetic Ganglion & Nerves

Sympathetic Ganglion & Nerves

Bones Of Vertebra

SECTION THROUGH THE SPINE

Illustration Number Fourteen - The Spinal Cord and Lower Brain

143

what there is beyond that". Tunnel vision occurs because we only want to see what there is immediately in front of us and do not want to look beyond a very narrow angle of view. We could go through each particular vision defect, but these examples should be enough to help understand the principles involved. Eyesight problems can be corrected, but it literally needs a change of focus by the sufferer.

The Ears

The ears are situated on the side of the head for the same reasons as the eyes are in the front, in order for us to hear in a forward direction.

The outer ear, the fleshy bit stuck on the outside, is shaped in a way that focuses sounds into the entrance to the middle ear. We grow hair in the outer ear in order to help prevent any unwanted debris from entering the middle ear. The middle ear is lined with mucous producing cells which help keep the ear clean on the inside, commonly called ear wax if it begins to solidify. At the back of the middle ear is the ear drum (the tympanic membrane). The inner ear really begins behind the ear drum. Connected immediately behind the ear drum are two small bones that form the basis for our hearing (see illustration number fifteen b). One bone is connected to the back of the ear drum and is called the malleus, this bone vibrates with the sounds entering the middle ear and strikes another bone called the incus. Through other connections, the sounds of the malleus and the incus vibrating against each other is transferred into a region known as the vestibule. Connecting into the space around these bony connections is the eustachian tube which connects the inner ear to the nasopharynx (see chapter seven). The vestibule throws the sounds around a region known as the semicircular canal which leads onto the bony and membranous labyrinth. Connected to the back of the labyrinth is the auditory nerve. The whole of this assembly is designed to amplify all of the sounds that enter the inner ear so that we can hear the world outside.

As with the eyes, health problems associated with the ears are to do with shutting out the outer world. "I do not want to hear what is going on around me" for whatever reasons. The reasons can vary from trying to silence a chattering partner (very common) to not wanting to know what the world has to offer. Very often it comes down to "why do I have to hear all of everybody else's noise when all I want to do is to get on with my own life". Shutting down and withdrawing from the world.

A withdrawing into the self and away from the universe that surrounds us. This is something that we cannot do. We have chosen to live amongst other physical beings. Shutting out the world around us breaks the soul's primary wish. Nobody is a soul in isolation, no matter how we might long for this, sometimes, to be the case.

Tinnitus is another version of the same thing. The sounds of tinnitus link into the fourth chakra, the lymph system, and is connected with expressions of love. Tinnitus usually occurs in situations where we are not expressing love for our self. It is the soul's way of shutting out the outside world in order for us to pay more attention to our own needs. If we cannot hear the world around us, we can only hear inwards.

No matter what situation we might find ourselves in, we have the choice to accept it or to move on. If you help lead someone out of the situation that they no longer wish to see or hear, their condition improves.

The Nose

We have described most of the functioning of the nose in chapter seven. At the top of the nasal cavity is a region covered in fine hairs, believe it or not, known as the olfactory hair (see illustration number sixteen). Attached to these hairs is the olfactory nerve. It is through these very sensitive hairs that we smell the world immediately around us. Human sense of smell is very poor in comparison with most of the animals we share

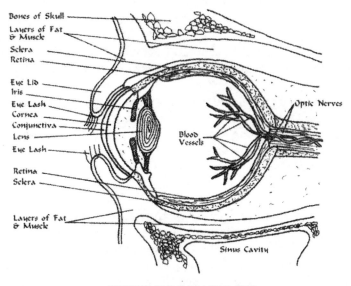

Bones of Skull
Layers of Fat & Muscle
Sclera
Retina

Eye Lid
Iris
Eye Lash
Cornea
Conjunctiva
Lens
Eye Lash

Retina
Sclera

Layers of Fat & Muscle

Optic Nerves

Blood Vessels

Sinus Cavity

SECTION THROUGH THE EYE

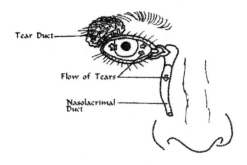

Tear Duct

Flow of Tears

Nasolacrimal Duct

Illustration Number Fifteen a - The Eyes

our world with, however, it serves its purpose as far as we are concerned.

The Tongue
The tongue fills most of the mouth. Its purpose is to taste the food that we eat and, to a lesser extent, taste the air around us. Again, in comparison to the other forms of life on the planet, our sense of taste is not very good and the number of sensory organs on the tongue is comparatively low (see illustration number sixteen).

The nose and the tongue are included together because their reason for a dysfunction is the same. We live in a world that has many smells and many tastes. Most of these sensations, as far as we are concerned, add a certain luxury into our lives. We do not necessarily need to smell or taste the food that we eat any more. With the advent of our modern consumer society these senses are needed less and less as we keep our food in refrigerated spaces that keep it fresh. In this way, these two conditions, loss of sense of smell and taste, are a fairly recent phenomenon. We do not need these senses to survive any more and they are, therefore, associated with luxury. It is the so-called luxury foods that give off the most smell and the most taste. If we feel that we are not worthy of luxury in our lives, we close down these senses.

The Pituitary Gland
The pituitary gland is one of the most important glands within the body. The endocrine system, covered in chapter six, is physically controlled by the hormones that this gland secretes. The hormone that most people will be familiar with is the growth hormone (somatotrophin). The pituitary is located just below the hypothalamus (see illustration number fourteen) and has very many connections in and out of the brain's central processor. All of the body's activities are monitored by the hypothalamus and the pituitary. The hypothalamus processes

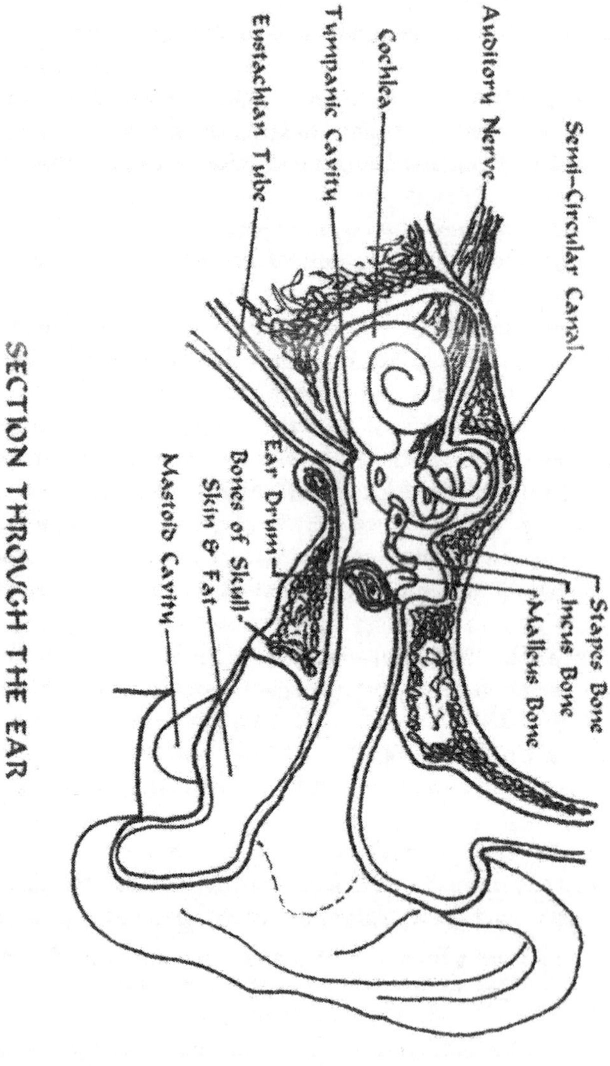

SECTION THROUGH THE EAR

Semi-Circular Canal

Auditory Nerve

Cochlea

Tympanic Cavity

Eustachian Tube

Stapes Bone

Incus Bone

Malleus Bone

Ear Drum

Bones of Skull

Skin & Fat

Mastoid Cavity

Illustration Number Fifteen b - The Ears

and distributes nerve impulses and information from the physical tissues within the body whilst the pituitary processes and controls the hormonal functions of the body and is the primary gland of the endocrine system. If you have read chapter six then you will understand just how important this gland is to the body's well being.

The sixth chakra is the highest energy chakra fully connected into the physical body. Although the seventh chakra does control certain bodily functions, they are more concerned with "higher" functions, see the next chapter. Essentially, the sixth chakra is the one which takes the directions of the higher self and processes these directions into how the physical body responds to the activities of the physical self. This is it's primary, spiritual, link. It is through these links that our psychic senses function.

Problems with the pituitary gland are very rare but where they do occur, they usually affect cell production and bodily growth. These problems are more usually associated with pre-pubescent children than adults. This is because children of this age have not reconciled the fact that their soul is now physical and they are going through a period of re-adjustment and reconciliation.

The only way of helping children through this phase is to help them to understand that they are wanted and loved and that their body is something that has its own beauty and worth.

Pituitary problems do occur in later life for very similar reasons. It is a withdrawal from the physical. The best means of approach to the problems is to take a very serious look at your life and see what it is you do not like about it and then try to understand why those feelings of rejection have arisen.

We are all living our physical lives for a reason and it was our choice, on a soul level, to live this lifetime. You need to look at what it is you are missing in your life and try to put it right. Somewhere or other you are missing the point.

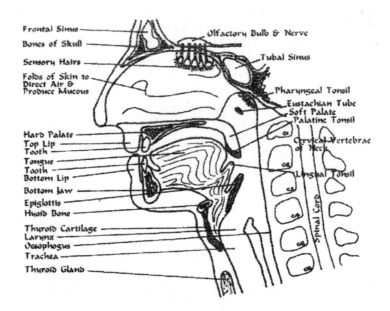

SECTION THROUGH NOSE & NECK

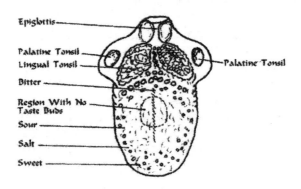

PLAN VIEW OF TONGUE

Illustration Number Sixteen - The Nose and The Tongue

In Conclusion

As far as the sixth chakra is concerned, it is our perceived place in the world that determines our response to it. We are spiritual beings, but spiritual beings made incarnate. If we try to close ourselves off from the physical world, we generate problems. This relates to the primary function of the chakra.

In secondary function terms, our psychic awareness, if we deny our senses on this level, we begin to affect the physical senses as well. Shutting down on one level, begins to affect the other. This situation works in both directions. Closing down the physical closes the psychic. Closing down the psychic closes the physical.

Everything that we do must be in a state of balance or the soul lets us know that we are going wrong.

Read the descriptions of the Bach Flower Remedies in appendix two and try to determine which of them will help you to begin to alter your perceptions of yourself and the world immediately around you. The Bach Remedies do work - even on this level.

Chapter Nine

The Seventh Chakra

The seventh chakra is located on the top of the head, in a direct line with the spine. This is the first of the energy centres to enter the developing fetus and is our link between the soul and the body. Most people will be totally unaware that this link exists. The western world's view of life is that we are totally physical and nothing exists beyond that. Even the views of our religions, that we have a soul, is taken as something that perhaps exists somewhere but we are not too sure where, nor do most people spend much time thinking about the concept. Our view of the world has become based upon materialistic values and the realms of the spiritual is something which belongs to a more primitive time.

However, the world is changing and our view of ourselves is changing along with it. What we are now seeing is a rapid return of a greater understanding and there is a gradual recognition of the higher realms of the self.

The seventh chakra is linked to the upper brain, the right eye and to the pineal gland.

The Upper Brain

Most of the functions of the upper brain are not understood. Medical research has managed to unravel the workings of some of the outer regions, but its inner workings are largely unknown.

The outer layers of the brain are where the hypothalamus directs the impulses and information from the rest of the body.

All of these impulses are then processed and interpreted by these regions, which extend inwards into the body of the brain itself, and are known as lobes. The brain itself looks a little like the nut inside a walnut shell, two scrunched up hemispheres with a connecting link in between. The material of the brain can be thought of as a flat sheet of tissue which has been folded in on itself a number of times in order for it to occupy less space.

As far as the body is concerned, the brain controls every function. If our brains were not there, the body would just be a collection of tissues and organs carrying out their mechanical functions, if they were alive at all. The brain is an organ of unbelievable complexity. The amount of activity that takes place here almost defies description.

Many people like to think of the brain as being like a chemically controlled computer but this view implies that there is a closed programme at work. The brain is really a giant processor that deals with all of the impulses and signals that keep the physical body functioning and stores the memories of those functions occurring. Our real memory systems are contained within our DNA structures and the higher self. The DNA deals with the energetic template of the physical body whilst the higher self (the soul) remembers everything that we do within our lives and provides suggestions as to what it is we should be doing within our lives. The upper brain is the interface between these three functions, the soul (higher self), the DNA and the physical body.

Ill health occurs because we ignore the prompting of the higher self and this break down in communication affects the way in which the physical body functions and, ultimately, alters the make up of our DNA. DNA stands for deoxyribonucleic acid and is contained within every single cell of the body. DNA tells every single cell what its function is within the body's structures. The soul, through the seventh chakra provides the energetic template for the location of the cells within the physical whole, the so-called etheric template, whilst the DNA provides the physical tissue, by building the appropriate types of cells. The chakras, especially the seventh, work with and through the DNA in order to provide the body's form and function*.

The upper brain deals with all of the sensory information that the body provides, therefore, if the problems discussed in chapter eight begin to manifest themselves, it is parts of the upper brain which shut down and the links through the seventh chakra begin to become disrupted. This is why the physical senses and the psychic senses are interlinked, closing one physical sense down affects some of the psychic senses.

The Pineal Gland

The pineal gland is located at the back of the brain in the region between the two hemispheres (see illustration number fourteen). It is a small pea shaped gland whose function is not fully understood by the doctors. The pineal gland produces a hormone called melatonin. This hormone serves three functions, the first is to regulate the body's clock (biorhythms), the second is to control the production of thyroxin and the third is to act as the body's major antioxidant. Thyroxin is actually produced by the pituitary gland (see chapter eight) and its distribution throughout the body is controlled by the thyroid gland (see chapter seven). Thyroxin controls the body's metabolism, the speed at which the cells function.

Melatonin is the hormone that tells us that it is time to get up in the morning or when we need to eat some food etc.. The way in which it works is through the amount of light the pineal

---

* For a fuller description of the Chakras and their role in building the physical body, see *The Fool's First Steps* by the authors.

gland receives through the right eye. If it is night time, no light entering the eye, it tells us that we need to sleep and the body's systems slow down their functions (high melatonin production). If it is morning, light entering the eye, it tells us that it is time to start the day and the body's systems begin to function fully (low melatonin production). This is why it is so difficult to change time zones or to work night shifts. Jet lag is caused by our telling the mind to work against the signals given by the pineal and its melatonin.

Conditions which come about because the body's clock has been disrupted are illnesses such as ME. ME is myalgic encephalomyelitus and is a condition where the sufferer experiences a total lack of energy or will to carry out any tasks or functions. All that they are capable of doing is to drag their tired bodies around the house and virtually nothing else (high melatonin levels). (Our findings on the link between ME and melatonin has recently been confirmed in a study carried out by Guy's and St Thomas's hospital in London).

ME comes about because we have totally ignored the prompting of the higher self and have got to a point where we desperately need to change our life and move in a totally new direction. In prompting terms, we have ignored the gentle tap, the heavier nudge and are suffering the baseball bat on the back of the head. Until we do something to change the direction of our lives, our life will be put on hold.

Every single ME sufferer that we have treated has been in this situation. We can alter the body's energy levels as much as we like and provide a temporary resurrection of energy, but until our client has begun to listen to the needs of the soul, we can do no more than that. Every single person that we know who has recovered from ME has done so by radically changing their direction in life.

Melatonin's third function, an antioxidant, is to remove toxins from the body, especially excessive free radicals. This process occurs when we are asleep. A free radical is an atom, or group of atoms, that contains at least one unpaired electron. Electrons are negatively charged particles that usually occur in pairs, forming a chemically stable arrangement. If an electron is unpaired, another atom or molecule can easily pair with it, causing a chemical reaction. Because they join so readily with other compounds, free radicals can cause dramatic changes within the body and a great deal of damage. Each free radical may exist for only a tiny fraction of a second but the damage it leaves behind can be irreversible.

Free radicals are normally present in the body in small numbers. Biochemical processes naturally lead to the formation of free radicals and, under normal circumstances, the body can keep them in check. Not all free radicals are bad. Free radicals produced by the immune system (see chapter six) destroy viruses and bacteria. Other free radicals are involved in producing hormones and activating enzymes that are needed for life. Free radicals actually produce a number of substances that the body finds useful. However, if there is excessive free radical production, damage to cells and tissues can occur. The formation of a large number of free radicals leads to the formation of more free radicals, leading to even more damage.

Excessive free radicals will be found in foods such as those containing hydrogenated fats (such as some margarines, etc.) and heat treated vegetable oils (most vegetable oils that are not cold pressed).

Insomnia

Insomnia is one of those odd conditions that has very many potential causes. The condition is included here as it usually manifests itself as an overactive brain.

Insomnia has two basic causes, the first could be seen as the opposite of ME and the second is related to hormonal patterns brought about by an upset in another chakra.

156

The first relates to a seventh chakra cause. This is when we are doing the jobs that we should be doing and the soul is trying to help complete the task that we are engaged in. These are the people who require no more than a couple of hours sleep per night, and every night, whilst they are completing a particular task or a role which it is desirable for them to complete (low melatonin levels). The pineal gland is stimulated and the body's clock is readjusted to allow more time for the task in hand to be completed. Usually, once they have completed the task etc. they slow down and their sleep patterns alter to a more normal pattern.

The second main cause for insomnia relates to an emotionally based problem. If you look at chapter five under the pancreas, you will see that the pancreas controls the function of a number of hormones. One of these, somatostatin, is a hormone which regulates the level of activity within the synaptic gaps within the brain. The region of consciousness which the pancreas relates to is emotional force in dealing with a situation. There are occasions where the soul feels as though an unresolved issue needs to be fully resolved and the issue settled. In these instances the hormone production will be stimulated and the situation, emotion, method of dealing with the situation, etc. will be replayed in the mind until the whole issue has been resolved in a satisfactory way, keeping us awake.

The first reason for insomnia means that we are doing something right. The second reason means that we have not resolved an issue and we need to replay the situation until we have arrived at a more appropriate answer. Suggested remedies for insomnia will be found in chapter twenty.

Aïðs

Acquired immunodeficiency syndrome (AIDS) is a disease which has come into being in recent years. We do not have any direct experience of dealing with this problem and cannot, therefore, pass any direct comment. This is a disease of the immune system and, assuming that the condition is naturally occurring and not produced in a laboratory, will be connected with the fourth chakra. However, as the disease is life threatening, then other chakras, especially the sixth and seventh will play a major role in the disease development.

As with all illnesses, we have heard of a number of Aids sufferers who have cured themselves.

Cancer

Another function of the seventh chakra is concerned with the generation of cancer. Cancer is the final piece of ammunition in the soul's armoury. The soul has tried to speak to us in every way possible and we have been unable or unwilling to listen.

As a psychic surgeon, one of us has the ability to "scan" the body and follow the course of an illness back to its originating cause. With cancer, the mechanism would appear to involve a particular sequence of events and involve several of the body's messenger mechanisms. These events appear to be present regardless of where the cancer growth has occurred.

All illnesses can be tracked and related to a chakra. The chakras are the physical, energetic manifestation of the consciousness and each chakra relates to a region of our lives and to a particular set of organs or system within the body. As we act against our intended route in life, the energies contained within one, or more, chakras become affected. If we do nothing to correct this energy imbalance, the associated organ or system becomes weakened. If we continue with our undesirable activities, the chakra becomes depleted to a point where the chakra begins a process of collapse. If a chakra fully collapses, death occurs as the body cannot survive without all of its energy components. Before a chakra does fully collapse, the consciousness releases a new DNA sequence. This DNA sequence is contained within everyone's genetic makeup, but remains inactive until the events described above occur.

It has proved a little difficult to read this sequence precisely, but it would appear to have the following designation: GATTAC CATTAG. We understand that this should be written in the format:

GATTAC

CATTAG

(we can read the letters but are unsure about the format - see below). This DNA sequence has a number of consequences within the body.

The most important is the blocking of a pancreatic hormone called "Galanin". We have been unable to find any details of the activity of this hormone within the medical literature (the literature says that doctors do not know what its function is within the body). However, from our research, the hormone has a cell modulation function ie. it regulates the size, composition and integrity of the cell walls.

With this hormone suppressed, it generates an area of weakened cell structures in the region of the affected organ etc.. Along with the suppression of the galanin, two other pancreatic secretions are stimulated into a much higher level of production than would be normal. These two substances are IGF-1, which increases the levels of insulin production, and a pancreatic polypeptide. We have been unable to put a name to this particular polypeptide as the medical literature is very sketchy about these substances.

The overall affect of this process is that the drop in galanin levels alters the structural integrity of the cell walls. The increased insulin produced by the IGF-1 is rapidly converted into glucose by the polypeptide and the cells begin to grow very rapidly, essentially, cancerous growth.

The DNA sequence remains active until the patient has dealt with the root cause issue which brought about the chakra imbalance in the first place*.

The process described above can also, unfortunately, work in reverse. Our environment, particularly work environment, is filled with toxic chemicals, many of which are carcinogenic (cancer causing). If our chakras are in a poor condition, these chemicals or substances can find their way into regions or organs which relate to that particular chakra. If we are constantly bombarded by these substances, their concentration will increase and begin to break down the cell structure of the organs, tissues, bones, etc. and trigger the DNA/hormone response detailed above. This is, essentially, how radioactivity can cause primary and secondary tumours.

As a note about the DNA sequence detailed above. The four letters used are abbreviations of the names given to the four basic components of the DNA spiral. A = adenine, G = guanine, T = thymine and C = cytosine. These four components link together in differing sequences to form the many millions of coding signals which make up the DNA molecule.

A comment about orthodox cancer treatments. The standard medical approach to cancer is to treat it by chemotherapy, radiotherapy or a combination of the two. With chemotherapy, the body is injected with a cocktail of powerful chemicals. These combination chemicals are intended to "scour" out the cancerous cells and cleanse the area affected. The only problem is that it also scours out the rest of the body. The way in which they do this is that the chemicals are designed to prevent the

---

* The full details of the mechanisms and the hormones involved have been copyrighted and a patent applied for by the authors.

generation and growth of new cells within the body. This is why chemotherapy will make patients go bald and sterile. Radiotherapy involves the cancerous region being bombarded with radioactive material to try to kill off the cancer cells.

In our experience, both of these treatments cause more damage to the body than the original illness, all secondary cancers are caused by these treatments, especially the radiotherapy.

Think about the mechanisms going on in the body. An area of the body has become weakened by a chakra being close to collapse. The DNA/hormone process detailed above has been activated and the whole body becomes weakened by the virtual loss of the energies of the associated chakra.

The immune system tries to adjust itself to the new situation and is placed under enormous stress. As the chemicals enter the blood supply, they are carried to all parts of the body and collect in any regions which have a weakness. These weaknesses become severely aggravated and the cells can begin to locally collapse, forming a secondary tumour. With radiotherapy, the weakened area is flooded with a substance that causes cancer in healthy cells. The radioactivity is not targeted at the specific cancer cells but floods the whole area, including the blood vessels in the area. The radioactive material enters into the blood and is carried to all parts of the body, collects in regions which have weaknesses and generates secondary tumours.

Detailed analysis of post mortem examinations has shown that many people have cancerous tissues within their bodies which have gone undiagnosed, possibly for a number of years. The cause of death of these people has been established as whatever cause it was and the cancer was proven not to be a contributory factor. This is a further indication that if we leave the body to deal with its own problems, it does so. If we interfere with the body's mechanisms with drug treatments, we end up with many complications. Cancer does not necessarily kill you as the body will take care of the problem, current cancer treatments disrupt these processes and generate problems which the body cannot fight.

The redirection of our behaviour to one more acceptable to the soul will undo all of our illnesses. If these redirections are combined with a healthy, balanced diet, the body can deal with anything.

Out of all of the choices that are available to us, the final one is, of course, death. The ending of a physical lifetime. This situation occurs for two reasons.

The first is that we have not listened to the promptings of the soul to a point where a chakra collapses and the energy contained within that part of our consciousness is, effectively, lost. If the soul loses an element of its energy potential, it cannot continue in it's physical realms. In misunderstanding the promptings of the soul, we have ultimately failed in the lessons we were intending to master. This is not as final as it sounds. We have further opportunities for learning on our journey back to "the ultimate source", we just didn't have quite enough courage to see this life through to its hoped for conclusion. We are, after all, human and to be human is to err. There is no judgement implied in this situation, the only judgement is by the individual soul involved. If a chakra fully collapses, life cannot continue as a connection within the soul has been broken. If this situation occurs, all of the energy contained within the physical body returns to the "total" soul and healing begins. The soul is made whole again and further physical life is possible, depending on the wishes of the soul.

The second reason is that we have lived out our lives, completed whatever goals we set ourselves and the need for a physical body is no longer required. The soul has completed its journey and will decide what it wants to do next. We always have a choice.

Whatever the circumstances, the physical body has served its purpose. The process involved is the same for everyone, whatever the circumstances of their leaving the physical. The first action of the soul is to break the connection to the physical body. This is achieved by withdrawing the energy of the first chakra. The first chakra contains the energy which keeps us in the physical, with that role no longer required, we let go. This is really what death is, a letting go of the physical, no more than that. As the root chakra releases, the other chakras follow, one by one until the crown chakra lets go. This is the final sigh of physical life. A letting go of the body. It is usually done with reluctance as physical life is considered to be a pleasure.

The body is a vehicle for the soul, but the body also feeds the soul in ways which cannot be experienced anywhere else and this is why we return to a physical life on more than one occasion - to enjoy.

In Conclusion

Nothing occurs within the body that the soul does not know about. If we listen to it's promptings, we have good health. If we fail to listen, we have illness. This is not any kind of judgemental comment. Illness is not a judgement.

Just because you have an illness does not mean that you are being judged. Rights or wrongs in health matters are, and can only be, determined by the individual concerned. The knowledge of the workings of the soul and its interconnectedness with the physical body has been forcibly removed from our understanding by those who wish to hold control over other people's lives. If we had been given a copy of the chakras and their relationship with the physical body on the day that we were born, we would all be in a position of greater understanding. Until that day arrives, we will always make an uninformed choice. We now need to take a fresh look at our bodies and welcome in the guidance of our soul. It is never too late to start from this point of new understanding.

Chapter Ten

Past Life Memories

We have taken a journey through the body and much of the soul. However, there is one element of our current health problems which relate to existences prior to the one we are currently living.

This is quite a controversial area and one which although treated by most people with fascination, is one which is not taken too seriously. Whilst every single illness can very definitely be related to an element of our lives and our behaviour within that element, the chakras are the energies of the soul made physical and the soul carries the memories of all that we are or have been.

We are a created consciousness, an immense quantity of energy. But we have been created to investigate our limitations or strengths. In order to do this we have total free choice. As an individual, we have ultimate free choice in what we do, where we do it and who we do it with. Our choices are not limited in any way. As discussed in chapters one and two, the total consciousness is comprised of two elements, the "physical self" and the "higher self". The higher self is the element of our being which makes these kinds of decisions. Whilst we live out a physical life, the physical self is too distracted and too constrained by the physical world to be aware enough to make these kinds of decisions. Once we pass out of the physical, we are re-united with our "higher" elements and our view, and the range of options available, changes.

As explained in chapter one, we ask our parents if we can be born to them or our parents ask us if we will be their child.

These are decisions which take place on these "higher" levels. We choose to be born or we choose not to be born. Within this range of choices is the option of experiencing more than one physical lifetime. If the concept of existence of life after death (heaven) can be widely accepted, why not life pre-birth?

Our view is that we have been created (born), at some time within the scope of universal time, and we will return to that "Creator Spirit" (die) at an appropriate time. We would consider this to be our lifetime, no matter how many hundreds, or thousands, of years that birth/death cycle might be. During our period of life, we have free choice in what we do, whether that is to be born into a physical body or not (those who choose not to be born into a physical life, we usually call "Angels"). If we make that choice to experience physical life, we also might choose to live another. If we have made these choices, the "total" soul remembers them and the total soul also comprises the seven bodily chakras. This is how physical illnesses can relate to previous lifetimes, the soul remembers a past experience and that experience is passed onto this lifetime through the DNA memory structures.

There are many theories and many concepts surrounding this idea, usually known by a Hindu word, "Karma", and we will go on to discuss some of the concepts implied by this a little later. In our experience, health problems of this kind are not very common. But, never the less, they do exist. The best way of illustrating the kinds of problems encountered is to give you a few case histories.

Case One
We were approached by a lady in her twenties who felt extremely lonely and not very comfortable within herself or her surroundings. There was nothing which she could pin down to anything specific, just a sense of "aloneness". She had physical symptoms of severe osteoporosis (close to twenty percent reduction in bone density).

By talking to her about her thoughts, feelings and life together with our ability to "read" the energies of the chakras, we were able to begin to unravel the root of her problem. She had been born in Scotland in the mid 1700s. Her family had decided to take the opportunities offered by the new world of Canada and had emigrated. When in Canada, she had met a man and married. The couple decided to make a fresh start and had moved to the plains north of Vancouver to begin a homestead farming existence. The farm was located a few hundred miles from Vancouver and totally isolated from any other farm or settlement. They were blissfully happy. The farm flourished and there was an abundance of game and fish.

One day, her husband went on a scouting/hunting expedition that took him into the foothills of the Rockies and he never came back. She had no way of knowing what had happened to him and for the next thirty years, the remainder of her life, she was alone. She had no problem in feeding herself as the farm flourished and she could hunt but she was too far away from any other people to move out of the area. She also hoped, day upon day, for the return of her husband and if she moved away, how would he find her? (from our reading of her chakras, the sense of love between these two was overwhelming).

We also had a sense of an Indian who approached her homestead to make contact but she could not find it in herself to trust him but he continued to keep an eye on her and brought her healing herbs whenever she fell ill.

So, here we have a lady who does not know what happened to her husband and could not move away in case he came back. She did not know if she could trust her Indian friend and so hid from him. Alone for thirty years. This experience was so profound that it left "scars" on her soul. However, by helping her to understand that her sense of aloneness belonged to another life and another time, it was possible for her to release the emotions connected with the experience and her sense of loneliness gradually disappeared. The osteoporosis was brought about by her sense of insecurity (first chakra) both from the past life and her feelings of aloneness and insecurity in her current life. She is now living a very happy, normal life and her bone density has returned to a normal level.

Case Two

This was a man who had panic attacks which were very unusual in their pattern. He was a very successful businessman with a thriving company. His position meant that he had to attend a number of social functions and this was when his problem would surface. Within his work he was very confident and self assured whilst the thought of attending any kind of social occasion turned him into a gibbering wreck. Once he arrived at the function, he would calm down, it was the anticipation and journey to the function that caused the problem.

As we began to "read" his chakras, it became clear that we were dealing with a past life situation. He had been a very successful businessman in 17th century Venice. However, his success was usually at the expense of someone else, very much an Arthur Daley character. Eventually, his fellow businessmen decided that they had had enough of his sharp practices. They all banded together to lay on a dinner in his honour and convinced him that they were genuine in wanting to honour him for his business success. On the way to the venue, he was set upon by two assailants, knifed and thrown into a canal.

By being a successful businessman in this lifetime, even though he was totally honest in his business dealings, every time he was invited to a social function, especially one connected with business, he panicked as he expected to be done away with.

By helping him to understand the origin of his fears, he was able to let go of the emotion and begin to enjoy his social life.

Case Three

This was a man in his early thirties with a large variety of physical problems. He had experienced sore throats and sinus problems since a baby; when he was eighteen one of his lungs had collapsed and since then had regular hot flushes and bouts of profuse sweating; at twenty one he had his tonsils out and his lung had collapsed again following the operation; he had extreme tiredness all of the time and needed to sleep at several times during the day; he had back, pelvis and rib problems which caused him a great deal of pain; two years ago he had begun to have bouts of severe depression and would burst into tears for no reason. Quite a mess.

As we began to examine him and to "read" his chakras, a story began to unfold which explained most of his symptoms. All of his chakras were disrupted and in a state of "trauma". His consciousness was desperately trying to release a memory (DNA sequence) but it had somehow become lodged within his body.

His story was this. In a previous life he had been born in Eastern Europe, in an area that relates to the current Czechoslovakia, and had worked as a tin miner. In 1742 he had become involved in a roof collapse in the mine and had been pinned to the floor by the collapsing roof. His body had been slowly crushed by the weight of the debris and he had been in total darkness and considerable pain for ten days before he died. All of his current health problems related to this accident. As his body had taken on many of the memories of the soul (see appendix one), he required a number of healing sessions before we could help his body to remove these "memories". He is still not fully recovered but his body is gradually letting go and many of his symptoms have gone.

Whilst these kinds of cases are quite dramatic, they are not very common. Only about five percent of our many hundreds of clients fall into this category.

Since the dawning of the "New Age" movement, many people have begun to adopt concepts and ideas from other cultures. With this spreading of knowledge has come a growing understanding of the workings and journeyings of the soul. Many of these new ideas have come from India where past life memories are quite strong. The Hindus, in particular, have concepts involving many lifetimes and out of these concepts has come the idea of Karmic debt (very similar in practice to the Christian concept of "an eye for an eye"). This has been a way of explaining many of the events and illnesses which people have to undergo in order to cleanse the soul of impurities. This has been their way of life for many centuries and the concepts are fully understood and accepted in their country. As the west has begun to look at and accept many of these ideas and beliefs, we have not fully taken on board the whole range of concepts inherent in these belief systems. This has led to many people using the idea of Karmic debt to walk away from their own responsibilities. It has been far easier to proclaim that "it is my Karma" than to take responsibility for their actions or their illnesses.

Whilst the case histories given above demonstrate that other lifetimes can influence this lifetime, the idea that we can behave in particular ways, usually irresponsibly, and blame it on a Karmic hangover is, in our opinion, pushing it a little. As Ghandi put it - living a series of eye for an eye existences only leads to a world of the blind.

What must be remembered is that even these kinds of problems belong to your "total" soul and problems arise, in this lifetime, because we have not let go of these kinds of memories. Whilst they can lead to quite serious problems, as in case three, we still have to deal with and clear these memories. There are two very good ways of doing this. Firstly, you can use the meditation exercises suggested in appendix one. Secondly, these memories can be explored through hypnosis - if you choose to try this method, be prepared for a few surprises! But, again, we would stress that health problems associated with past life trauma are extremely rare - do not try to use this as an excuse for not dealing with your current lives.

Incidentally, the whole cycle of Karma stopped at Christmas 1996. We are no longer creating any kind of Karmic debt. This is our last lifetime where Karma has any kind of role to play. What we have begun to do since 1996/1997 is to clear our accumulated debris. We will all shortly arrive at a new, clean, page of existence.

The ideas and concepts raised by these issues are discussed in detail in the author's two previous books *The Journey Home* and *The Fool's First Steps*.

Chapter Eleven

Conclusions

We have arrived at the end. All of the body's systems are in place and the chakras that control them are also in place. The body and soul are complete.

From the most basic physical structures to the most complex chemical signals, the body and soul function together with a rhythm and complexity that is breath taking. In describing the body's organs and systems we have tried to use language that is as simple as possible. This has been in order to avoid the words of forty three Latin syllables that the medical profession uses. In simplifying the descriptions, we hope that we have not taken away from the wonder that is the human body. Because that is what the body is, a wonder. As healers, we can "see" into the body and all of its workings and we are still awestruck by the complexity and the immensity of the whole. Every day is a trip into the wonders of the soul and the physical body. The energies contained within our physicalness are immense and yet we take it all for granted. If you could see what we see, you would never do anything to harm this masterpiece. When the body is working correctly and the body and soul are in harmony, it glows and sparkles with an intensity that is blinding. This is why we work as healers, we have seen the immensity and sheer beauty of the soul and once you have touched the soul, everything else pales into utter insignificance. Every day we touch the spirit of the Creator and we are very fortunate, and every day we see the damage that can be done by our not being true to ourselves.

That is all that is asked of us - to be true to ourselves. Everything that occurs in our lives attempts to turn us away from our own truth and the more we turn away from that promise, the more we create illness and disease. Nobody needs to suffer. We'll say that again because it is probably the first time that you can stand in a position where you can understand what the expression means.

Nobody needs to suffer.

All illnesses occur because we have not fulfilled the promise that our chosen life has to offer. We have taken a wrong turn in carrying out the wishes of the soul. This is what illness is, a wrong turn. Everyone of us arrives in our lifetime with a blank page of possibility. It is how we respond to those possibilities that creates an illness. There is no easy way to say that we create our own realities, our own illnesses. We have total freedom of choice in how we live our lives. If we listen to our own inner voices we survive unscathed. If we fight against them, we falter and illness occurs. How far we turn away from the soul determines how severe that illness is. We have said several times during the course of this first half that there are three stages to illness; there is the gentle tap on the shoulder, then, if we ignore it, there is a harder nudge, if we ignore the nudge, the baseball bat.

Only we can judge how we are doing in our lives. We can state with absolute conviction that nobody else stands in judgement of us. Only we judge ourselves and our actions. If we act against our own choices, we become ill. If we act with our own choices, we glow. It is as simple or as complex as you choose to make it.

The problem with our western world is that we have been pushed into a situation where we see the world around us as being ruled by others, we have no power of our own. What we are trying to say with this book is that it does not need to be this way. We all have control. What we have done is to give that control to others. The scientists, doctors, politicians, priests, etc. have, collectively, convinced us that we do not need to do anything, they will take care of us and we have listened. It is only now, at the end of the twentieth century, that we are beginning to realise that we have been duped.

Northern Ireland is a wonderful example of how we, individually and collectively, can regain control of our environment. As we write, the politicians are still posturing and fighting each other. The peace was arrived at by the people saying, enough.

It is this same realisation that we can bring to bear upon ourselves. We can be in control of our own bodies. All that is, usually, needed is for someone to give you permission to do so. Most people have forgotten that they have a voice. There is no need to accept the outside world when your inner voice is saying no. This is what happened in Northern Ireland, each person found their voice and said NO. The world stopped turning and the politicians, the terrorists and the priests had to listen.

This is what this book is all about. You have permission to say no.

Good health only comes about because we realise that we have the power to be ourselves. We *can* be whole, we *can* listen to our souls, we do not have to be pushed into situations which go against what *we* want. If we start to shout, the world has to listen.

We are not proposing anarchy. Don't misunderstand us on this. You are an individual and you need what YOU need. Nobody else can tell you what you need. Only you can decide and only you can act on that decision. What we have tried to say in this book is that the body works, despite all of the rubbish that we put into it, and to keep it working properly you need to listen to it. Ill health occurs because we stop listening.

The chakras are a representation of the soul made physical. Each of the chakras represents an element of our personality. As we live our lives, certain opportunities or choices present themselves. What we have to do is to choose. We can go down the route that looks the easiest or we can do what we know is the best, even if it appears to be the most difficult.

All that the soul asks of us is that we make the choice. No more, no less than that. We can choose what we want or we can choose what we think the other person involved wants. If we choose what we want, we walk away knowing that we made the right choice. If we choose what we think the other person wants, we have made a decision on behalf of that other person. This is what our choices come down to in the end. Do we do what we know is right for us or do we try to judge what is right for the other person? They are a way of helping you to realise that matters involving you and your life can only be decided by you. The right decision is not an act of selfishness. If we stay true to ourselves, we make the right decision. If we make a judgement, believing that we know what is right for the other person, we compromise ourselves and are setting ourselves up for a new career in politics (and an illness). How can you judge what is right for someone else? The American Indians have a wonderful expression; before you judge someone, walk a mile in their moccasins. What this means is that we cannot know why someone makes their decisions because we do not live their lives for them. Until we walk a mile, live as they live, see the world as they see it, we cannot possibly comment on their actions or decide what they need.

We can only make decisions based on what *our* needs are. If we ignore those needs, the soul and body respond in a way that lets us know we have taken an inappropriate turn.

How many books have you read about people who have overcome their major illness such as cancer. All of these people have been in a position where they were staring death in the face. When you stand in this position it is easier to see your life and what it means to you. Those who have recognised what their soul is trying to tell them through illness, and take steps to correct their actions, go on to survive and live more fulfilling lives.

We do not need to wait this long before we take action to correct the imbalances that we have created. What we have set out in this book is the way in which the soul is intimately linked with our lives and our bodies. If we all took the actions and decisions that we know we should do, all illness would be eradicated on a global level.

It really does not matter what the illness is. It can be a cold or terminal cancer, all illnesses can be cured if you begin to track the illness back to it's source. The chakras, as a tool for diagnosis, are totally foolproof. Once you have determined the area of your life which has been neglected or misunderstood, you can begin to undo the damage.

Even cancer is something which can be undone. We mentioned one particular case history in chapter five, the lady with stomach cancer, where despite being given a very short time to live, the lady turned it around. Cancer is only another tool in the soul's armoury to try to help us to understand ourselves. All that it takes to reverse the process is to recognise the power to change within yourself and the hormone production can be stopped and the damage undone. We have seen too many cancers put into remission for us not to accept that we have understood the process.

On the other side, we have also come across many people who were more afraid to change their lives than they were of death. For those people, all that we were able to do was to remove the symptoms for them to see that change was possible.

When you are in a position where you have a life threatening disease, the distance from where you are to the point where the disease has gone can seem an extremely long way. It is then a question of whether you have the strength to carry on the fight. This is where many people begin to falter, "how can I fight any more when I feel so weak, it would be a lot easier if I just gave in". It does not need to be this way. Huge strides begin with the smallest of steps and the first step is to realise why you have the disease in the first place. It is only from that point of understanding that a genuine choice can be made.

One of the biggest problems we have faced is that we have been unaware of the true links within the body. As our western "civilisation" has developed we have moved further and further away from the energetic and spiritual nature of the body. As materialism took hold, the soul was cast onto the scrap heap of superstition. It is time for us to dust off the soul, take another look and begin to live our lives with a new understanding.

Do not wait until you have your own near death experience.

As a final note to any medical practitioners who have read this far into this book. Most of you are probably feeling extremely sceptical about the explanations and connections given. We can understand your point of view. The way in which medical training is taught only accepts the body as a collection of parts which can be totally separated out from each other. To relieve symptoms, a pill is given or surgery performed to solve a medical problem.

Try a new approach. Make a list of the chakras and the organs and systems associated with them. Next time you see a patient, spend an extra two minutes talking to them and ask them about their lives, especially about the regions that are associated with their particular ailments identified in the chakra list.

Give it a try. What harm is it going to do to find out if there is something to the chakras after all?

THE SECOND HALF

Self Diagnosis
and
Treatment of Symptoms

Chapter Twelve

A New Way of Looking

We are a soul that has a body. This much should now be becoming clear. Everything that we do within our lives, how we respond to the day to day living of those lives has an affect upon our consciousness. If we respond to these situations in ways which our consciousness finds acceptable, we live to fight another day. But, if we respond in ways which are unacceptable, small "ripples" are set up within the chakra that correspond to the regions of our consciousness that deal with those particular situations.

These ripples do not have much of an immediate affect, all that they do is to set up minor weaknesses within the organs that correspond to the chakra. If we do not make the same mistake again, the ripples smooth out and the chakra returns to normal. If we find ourselves in a similar situation and we respond in a similar way to the first time, the ripple becomes larger and can set up "wobbles" within the chakra.

When working correctly, the chakra spins with a bright, clear colour. If these "ripples" begin to form, the colour begins to lose its clarity and the spin begins to slow. It is a little like a spinning top. If it is allowed to spin by itself, it spins and hums away to itself quite happily. If the top is nudged, it begins to wobble. If it was not nudged too hard, it can correct itself. If it is nudged again, especially when it was still wobbling from the first nudge, it can topple over. This is how illnesses can begin to form. If the chakra is "nudged" it will begin to wobble. If it is nudged again it will begin to affect an associated organ. If the "wobble" within the chakra is not corrected, it will create a kind of pressure within the organ forcing the organ to not perform

178

its function correctly. If the wobble remains uncorrected, the organ can begin to fail.

This is how illness can begin.

If the chakra can be made to spin correctly again, the pressure comes off the organ and the illness will disappear. All of the pressure that the organ was experiencing will be drawn out through the now correctly spinning chakra and its function returns to normal.

This is how healing can begin.

This is the basis of the healing process that we are describing. It sounds very simple, but then most correct solutions are very simple. This is the theory, it is putting the theory into practice that can be the difficult part.

What we have explored throughout the first half is the illness and healing process. Each chapter has taken each chakra in turn and explained, in detail, what regions of the body it relates to and how our actions can affect those regions and the illnesses that are associated with those regions. It has not been possible to cover every single illness in this way, but a number of the common ailments are included, some of which are serious life threatening illnesses. Even for illnesses that are not included here, if the same approach to establishing the root cause is used, then their root causes can also be determined.

Each chapter has taken a similar format. It describes the chakra, the organs or systems affected by it and some of the ailments that can arise because of imbalances within the chakra. They also describe ways in which the primary underlying cause of the illness can be dealt with on a chakra level. We have also given ways in which it is possible to deal with the situations that brought about the chakra "imbalance" in the first place. If these methods are fully put into practice, then all illnesses can be healed. This is no idle statement, but is based upon many years of research helping our clients to correct their health problems. They do work.

As a second line of approach, this section of the book looks at a number of methods of dealing with the symptoms of the problems whilst the root causes are being dealt with.

These methods are "alternative" in their approach. The reason for suggesting these methods is that prescriptive drugs have many adverse side affects, especially when taken over a prolonged period. The methods of approach suggested here work with the body to gently cleanse and heal the symptoms. They work in subtle, but effective ways, which can take a little more time to fully work than prescriptive drugs. The reason for this is that prescriptive drugs are designed to mask the symptoms very quickly. You think that you are getting better because the symptoms are not so pronounced, whereas what they also do is to take over some of the functions of the organs or systems that the drugs are being prescribed for. This is not so bad in the short term, but in the long term the body becomes dependant on the drugs and forgets about the organ, ultimately making the situation very much worse.

The remedies that are proposed here work in a different way. They can gently coax the organs or systems to begin to return back to their normal function. This means that the symptoms are not fully hidden but are gently and gradually eased until the remedy is no longer required.

The remedies that are proposed here are: Bach Flower Remedies®, Tissue Salts, Herbal Remedies, Reflexology, and where appropriate, Homeopathy. See appendices two, three and four for full details of these particular remedies.

The remedies given here are as a suggestion only and are designed to treat general symptoms. If you decide to switch to an "alternative" approach and away from prescriptive medication, then we strongly suggest that

you consult a fully qualified practitioner for that particular remedy in order to treat your specific symptoms, particularly if you are pregnant or have been taking prescribed drugs for a prolonged period.

If these types of remedies are new to you and you intend to make use of them instead of your prescribed medication, then you should consult with a qualified practitioner to ensure that coming off the drugs will not have a harmful effect upon your body. Most prescriptive drugs have the affect of creating a dependency within the body. If you stop this type of medication too quickly, it can result in withdrawal symptoms occurring.

In some instances, it should be possible to use both the remedies and your prescribed medication together whilst, hopefully, reducing the medication doses as the other remedies begin to work. It is advisable to consult the medical practitioner who prescribed the medication to ensure that this approach will not cause any harmful side effects, although you should be prepared for a sceptical response to your decision from the medical profession.

None of the remedies suggested here are harmful. What creates a potential problem is making a sudden change to your prescribed medication or not adhering to the recommended dosages, so it is always best to check first.

The "alternative" remedies and practices that are recommended here are well known and have been proven to work over many years, in some instances, centuries but, for some people, this form of approach will be new and so here is a brief description of how they work.

Bach Flower Remedies®

These are remedies developed by Dr Edward Bach (pronounced Batch) during his career as a pathologist, a Harley Street consultant, bacteriologist, and homeopath until he passed away in 1936. Instead of using herbs as the basis for his remedies he used the flowers of wild plants, bushes and trees.

These remedies take the form of tinctures, that is an extract suspended in alcohol, in this case, brandy. They are intended to be used as primary remedies. They are aimed specifically at the state of mind of a person with a health problem and are aimed at the person's worry, apprehension, sense of hopelessness, irritability, etc. These states of mind can have a major depleting effect on someone's health, and consequently, the energy they have available to fight those health problems. These remedies are designed to alleviate these aspects of health problems. In other words, they are intended to be used to bolster your morale and help bring your mental state back into a more helpful, positive balance, whilst at the same time, helping to work on the root causes of your problem.

There are thirty eight remedies, all of which have a very specific function and treat specific aspects of our mental well being. Bach Flower Remedies are registered products and care should be taken to ensure that the ones purchased are the genuine article. These remedies work in very subtle but powerful ways. They are very gentle and safe and can be taken alongside any other treatments without undue concern. However, if you do experience any difficulties then you should consult a qualified Bach practitioner.

The suggested remedies are given as number of drops of a particular remedy. These drops should be put into a glass of water and sipped slowly throughout the day. If you accidentally add a greater number of drops than specified, it does not matter, it will not cause any harm neither will it, unfortunately, make them more effective.

There is one particular Bach Flower Remedy which would be useful to carry with you at all times and this is the "Rescue Remedy"®. This remedy is intended to be used when you are in stressful situations and can help to calm and reassure. It is available in tincture or cream forms and can be applied internally as well as externally. It can also be used on animals.

Biochemic Tissue Salts

Biochemic tissue salts were first developed by Dr Wilhelm Schuessler in the 1870's. Dr Schuessler was a physician and a homeopath. He described twelve tissue salts as being vital for health and vitality within the body. Each of the salts treat a particular element of health and the body's well being. There are also a range of eighteen combination salts which have been formulated for specific ailments.

The tissue salts are usually described under homeopathic treatments but they are very different to homeopathic remedies. They should be taken in the same way as homeopathic remedies i.e. the required dose should be "tapped" into the lid of their container and the tablets put under the tongue directly from the lid. The tablets should not be touched with the fingers. The tablets are prepared in a lactose base (from milk products) and should, therefore not be taken if you have any kind of allergy or intolerance to milk products.

Herbal Remedies

Every single country throughout the world has a herbal remedy tradition. Some of these remedies have been in use for several thousands of years and so their effectiveness is well known. All modern medicines are based upon the use of the active ingredients found in herbs and plants. The drug companies are currently scouring the planet for new plants to treat our illnesses as it is believed that their artificial chemical versions of these original extracts are increasingly failing to work.

The original forms of these drugs were manufactured from the plant and mixed with a suitable powder. These powders were then dissolved in water and taken as a medicine. Eventually, what was considered to be the active ingredient from the plant was artificially manufactured and the powders pressed into a tablet form.

Over the years, the drug companies have moved further and further away from the original plant extracts and produced chemically modified versions of the active ingredients. In our opinion, the further the further the pharmaceutical companies have moved away from the original plant extract, the less effective their drugs have become.

If we return to the use of the original plants, we can overcome many of the problems that the drug companies have experienced. The best way of using herbs as a means of keeping healthy - or of clearing up ailments - is in your daily diet. They provide vitamins and minerals as well as giving extra flavour to food. However, it is not always practicable or pleasant to use herbs in food, for example, some people do not like the taste or smell of garlic. Some of the commoner herbs can be bought from health food stores in a tea bag form and the herbs drunk as tea. Many of the herbs mentioned throughout this text are not available as tea bags and, therefore, other forms of preparation are required.

Like all vegetable products, mass produced herbs can be treated with pesticides and chemical fertilisers. It is best to ensure that your suppliers are as organic as possible.

Herbal Drinks

There are four main ways in which herbs can be taken as drinks.

Infusion. Fresh or dried herbs can be used in either loose or tea bag form. To make an infusion, warm a teapot and put in one dessertspoon of herb, or mixed herbs, for each cup required. Pour in a cup of boiling water for each cup of tea and allow to stand for 10 - 15 minutes. Strain before drinking.

Decoction. This is the name given to an infusion made from roots or "twiggy" herbs. To make a decoction, put a heaped tablespoon of the powdered dried herb, or herb pieces, into a stainless steel or glass saucepan (never an aluminium saucepan). Add about one pint (600ml.) of boiling water. Bring to the boil and simmer for about 10 - 15 minutes. Strain while the tea is hot and drink. You can make decoctions from your own herbs but you need to allow the root or stems to dry thoroughly. Store the herbs in an airtight container for use.

Tincture. Herbalists prescribe more alcohol based tinctures than any other form of remedy. They are long lasting, highly concentrated and taken in small dosages. They can be made at home with a forty percent spirit (alcohol content) which depends upon your own taste. Vodka, gin, etc. can be used but the most common is brandy. Put about 4oz. (120g) of ground or chopped dried herbs into a container. Pour one pint (600ml) of alcohol onto the herbs and seal the container. Leave it in a warm, dry place for two weeks, shaking it well twice a day. Decant the liquid, straining off the residue, into a dark wine bottle (or similar) and seal until needed.

Tisane. This is, essentially, a milder form of an infusion. Make in the same way as an infusion but do not allow to stand for more than a couple of minutes to your own taste.

Herbal Dressings
Herbs can be used in two ways to dress wounds, bruises, injuries or local infections.

Compress. To make a compress, soak a clean cloth, or a piece of cotton wool, in a hot herbal decoction or infusion made from as many herbs as are required. Place the cloth against the affected area and, for large areas, maintain the heat by holding a hot water bottle against it.

Poultice. The leaves of fresh, untreated herbs can be placed directly onto the skin. Alternatively, put the leaves on a piece of gauze and place on the skin. With dried herbs, make a paste with hot water and apply accordingly. Maintain the heat by holding a hot water bottle against the poultice.

Other Herbal Preparations

Creams and ointments are available that are made up of herbal mixtures put into a hypo-allergenic cream. Many different types of creams and ointments are available ready prepared from chemists, health food shops and herbalists. Herbs are also the source of most essential oils.

An alternative method, which is being increasingly used, is where the infusion is dried and pressed into a tablet or capsule form.

The herbal remedies suggested in the following chapters are taken from a variety of traditions. We have taken many sources for these suggested remedies and have tried to find a balance between the most effective and what is readily available to purchase or easily grown.

When these traditions began, many centuries ago, the people who made up these remedies were the tribal shaman or medicine man, or woman. These were people who had psychic capabilities where they could "look" into a plant and "see" what healing properties it had. It is still possible to find people with these abilities in many of the tribal cultures that still exist in the more remote parts of the planet.

The remedies suggested here are recognised as being effective for particular symptoms. If you decide to use these remedies and find that they are not particularly effective for you, then you should consult a qualified herbalist who will be able to recommend a more suitable mixture that is specifically formulated for your particular health problems.

Most of the herbs listed will be available from health food shops many of which will also sell pre-prepared remedies in a tablet or capsule form. There are also a number of specialist herbal suppliers who will be able to mix herbs for you and further advise you on suitable remedies. The other alternative, of course, is to grow the herbs and plants for yourself.

These remedies are effective and often quite powerful. Although herbal remedies are well tried and trusted and have been prepared from natural sources, it should not be assumed that they are harmless. Remember, these are the source for Western type drugs and they do have very strong healing capabilities, so they should be treated in the same way as prescriptive drugs and only take the prescribed dosages. They should be used with common sense and understanding and not taken for prolonged periods.

If you experience any difficulties or fall into any of the following categories, you should consult a qualified herbalist:

1. Pregnant.

2. Taking prescribed medication.

3. Have a chronic condition.

4. If an acute condition does not respond in a suitable time or worsens.

5. Do not take herbs over a prolonged period without a break or without professional advice.

Reflexology
This is another practice that was first developed by the ancient Sumerians. As was briefly mentioned in chapter two, the body

is criss-crossed by energy channels that are more commonly known as the "Meridians".

These meridians carry the energy from the chakras and distribute it around the body to the appropriate regions and organs. All areas of the body are covered by the meridians. It is these meridians that are treated by those who practice acupuncture, acupressure and kinesiology. The meridians are also represented on the palms of the hands and, especially, on the soles of the feet. This is how reflexologists work. Each of the meridians that connect to the body's organs connect into particular regions of the palms of the hands and to the soles of the feet. Applying pressure and massaging particular regions will correct any energy imbalances within the meridians and relieve the pressure on the organs (see illustrations numbered seventeen and eighteen).

This method is also a very good way of providing a secondary diagnosis, the chakras being the primary diagnostic tool. You can use this method to diagnose and treat yourself on the palms of the hands but asking somebody else to work on the soles of the feet is a much more effective way of working.

The way to work with this is to place yourself in a comfortable position where the person working on your feet can gain easy access to the soles. The "reflexologist" needs to apply *gentle* pressure to each region over the whole of the foot. What you will experience is a sensation that ranges from a mild "tingling" to a sharp pain depending on the level of problem with a particular region or organ. This is why it is important to begin with very gentle pressure. If the region or organ is badly affected then the pain can be quite sharp when pressure is applied to the reflex point. When the "reflexologist" has gone over the whole foot, they should go back to the areas where you experienced a reaction and begin with a very gentle massage of these regions. The massage should be with gentle circular movements of the fingers or thumb, beginning with a very light pressure but gradually increasing the pressure as the reflex point becomes less sensitive. Continue with the massage until you have completed twelve to fourteen clockwise circular motions on each reflex point. Excessive stimulation of a blocked reflex point can cause bruising, so it is best not to exceed fourteen motions. You can carry out the massage yourself using the reflex points on the hands.

This approach can be used on virtually any symptom and has the added advantage of being very relaxing, once you have gotten over the initial shock of the reflex point's sensitivity. Reflexology works and is designed to stimulate the organ etc. into its proper function. If you use reflexology massage, you should be aware that you will probably require a reduced dosage of medication.

You can also colour in the illustrations using the chakra colour for each corresponding region.

Homeopathy

Homeopathy is a method of healing which is, in some ways, the exact opposite of western medicine. Western medicine is described as being allopathic, that is working against the body. Homeopathic is working with the body.

The basic principle of homeopathy has been known since the time of the ancient Greeks. Derived from the Greek word "Homoios", meaning "like", homeopathy is the medical practice of treating like with like. That is to say, treating an illness with a substance which, when taken by a healthy person, produces symptoms similar to those displayed by the person who is ill. Current medical opinion takes the view that symptoms are a direct manifestation of the illness and, therefore, treats the ailment by suppressing the symptoms. Homeopathy, by contrast, sees the symptoms as the body's reaction against the illness as it attempts to overcome it, and seeks to stimulate and not suppress the reaction.

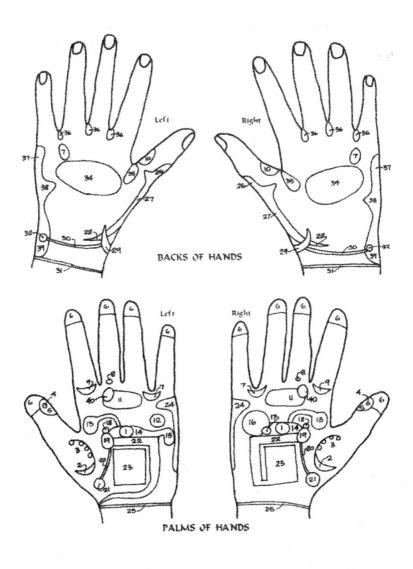

Illustration Number Seventeen - The Reflex Points on the Hands

Key To Illustration Number Seventeen

1. Solar Plexus
2. Thyroid
3. Parathyroids
4. Pituitary
5. Brain

6. Sinuses
7. Ear
8. Eustachian tubes
9. Eye
10. Throat

11. Lungs
12. Heart
13. Stomach
14. Pancreas
15. Spleen

16. Liver
17. Gall Bladder
18. Adrenal
19. Kidney
20. Ureter, Urethra

21. Bladder
22. Large Intestine (Colon)
23. Small Intestine
24. Shoulder and Arm
25. Sciatic Nerve

26. Neck
27. Spine
28. Coccyx
29. Uterus or Prostate

30. Fallopian Tubes
31. Groin and Leg Lymph
    Tissue
32. Ovary or Testicle
33. Hip and Pelvis
34. Breast
35. Neck and Throat Lymph
    Tissue

36. Arms and Chest Lymph
    Tissue
37. Shoulder and Arm or
    Ankle and Lower Leg
38. Knee or Elbow
39. Thigh or Forearm
40. Thymus gland

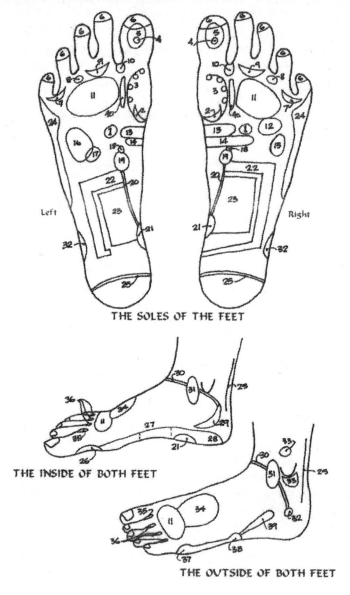

THE SOLES OF THE FEET

THE INSIDE OF BOTH FEET

THE OUTSIDE OF BOTH FEET

Illustration Number Eighteen - The Reflex Points on the Feet

Key To Illustration Number Eighteen

1. Solar Plexus
2. Thyroid
3. Parathyroids
4. Pituitary
5. Brain

6. Sinuses
7. Ear
8. Eustachian tubes
9. Eye
10. Throat

11. Lungs
12. Heart
13. Stomach
14. Pancreas
15. Spleen

16. Liver
17. Gall Bladder
18. Adrenal
19. Kidney
20. Ureter, Urethra

21. Bladder
22. Large Intestine (Colon)
23. Small Intestine
24. Shoulder and Arm
25. Sciatic Nerve

26. Neck
27. Spine
28. Coccyx

29. Uterus or Prostate
30. Fallopian Tubes

31. Groin and Leg Lymph
   Tissue
32. Ovary or Testicle
33. Hip and Pelvis
34. Breast
35. Neck and Throat Lymph
   Tissue

36. Arms and Chest Lymph
   Tissue
37. Shoulder and Arm or
    Ankle and Lower Leg
38. Knee or Elbow
39. Thigh or Forearm
40. Thymus gland

Homeopathy is essentially a natural healing process, providing remedies to assist the patient to regain health by stimulating the body's natural forces of recovery. The remedies appear to trigger a healing process within the body, leading to the correction of the illness.

Homeopathy was begun in the eighteenth century by Dr Samuel Hahnemann. Dr Hahnemann was a leading German doctor who was appalled by the medical practices of the day and sought a method of healing which would be safe, gentle and effective. He believed that human beings have a capacity for healing themselves and that the symptoms of disease reflect the individual's struggle to overcome their illness. He reasoned that instead of suppressing symptoms, he could seek to stimulate them and so encourage and assist the body's natural healing process.

Dr Hahnemann discovered that when he took an infusion of chinchona bark (quinine) it produced the symptoms of malaria. When given to a patient, suffering from the disease, it alleviated the symptoms. From this, Dr Hahnemann deduced the first principle of homeopathy - similia similibus curentur - "let like be treated with like". In other words, a substance which in a healthy person produces the symptoms of a disease will, in a person suffering from that disease, have a curative effect.

Dr Hahnemann went on to discover that remedies obtained from animal, vegetable and mineral sources were just as effective in extreme dilutions. This was especially apparent in the case of poisons which often produced symptoms similar to those of certain illnesses and which, in very diluted doses, suggested themselves as remedies on the "like cures like" principle.

Over a long period, Dr Hahnemann and his assistants took small doses of various substances, carefully noting the symptoms they produced. These were called "provings". Subsequently, patients suffering from similar symptoms were

194

treated with these substances. The results were usually encouraging and often remarkable. Dr Hahnemann then worked to establish the smallest effective dose, for he realised that this was the best way to avoid side effects. In so doing, he unexpectedly discovered the second principle of homeopathy: the more a remedy is diluted the more effective it becomes.

The third principle of homeopathy is that people vary in their response to an illness according to their basic temperament.

Homeopathy concentrates on treating the patient rather than the disease and it follows, therefore, that a homeopath does not automatically prescribe a specific remedy for a specific illness. Instead, they try to determine the patient's temperament and responses and so prescribe on a more individual basis.

The more closely a remedy imitates a patient's symptoms, the more it promotes healing, and the more dilute the dose, the greater its effect. Remedies rarely cause any side effects other than the symptoms already present. These symptoms may worsen at first, known as a healing crisis, but they do not usually last for very long. This increase in symptoms is taken as a good sign as it signifies the beginnings of an improvement. Homeopaths pay most attention to symptoms which have the greatest effect on the patient's overall ability to function. The severity of symptoms within each bodily system is graded in order of importance, but unusual symptoms have a greater significance. So a patient's mental and emotional state, general problems and any additional "peculiar" symptoms may receive more attention than say, a rash, even though this was your reason for consulting the homeopath in the first place.

The remedies are made from a variety of plant, animal or mineral substances. These substances are first soaked in alcohol to extract their active ingredients. This solution, known as a "mother tincture", is progressively diluted many times over in measures of tens or hundreds, with a vigorous "shaking" (or succussing) at the end of each dilution.

Succussing "fixes" the energy of the remedy into the solution, a process called "potentising". This means that homeopathic remedies become more powerful with each dilution. As the remedy is further diluted, the active ingredient reduces but its energy rises. Once the final dilution has been made, sugar is added and the mixture is pressed into small tablets.

The homeopathic remedies given in this book are effective, but they are also quite general. If you decide to change to a homeopathic approach to your health symptoms, then you should consult a qualified homeopath. Qualified homeopaths undergo several years of rigorous training and can advise you on treatments for all ailments. They can also advise you on your existing medication and how best to make the switch from prescribed drugs to a homeopathic approach.

In suggesting the remedies detailed above, we have tried to find ways which are effective in treating symptoms that do not involve artificial methods. As psychic surgeons, the authors can "see" the many adverse affects that prescribed drugs can have on the human body. Many of the symptoms that we are called upon to treat are as a direct result of drugs "invading" regions of the body which they were not intended for. The damage that we have seen caused by these drugs can be worse that the conditions they were meant to treat. This does not mean that all prescribed drugs are this harmful but many are, especially when used over a prolonged period.

The remedies suggested in this book are effective and tend to work with the body in ways which do not cause further harm.

As healers, we would obviously promote healing as being an extremely effective way of dealing with virtually all health problems. Healing is also known as Spiritual Healing, The Laying on of Hands, Hands on Healing, Faith Healing, Chakra Balancing, etc. All illnesses come about by the energy contained within the chakras becoming depleted. This energy depletion creates stresses and pressures in associated organs and structures. Healers work by adding energy into these particular regions to "top up" the energy deficiency thereby producing a state of balance of energies. A stabilising of the "wobble" within a chakra or an organ.

Healing has not been included here as a suggested remedy because it is generally not possible to heal yourself in this way (the "hands on" approach). However, whatever your symptoms, we would recommend a visit to a healer to help relieve your symptoms and to help balance all of the body's energies. Healing does not affect your current medication or alternative remedy in any way, except to reduce the need for any form of treatment. By adding energy into the chakras, the healer can also help relieve the originating cause for the illness. To a certain extent, healing can be carried out using meditations designed to help boost the chakra system. Details of this approach will be found in appendix one.

Other therapies and treatments are described in appendix six.

As a final note about remedies and treatments. All of these remedies and suggested treatments work, otherwise there would have been little point in recommending them. If you are on any kind of prescribed medication, but choose to adopt a more alternative approach to your health, it is advisable to consult your medical practitioner on a regular basis to monitor the effects. What should occur is that you will require reduced dosages of your medication and, hopefully, a point where no prescribed medication or any kind of surgery is required. This suggestion applies particularly where you are taking high dosage medications.

There is not an exhaustive list of remedies as we have not included every possible ailment. As with the first half, we have attempted to establish basic principles and some of the symptoms that can arise from chakra imbalances. The remedies suggested treat the ailments described, if you fall outside of the list given, many health food shops can supply pre-made remedies for other ailments or you should consult your chosen therapist.

To many, the idea of taking a tincture to deal with an illness will be a new one. All that we can say is that they work. To help us to reinforce this view, we can supply you with a case history which illustrates their effectiveness.

We were telephoned by a friend whose mother had been into hospital for an examination of her throat. The doctors had examined her by endoscope and x-ray and had come to the conclusion that she had polyp type growths on the inside of her throat which were "possibly cancerous". As our friend and her mother live over three hundred miles away, it was not possible for us to visit them very easily so we recommended that her mother take a combination of two Bach Flower Remedies and a tissue salt.

The doctors had arranged a further appointment, six weeks later, where the mother would return to discuss the surgical removal of the growths. During the six weeks, the mother took the Bach remedies and the tissue salt. When she returned to the hospital, she was re-examined by the same doctor and was advised that surgery was not required as the growths had disappeared and her throat was normal. Whilst this one case history cannot be taken as any kind of guarantee for the effectiveness of these remedies, it does suggest that they can work very effectively.

As a note about alternative therapies and therapists. The medical profession is usually very scathing and sceptical about any form of "alternative" treatments. This reaction is usually brought about by a sense of insecurity in the doctors as they are concerned that western drug treatments are becoming less and less effective whilst at the same time becoming more and more toxic leading to situations where side effects are increasingly common and life threatening. Alternative therapies, on the other hand, are perceived as becoming more and more effective

198

without the use of any prescriptive drug. So we have a medical profession which is perceived as being increasingly ineffectual in treating ailments and alternative therapies being perceived as being increasingly effective, leading to our doctors feeling increasingly threatened and insecure. From this viewpoint, most doctors will not promote or even investigate alternative practices as it puts their position at risk.

This is not true of all doctors. There are many who have seen alternative remedies work and work in situations where western drugs have failed. Some medical practices are employing alternative practitioners within their surgeries as some therapies have been shown to reduce the doctors' drug bills by well over 50%. The argument used by most doctors is that there are insufficient studies carried out into alternative therapies for them to take them seriously. The kinds of studies they have in mind are called "fully randomised, double blind, placebo" studies. The way in which these work is by taking a group of patients with similar symptoms and randomly dividing them into three groups. The division needs to be random so that nobody knows, including those evaluating the study, which patient is included in which group. The first group is given the full treatment being studied, the second is given an imitation (placebo) of the treatment and the third, or control group, is not given any treatment (or they continue with their normal medication). At the end of the study each patient is evaluated for changes in their symptoms. The evaluation is carried out without the evaluators or the patients knowing which has had the treatment or the placebo and their improvement, or otherwise, is measured against the control group symptoms.

Unfortunately, studies such as these cost money and as well over ninety percent of medical research is paid for by drug companies, there is very little money available for research into alternative remedies as the drug companies will not fund studies into treatments which are not based on drug usage.

Where such double blind, randomised studies have been carried out into alternative therapies, the results have usually shown that the treatments are extremely effective (see appendix two and appendix four). Even with these positive results, the medical profession tends to ignore them. This is mainly because there is no benefit to the doctors or the medical profession or the drug companies as they are shown to be failing in their treatments.

Given the doctors' insistence on randomised, double blind, placebo studies for alternative therapies, it would be anticipated that all of the procedures and drugs used by doctors would have undergone a similar study to determine their effectiveness. This is not the case. Ninety percent of all medical procedures or prescribed drugs have not been tested before they are tried out on patients (source: WDDTY, see appendix four).

As mentioned above, virtually all medical research is paid for by the drug companies. Most of this research involves studies into new drugs before they are licensed. These studies are only interested in finding out if the drugs suppress the symptoms they were designed to treat. The studies are not designed to determine if the drugs are safe to use or what the effect of taking the drugs over a prolonged period are. Long term studies of drugs are virtually never carried out before they are prescribed to patients and randomised, double blind, placebo trials are virtually unheard of. When a new drug is prescribed for the first time, its effectiveness or side effects are virtually unknown. The commercial pressures are such that new drugs come onto the market before anyone knows what their real effects are. Given the dangers inherent within this type of prescribing, alternative therapies are rapidly becoming the only source of effective and safe treatment for symptoms.

There is only one way to cure your health problems and that is to deal with the root problems that caused them in the first place. No other course of action can cure you. The remedies suggested are given as a way of dealing with the symptoms and to provide you with extra time in order for you to tackle the root causes of your particular problem.

Any remedy, whether it is one of the ones suggested here or prescribed medication, can only deal with the symptoms. Removing health problems can only be achieved by working with the chakras to give you the answers to where your problem first originated.

Total health is achievable by using this approach. Everything else just deals with the symptoms.

Chapter Thirteen

Self Diagnosis

During the first half of this book we looked at the underlying causes of all illnesses. The primary, and only totally accurate, means of diagnosing the root cause of a health problem is through the body's consciousness energy centres, the chakras. Illnesses manifest themselves in ways which help us to understand where in our lives we have taken a wrong turning. Most of us try to look for reasons that are as complex as possible to make our illness something unique and special. What should have become clear from the first half of this book is that the soul speaks to us in ways which are quite literal and often quite simple. Having said this, there are times when our problems are a little more obscure and accurate diagnosis can become complex. However, by staying with the basic principles detailed above, even the most complex health problems can be understood and related back to a primary cause that is related to the function of one, or more, chakras.

What we need to do is to look at our lives quite closely and seek out the region where we have strayed from the soul's required route. It sounds difficult, but all that is really required is an honest look at ourselves and the way in which we respond to our lives and the people we share those lives with.

So, where to start? We can begin with what our doctors have to say. For most of us, any illness is first taken to a doctor for them to try and tell us what is wrong. In our experience, the medical diagnosis is very often inaccurate. However, it does at least give us a clue of where to start to look to understand where the illness came from in the first place.

Take the medical diagnosis that you have and look through chapter two. This will give you the chakra that relates to the organs, regions, systems etc. affected by your illness. The chakra has a primary and a secondary function. All illnesses will relate to either of these functions. Once you have found the corresponding chakra, look through the appropriate chapter for a more in depth view of the chakra's function and how it relates to your illness. The same principles apply if you have more than one organ, region or system affected. All illnesses relate to a chakra. If there is more than one region of your body affected, then more than one chakra has been affected.

One region of the body becomes affected because of a problem in one chakra. If two or more regions are affected, two or more chakras are affected and you will need to look at several regions of your life to understand what is going wrong.

To best illustrate what we mean, we can give you a few case histories from clients who have come to see us for healing.

Case One

We were approached by a lady in her thirties with several problems. There was a lot of pain and stiffness in her neck and shoulders. She had had a non-cancerous lump removed from a breast a couple of months before seeing us. There were quite bad period problems and there was a weakness and pain in her left hip and thigh. All of these problems had appeared about two years previously. The medical diagnosis was inconclusive and her prescribed medication was not very effective.

If we start at the top. The breast lump gave us a clue of where to start with tracking down her problems. The upper body lymphatic system is controlled by the thymus gland. Lymph tissue problems in the upper body are caused by blockages in the thymus. All of this lymph tissue was "tender" to the touch, across her chest, her underarms (underarm lymph blockages feel like swollen grains of rice and are painful to the touch) and across her back. The neck and shoulder problems were caused by the lymph tissue being unable to drain through the blocked thymus, causing a build up of salts etc. within the muscles.

The period problems were due to the right ovary not functioning properly causing fluctuations to her progesterone levels which affected the uterus lining. The hip and thigh problems were caused by the sacrum/illium joint being slightly displaced causing the pelvis to "rock" slightly and slacken the tension in the cartilage which holds the thigh bone into the hip socket.

At the time that her health problems started, she was having major marital problems. What she thought was a secure marriage, turned out not to be. This generated a major insecurity within her life (first chakra), but especially within her marriage (second chakra). This insecurity and shock to the first and second chakras brought about the hip and pelvis problems. The relationship problems brought about the ovarian dysfunction. As a result of the whole situation, she lost much of her self confidence and how she thought about herself (fourth chakra) resulting in the thymus and lymphatic system becoming blocked, bringing about her other problems.

From our healing work, we were able to remove most of the symptoms. She began a programme of work on herself to try to remedy the underlying issues. The situation with her husband was improving, but there was still an underlying mistrust. This element of a health problem is always the most difficult to deal with as it is not always possible to forgive and forget within a relationship. However, she started to attend an exercise class (aerobics type) which helped to reinforce the root chakra and her spine and pelvis began to stabilise. She also took up a creative hobby which helped to override any lasting relationship problems. Both of these activities helped her to regain her self esteem and the lymph problems began to clear.

Case Two

This was a middle aged man with a lot of pain in his middle and lower back. He also had recurring gall bladder and pancreas (digestive) problems. He was in a fairly responsible job but had a tendency to panic attacks and he was a self confessed hypochondriac.

The lower back problems turned out to be stress related. All of us store stresses in either the shoulders or in the muscles of the lower back. A regular massage to the regions does more good than anything else. The middle back problem was chakra related. Although in a responsible job, he could not help feeling that he was not doing as well as he could. This gave him a constant sense of insecurity (first chakra), which manifested itself in the region of the chakra which he felt insecure about (third chakra - personal power). Fortunately, the damage was only in the muscles and the spine was not affected. As he was always insecure about himself and his work, he tended to bury his emotions away. "I'm not going to complain or be assertive as I don't feel confident enough to state my opinion". This meant that many of his emotions went into the related organs - in this instance, the gall bladder (unexpressed anger) and the pancreas (not enough force in expressing his feelings).

By helping him to understand the root cause for his conditions, it meant that he was able to concentrate on these issues and bring about a change in the way in which he approached his work. By accepting that he had achieved a position of responsibility within his company, he was able to relax about his abilities and the anxiety attacks virtually disappeared. If he had another attack, he remembered that he was in control and was more able to deal with it. As his confidence grew, the hypochondria also disappeared and he began to see himself as healthy.

Case Three

This was an elderly lady with a severe leg ulcer. The problem had begun about two years before coming to see us. She had been prescribed steroid creams but had a severe reaction to them, the skin of her leg had swollen and become covered in small lumps. The steroid creams had also thinned the skin so that any minor knock or insect bite took off several layers. She had also been prescribed antibiotics which she was allergic to. Whilst taking the antibiotics, her leg had been bandaged. The reaction to the antibiotics had been so severe that the bandage had dug into the leg and opened it up to the bone. She also had a mild form of diabetes mellitus and stomach problems.

About a year before the problems began, she had re-married someone who was very domineering. The root of her problems lay with the relationship with her new husband. Although there were problems with the relationship, they did not manifest themselves in the regions related to the second chakra. This was a little unusual but the lady was able to deal with the relationship issues by other means (she had accepted her husband as he was and could deal with his domineering ways without allowing it to affect her too much). However, his behaviour did make her feel insecure (root chakra) and she was unable to express her feelings fully (third chakra - pancreas). She also felt very frustrated by the situation as she was a warm, giving person and felt stifled by his domination (third chakra - spleen). This frustration badly affected her spleen in both aspects of its functions. Her stomach was affected by the spleen being blocked and not feeding the correct vitamins etc. into the stomach walls. Her immune system was affected as she could not fight infections efficiently, leading to a growth of infected tissue in her leg.

She started to use the giveaway as a means of clearing out her emotions. At the same time, she decided to take her doctor's advise and have the infected area surgically removed. She felt that by having the infection cut out, it would "cut" the problem out of her life. Unfortunately, the surgical wound would not

206

heal for the same reasons as the ulcer would not heal. When she used the giveaway after the operation, she released the underlying emotions and has now, finally, recovered.

We have given these cases to try to illustrate how our health problems can manifest themselves in varying ways. If you put these together with those given in chapter two and other chapters, you should be able to begin to build up a picture of how your illness arose and how to deal with the root causes. The remedies given in the following chapters will help to relieve the symptoms without prescribed medication, but you will need to work on the root causes before the problem can be totally removed.

The examples given above show how to relate symptoms to the chakras which is fine when you know which regions of the body are affected. Unfortunately, we very often find that medical opinion is not as good as it could be. This is not necessarily the doctors' fault. They tend to be under tremendous pressure these days and they are not always able to spend as much time as they would like with their patients. This leads to situations where they will try to fit symptoms to illnesses without fully looking at the symptoms. There are also times when you have symptoms but, for whatever reason, you do not consult with your doctor and they remain undiagnosed. In these situations there are two other means of approach to understanding what your body is trying to say to you.

The first is to investigate the problem for yourself. What you need to do is to find a quiet time in your day when you will be able to relax fully. Sit or lie down and try to empty your mind of your every day troubles (see appendix one). As you begin to relax, start to travel inwards into your body. We know how silly this sounds, but give it a try, you might be surprised at how easy it can be. As you travel inwards, ask your body what is wrong. It is as simple as that. Just ask and listen to the answer. The answer will come, we just need to listen. If you are able to visualise easily, you can travel throughout the organs of the body and ask each one in turn if they need any assistance. We know a lady who was very good at these kinds of exercises and found that as she asked each organ what it was hanging onto she received images that were very similar to a video tape of events in her life. Each of her organs held specific memories of events and emotions and, by asking each one in turn what it stored, she was able to see what it was she needed to do to clear out the organ concerned. Not everyone can do this, but, if you ask you will receive an answer. These answers take many forms but will usually be along the lines of either:

- a specific memory will come to mind of a particular event;

- an inner "knowing" of the problem, this is a sense that a particular organ or region is affected;

- the sense that a particular chakra, or chakras, need some help;

- a region of your life will come to mind which you know needs to be sorted out.

The answers received will arrive in many ways which will suit you as an individual. No two people are the same so we cannot say that you will receive answers in a particular way, just that you will receive an answer. If you listen to your body you can track down any health problem. This will give you the region of your life which has brought about the problem in the first place. Once you have your answer, you can begin to remedy it and the symptoms. The only thing you have to be is honest with yourself. If you want to heal your health problems, you have to listen and accept the answer.

The second form of diagnostic is to use the reflexology charts. Ask your partner or a friend to rub their fingers over the whole of the area of your feet, one foot at a time. They will need to use a certain amount of pressure whilst they do this as gentle strokes will just move the skin around and will not activate the reflex points. Any areas which require attention will feel sensitive or tender. Make a note of the areas which are tender and look at the charts (see illustrations seventeen and eighteen). This will give you the organs or regions which require some attention. Relate these organs etc. to the chakra concerned.

Another approach is to go and ask someone who can find the answer for you. The best people to do this are kinesiologists. Kinesiologists work by asking your body to tell them what is wrong. These practitioners have developed methods of asking the body questions which the body has to answer. Crazy as it sounds, it works extremely well. In the same way as the exercise suggested above will give you the answer, kinesiologists have ways of asking questions which can arrive at the full story of your symptoms and, very often, the underlying causes. If you consult with a kinesiologist, you have to ask them to investigate what your problem is. Once you have arrived at your answer, you can relate it to the chakras and find out what it is you need to do to remove the problem. Kinesiologists are also able to help you remove some of the problems, by freeing energy blockages, and advise you on suitable remedies.

A further approach is to consult with an Irridologist. The patterns of energy displacement (illnesses) contained within the body manifest themselves in several locations. The patterns shown on the hands and feet have been described under Reflexology, but Irridologists believe that the same information can be read in the eyes. The Irridologist takes a photograph of the eyes and, by reading the patterns of colours, lines and patches around the pupil can read where illness is occurring within the body.

We have experience of both of these types of diagnosis and they can be extremely accurate. Dowsing and the diagnostic techniques used by acupuncturists can also be very accurate, see appendix six. In addition to the diagnostic methods suggested above, there is another approach which can provide you with the beginnings of your answers.

For this you will need to be totally honest with yourself. Find a quiet time and think about how your life is. Write down all of the activities that you undertake in your normal daily life. Everything. Then, against each activity, put down the amount of time that you spend doing it. Rearrange the list so that the activity you spend the most time doing is at the top with the next most time consuming activity below that, the next below that and so on.

Now begin a new list. Try to imagine that you are in a perfect world where all of your wants, dreams and desires can be satisfied. You can be or do anything that you want to, without limit. In the new list, write these down.

Now compare the two lists.

How many items from the second list do you actually have in the first list? Try to think of ways in which you can rearrange your daily or weekly schedule to include one or some of the items from the second list. At first, it will probably look very daunting. "I fill my life with all of these activities, I have no time to begin something which I long to do". This will probably be your first reaction. But, think about it very seriously. We bet that if you made one or two minor adjustments to the first list, you will find that you can squeeze in one, or a part, of the items on the second list.

So, what is stopping you? It can't be time, you have just proved that you can find that. It can't be money, many day and evening classes are free or priced for those on low incomes. It can't be other commitments as you have already found the time. So, what is stopping you?

There are no excuses left. Take the first little step. Find out what is available in your area, if what you have chosen involves some training. What resources do you have around the house? How can they be utilised to take you to where you want to be? What about all of those bits and pieces that have been put into storage, how can they be brought back into your life and re-used for something that you want to do or to begin doing again? See, there are no excuses left, so what is stopping you? Giant strides begin with the first tentative steps. The change to your life and your wellbeing can be immeasurable just by taking that first step. Don't be afraid of evening classes or workshops, everyone else there will be in the same position as you - so what are you afraid of? Give it a try, you have nothing to lose, but everything to gain.

The way to approach your health problems is through an accurate diagnosis. Once you have achieved this, the next stage is to discover the root causes through the chakras. This system is totally infallible. If you have been honest with yourself you can find the underlying cause.

It works.

It is effective.

Nobody falls outside of the chakra patterns.

This is no idle statement. In nearly twenty years of working with people's health problems, we have yet to find an illness which does not fit into the pattern of the soul's messengers, the chakras. We just need to listen with fresh ears. Give it a try - you will be amazed at what you can find out about yourself! If you do experience difficulties in arriving at an accurate diagnosis, or how to deal with your problem on a chakra level, you can write to us using the questionnaire at the end of appendix eight. From the answers you supply, we will be able to provide a chakra diagnosis and "homework" appropriate to your circumstances.

Chapter Fourteen
The First Chakra

As a general remedy for the first chakra ailments, the following Bach Flower Remedies can be taken either individually or in combinations of no more than six. These suggestions are based upon an intuitive use of the Bach rather than their original uses. These are for the chakra itself and not for specific conditions. For specific remedies, see throughout the text.

Aspen, Crab Apple, Elm, Gorse, Sweet Chestnut, Walnut, White Chestnut.

The Skeleton

Osteoporosis

During the course of our research for this book, we have encountered a great deal of conflicting information on the benefits, or otherwise, of consuming dairy products for calcium maintenance. The outcome of current independent research is that the body cannot readily absorb the calcium contained within dairy products (the protein contained within dairy foods actually blocks the body from absorbing calcium easily, skimmed milk actually makes the situation much worse as it contains double the protein levels of whole milk) or artificial sources for calcium, such as supplements, these actually rob the body of calcium (various sources - and in particular an article in *Nexus* October '98). The body IS, however, designed to extract and absorb the natural calcium contained within organic plants and their produce (that includes herbs). Here are a few calcium rich food sources (see also appendix five): broccoli, green leafy veg, watercress, kelp, parsley, hazelnuts, brazil nuts, dried apricots, broad beans, dried beans, tahini, and sesame and sunflower seeds. Include onion and garlic in the diet as they contain sulphur which is a bone requirement. Foods rich in Vitamin D such as oily fish, cod liver oil, sprouted seeds, eggs, etc. all help the body to use calcium efficiently. Sunshine is of course another valuable source of Vit D.

Moderate exercise (excessive can be counter-productive) is very beneficial: aerobic type exercise (these are types of exercise which use the muscles and weight the bones), weight training, walking (considered by some as the best exercise for maintaining bone mass), yoga, T'ai Chi, cycling etc. all fall into this category, all help the body to absorb, retain and use calcium for bone reconstruction. Joining a dance class brings not only aerobic exercise but usually laughter and friendship as well, thereby covering the needs of some of the other chakras.

All forms of regular exercise help the bone structure. A recent study found that in less than 22 months, women who exercised three times a week increased their bone density by 5.2 per cent, whilst sedentary women actually lost 1.2 per cent (Nelson, M.phd, *Strong Women Stay Slim*, 1998).

There are at least 18 key bone-building nutrients essential for optimum bone health. If one's diet is low in any of these, not just calcium, the bones will suffer. They include, phosphorus, magnesium, manganese, zinc, copper, boron, silica, fluorine (not fluoride), vitamins A, C, D, B6, Bl2, folic acid, and essential fatty acids (food sources are in Appendix five). There are a number of supplementary remedies specifically formulated for osteoporosis available from various sources. Read the labels carefully to ensure that these supplements contain as many as possible of the above minerals as some pre-prepared formulations for this condition only contain calcium which can actually make the condition worse. See chapter 21 for further information on osteoporosis.

Bach Flower Remedies

Centaury. Weak willed; exploited or imposed upon.

Cerato. Those who doubt their own judgement, seeks confirmation of others.

Chestnut Bud. Refuses to learn by experience - continually repeats the same mistakes.

Oak. Normally strong/courageous, but no longer able to struggle bravely against illness and/or adversity.

Pine. Guilt complex - blames self even for the mistakes of others. Always apologising.

Read the full description in appendix two to determine the best remedy or combination for your circumstances.

Tissue Salts

Cal. Phos. helps the bone to hold onto calcium and helps attract calcium to the bone.

Silica.

Combination G.

Herbs

Quite a large number of herbs contain calcium and hormonal balancers, a herbalist or herbal supplier will be able to advise you on a number of helpful combinations made up into tinctures.

Reflexology

Massage the following reflexes: *solar plexus, pituitary gland, lungs, thyroid* and *parathyroid, liver, spleen, pancreas*, and all of the *spine*.

Fractures (damaged bone)

Fresh pineapple contains bromelain, an enzyme that acts to reduce swelling and inflammation (also a natural antibiotic). The suggested intake is half a pineapple a day until the fracture heals. Avoid processed foods and soft drinks due to their phosphate content as too much phosphorus can lead to bone loss. Boron is important in bone health and healing and studies have shown that Boron can increase calcium uptake by up to 30 per cent. See appendix five for food sources.

Bach Flower Remedies
Chestnut Bud. Refuses to learn by experience - continually repeats the same mistakes.
Rock Water. Rigid minded, self denying.
Vervain. Over enthusiasm - fanatical beliefs.
Vine. Dominating/inflexible/tyrannical/autocratic/arrogant. Usually good leaders.
Wild Oat. Helps determine one's intended path in life.
Read the full description in appendix two to determine the correct remedy or combination for your circumstances.

Tissue Salts
Calc. Phos. helps to strengthen bones and can be used when the bone is slow to heal.
Combination B.

Herbs
To speed up the healing process of broken or damaged bone the world of herbs has the very thing to help. *Comfrey (Symphytum)* comes up again and again in herbal medicine. The ointment (available at most health food stores) when applied liberally around the fracture, helps to heal the bone and tissue as can a poultice or compress made from the fresh leaf or infusion.

Comfrey tea is also beneficial. You can make this yourself by pouring a cup of boiling water over one teaspoon of dried comfrey leaves, leave to stand for ten minutes, strain. Drink this tea once a day until the bone is healed (or a maximum of two weeks).

For contraindications of herbs, see appendix four.

Reflexology

Massage the following reflexes: *solar plexus, parathyroid* and the *reflex of the injury*.

Homeopathy

Arnica: this is the number one first aid remedy in homeopathy. It helps with the physical and emotional trauma. Take it as soon as possible after the fracture has occurred.

Symphytum: this remedy follows the Arnica well and helps to promote the healing and bone growth.

Osteoarthritis and Rheumatoid Arthritis

Check your food intake. There are foods which can irritate and foods that can soothe. Personal research is advised here as everyone seems to come up with different reactions. Tomatoes, apples and citrus fruit, such as oranges, grapefruit or rhubarb are reported by some sufferers to be severe irritants. Start omitting certain foods from your diet and see if there is any improvement in your symptoms, if not re-introduce those foods omitted and try with another group.

There really is too much evidence that certain foods affect arthritic conditions to ignore this avenue of approach. Restrict refined foods, such as sugar, tea, coffee and alcohol and increase herbal drinks and fresh ingredients. Eat more foods containing sulphur. Sulphur is needed for the repair and re-building of bone, cartilage and connective tissue and aids in the absorption of calcium; it is found in foods such as garlic, onions, eggs, asparagus, etc..

Try the traditional remedy of cider vinegar and honey to help rid the body of the accumulation of toxic wastes. Mix two teaspoons of cider vinegar with water and add some honey and drink daily in the morning and again in the evening. Cod liver oil taken regularly is a tried and tested remedy. As the seas are increasingly polluted and fish stocks depleted we can recommend flax seed as an alternative. Take fresh flax seed (a spoonful 2 or 3 times a day) or the oil. Flax contains the same anti-inflammatory E.F.A's (essential fatty acids) as Evening Primrose. Evening Primrose oil is especially helpful for sufferers of rheumatoid arthritis. Alfalfa contains minerals essential to bone formation and may be helpful for arthritis. You can take it in capsule form or in whole, natural form. Moderate exercise, particularly walking, swimming and cycling, is essential for reducing pain and slowing up joint deterioration.

Bach Flower Remedies
A little bit of honest reflection is required here in order to select the most helpful remedy.

Oak. Normally strong/courageous, but no longer able to struggle bravely against illness and/or adversity.
Beech. Critical and intolerant of others.
Pine. Guilt complex - blames self even for mistakes of others. Always apologising.
Willow. Resentment, embitterment, "poor old me".
Rock Water. Rigid minded, self denying.
Vervain. Over-enthusiasm - fanatical beliefs.
Read the full descriptions in appendix two to choose the right remedy or combination for your condition.

Tissue Salts
Combination Remedy Q. is recommended.
Zief for all rheumatic conditions.

Herbs
Prickly Ash, Celery Seed, Cornsilk, Devils Claw, Marshmallow, Meadowsweet, Dandelion, Boneset, White Willow, Feverfew.
These herbs help to clear uric acid and toxins, relieve the pain, and reduce inflammation. Make an infusion of at least six of these and drink twice a day or ask your herbal supplier to make up a tincture containing these ingredients.
Nettle tea and/or *Parsley tea* is also recommended to help

reduce inflammations as is an infusion of *parsley* and *ginger root* (a dessertspoon of fresh or dried parsley and a teaspoon of grated ginger per cup of hot water).

It is quite beneficial to take a seasonal herbal liver, colon or kidney cleanse. A herbalist can advise you of the most beneficial herb combination.

For contraindications of herbs, see appendix four.

Reflexology
Massage the following reflexes: start with the *solar plexus* as this is the best way to relax the whole system, *thyroid, parathyroids, adrenals, kidney,* and then a general massage of the reflex areas relating to the joints affected.

Acupuncture, Alexander Technique and massage have also been found to be particularly useful for arthritic conditions, see appendix six.

Muscles

Cramp, strains and sprains
Cramp is caused by a sustained and painful contraction of the muscles. It can be caused by poor blood circulation to the muscles, salt or other mineral deficiencies. Muscle problems can also be caused by blocked lymphatic tissue being unable to clear salts etc. A lymph drainage massage can be very helpful in clearing these kinds of problems (see also chapter six).

Foods rich in vitamin B6 are essential for assimilating proteins in the body, healthy muscular tissue, nerves and skin. Vitamin B6 is found in a wide range of food (see appendix five).

Bach Flower Remedies
Chestnut Bud. Refuses to learn by experience - continually repeats the same mistake.

Chicory. Over possessive - (self-centered) - clinging and over-protective especially of loved ones.
Holly. Hatred, envy, jealousy, suspicion.
Hornbeam. "Monday morning feeling" - procrastination.
Olive. Fatigued - drained of energy.
Walnut. Assists in adjustment to transition or change.

Read the full descriptions in appendix two to determine the right one or combination for your circumstances.

Tissue Salts
Mag.Phos. helps cells to eliminate waste and is a nerve and muscle fibre stimulant.
Combination Remedy Elasto.

Herbs
Cramp. Use half a teaspoon of *Crampbark* tincture in a quarter cup of sweetened warm water and sip. This should bring quick relief.

Infusions of *ginger* can help. Pour boiling water over a teaspoon of chopped fresh ginger and sip when cool. As the vast majority of us have blocked lymph tissue, a tincture of *cleavers* would be beneficial as a tonic for the lymphatic system and to promote healing.

External
Rubbing *Lobelia extract* on the affected area helps to relieve muscle spasms/cramp.

Massage is an excellent therapy for aching muscles. There are many pre-made massage oils available with essential oils added - read the labels and take your pick. *We would warn against the use of Lemongrass if you suffer from any form of eczema or skin disorder.*

Comfrey and *Witchhazel* are good herbs to infuse and use as a compress. Use one tablespoon of the combined herbs to half a pint of boiling water, soak a cloth in the infusion when it is a little cooler, and place on the injury.

For contraindications of herbs, see appendix four.

Reflexology
Massage the *solar plexus, thyroid* and *parathyroid, hip, thigh,* and *leg reflexes*, and the *sciatic nerve reflexes*.

Homeopathy
External Ointments
Arnica: immediately after injury for bruising and pain. This is not to be used on broken skin.
Rhus. tox: for injury to muscles with swelling and pain.
Ruta: for injuries to ligaments and tendons. Massage well into the joint.
Internal Remedies
Similar homeopathic remedies can be taken in tablet form.
Arnica: immediately after injury, for shock, and for aching muscles after over-exertion from sport or gardening.
Rhus. tox.: for sprains that are stiff and sore.
Ruta: injury to ligaments, tendons and cartilage.
It is suggested that pulled tendons and sprains should first be treated with *Arnica* and then *Ruta*.

The Skin
Eczema and Psoriasis
There are self help treatments available and a few are listed below but in our experience there are many complex issues involved and a qualified practitioner should be consulted to obtain the best results. Watch your diet for food intolerances and sensitivities, and be aware of any toxic substances that may create a reaction. If you use a herb or combination of herbs and feel any adverse reaction then stop using it and try another recommendation.

Bach Flower Remedies

Agrimony. Those who hide worries behind a brave face.

Centaury. Weak willed, exploited or imposed upon.

Cerato. Those who doubt their own judgement, seeks confirmation of others.

Crab Apple. The "cleanser". Self disgust/detestation. Ashamed of ailments.

Elm. Overwhelmed by inadequacy and responsibility.

Larch. Lack of self-confidence. Feels inferior. Fears failure.

Mimulus. Fear of known things. Shyness, timidity.

Pine. Guilt complex - blames self even for the mistakes of others. Always apologising.

Walnut. Assists in adjustment to transition or change.

Rescue Remedy Cream to relieve the itching.

Read the full descriptions given in appendix two and choose the right one or combination for your condition.

Tissue Salts

Nat.Mur: when eczema is at the borders of the hairline.

Combination Remedy D. for mild skin complaint.

Herbs (for Eczema)
External

Chickweed and *Marigold:* use one tablespoon of the herbs to one pint of boiling water, infuse, allow to cool and bathe the affected area. *Chickweed (Stellaria)* cream and *Calendular (Marigold) ointment* are readily available in chemist shops. Both of these soothe itchy skin.

Internal

Burdock, Red Clover, Yarrow, Yellow Dock, Chamomile, Chickweed, Marigold, Fumitory. Combine the herbs and infuse one teaspoon per cup of boiling water. Drink when cooled, up to three times a day for four to six weeks.

Marigold tea is recommended to relieve symptoms of itching, flaking skin and blisters. Use loz. (30g) of petals or flowers to l pint of boiling water, leave to soak for ten minutes, strain, and drink the resulting tea.

Chickweed seems to be a herb of great value for skin problems and we have personal experience of its healing properties.

For contraindications of herbs, see appendix four.

Psoriasis

Psoriasis is thought to have a lot in common with arthritis in that there can be deficiencies in selenium, calcium, zinc and folic acid. See appendix five for foods rich in these minerals. Eat a diet that is composed of at least fifty per cent raw foods and include plenty of fruits (not citrus as the acids can cause the problem), grains, fish (fish oil is the important ingredient, flax seed oil or primrose oil are suitable alternatives) and vegetables. It is important to have a clean colon and these foods can help to achieve this. Also have yourself checked for food allergies or intolerances.

If your psoriasis has developed following the menopause, it could be due to oestrogen dominance from the artificial oestrogens contained within HRT. If your psoriasis has developed since you began taking the pill, it could be for the same reason. Natural progesterone creams could help, see chapter fifteen for details.

Bach Flower Remedies
Crab Apple. The cleanser. Self disgust/detestation. Ashamed of ailments.
Willow. Resentment, embitterment, poor old me.
Rescue Remedy Cream applied on the skin to relieve itching.
See the full descriptions in appendix two to determine the right remedy or combination for your condition.

Tissue Salts
Kali. Sulph: promotes and maintains skin.
Combination Remedy D.

Herbs

Blood cleansing herbs such as *Dandelion root, Red Clover, Yellow Dock, Walnut Leaf* and *Burdock* are recommended. Make an infusion by placing a dessertspoon of the combined herbs in a teapot and adding boiling water, leave for 10 to 15 minutes, strain and drink. These are also available as tinctures. *Milk thistle* tincture is also a good liver toner and cleanser.

For contraindications of herbs, see appendix four.

Reflexology

Massage the following reflexes: *solar plexus, thymus, thyroid* and *parathyroid, pituitary, liver, spleen, kidneys, adrenal glands*, all of the *lymphatic* and *digestive system*, and *ovary* or *testicle*.

Conditions such as boils, pimples and acne are helped by reducing the intake of fats, sweets, carbohydrates and by including more fresh fruit and vegetables. Foods rich in zinc may be beneficial.

A general cleansing herbal infusion may help. *Burdock, Echinacea, Red Clover, Yellow Dock* and *Cleavers* - combine all of the herbs, make a pot of tea with one dessertspoon of dried herbs per cup of hot water. Drink three cups a day for three weeks or ask your herbal supplier to make up a tincture combining these herbs.

Organic red wine, red grape juice, or grape seed extract are also good blood cleansers (the active ingredient is also found in pine bark extract) - see appendix five for details of antioxidants.

A good general skin soother is to place a handful of *oats* into a muslin or net bag and suspend the bag in the flow of water as you are filling a bath and bathe in the milky water.

For contraindications of herbs, see appendix four.

The tissue salts recommended above may be helpful.

Leg Ulcers

Varicose ulcers are particularly difficult to heal and if resistant to treatment professional advice should be obtained. Vit E oil applied to the area can be helpful as can eating foods rich in zinc, and vitamin C. Include plenty of fresh garlic and onions in your diet as they promote circulation and healing. They contain the trace element germanium which improves tissue oxygenation and boosts the immune system.

Tissue Salts
Silica.
Nat. Mur.

Herbs

Make *comfrey* tea and use it as a compress; soak a clean cloth in it and place on the inflamed leg ulcer. You can use it on its own or combine it with *Marigold* and *Marshmallow*. It makes a healing and soothing compress. Make a decoction by simmering a dessertspoon of the herbs in a half pint of water for 15 minutes. Strain and allow to cool, soak a piece of clean lint and place it on the area.

A wash can be made from an infusion of *Marigold* and *Hypericum* or from a combined tincture, dilute ten drops into a cup of warm boiled water. Soak some cotton wool and wash the area twice daily.

Applying a paste of *Slippery Elm* powder can also be good.

Echinacea taken daily for ten days improves the immune system and aids healing.

For contraindications of herbs, see appendix four.

Reflexology

A general workout of the whole foot will stimulate the circulation and improve wound healing, or use the reflex points mentioned under psoriasis.

The Kidneys and the Urinary System

Cystitis

This is a urinary tract problem. The symptoms are an urgent need to urinate frequently accompanied by the sensation of burning and sometimes stabbing pain. It is certainly possible to treat mild attacks but if there is blood or sediment in the water, lower back pain or a temperature, or the condition is recurrent, it is important to seek professional attention as the kidneys may be infected.

As soon as you have any symptoms it is advisable to drink plenty of water and/or Chamomile tea to flush the system. Drink at least one eight ounce glass of quality water hourly. Barley water is believed to be of great benefit. Put 4oz of pot barley, with just enough water to cover it, in a saucepan and bring to the boil. Strain off this first juice, add a pint of water and allow to simmer until the barley is soft. Remove the barley when the water is lukewarm and drink the liquid. Drink as often as required.

Cranberry juice (unsweetened) helps slow down the reproduction of the bacteria in the bladder as it contains a substance which makes it harder for the bacteria to adhere to the bladder wall and, along with the other fluids, helps to flush them out. If pure Cranberry juice is not available, it can be taken in tablet or tincture form.

Keep yourself warm and relaxed, apply extra warmth to the pelvic and lower back area. A salt bath should help.

If cystitis does not respond to anti-bacterial measures, consider that the cause may be fungal (thrush, etc. - see chapter fifteen).

Bach Flower Remedies
Honeysuckle. Living in the past - nostalgic. Home sickness.

225

Scleranthus. Uncertainty/indecision/vacillation. Fluctuating moods.
Walnut. Assists in adjustment to transition and change.
White Chestnut. Persistent unwanted thoughts. Preoccupation with some worry or episode. Mental arguments.
Wild Oat. Helps determine ones intended path in life.

Read the descriptions in appendix two to determine the right remedy or combination for your condition.

Tissue Salts
Mag. Phos: when there is unproductive but urgent need to urinate.
Kali. Phos: for cutting or scalding pain.
Ferr. Phos: when there is frequent and burning urination.
Nervone: if there is an obvious emotional connection.
Combination Remedy N if there is infection.

Herbs
An infusion of *Yarrow leaves* or *Nettle leaves* may help clear up single attacks of cystitis. Infuse one dessertspoon to one cup boiling water, leave for 15 minutes, and drink frequently.

For persistent cases of cystitis: *Cornsilk, Couchgrass, Bearberry* and *Yarrow*, mix together and infuse one dessertspoon per cup of boiling water and drink three times a day. Tinctures of these herbs are available but you will need to order it from a herbalist. *This should only be a short term remedy as irritation may result if these herbs are used over a prolonged period.*

For contraindications of herbs, see appendix four.

Reflexology
Massage the following reflexes: *solar plexus, pituitary gland, adrenal glands, kidney, ureter, bladder, lymph nodes of the pelvic area* and, in men, the *prostate gland*. Always work from the kidneys, down the ureter and into the bladder.

226

Homeopathy

Cantharsis: for the typical burning pains on passing urine.

Mer. Cor: when the urine is dark in colour, burning sensations and worse at night.

Nux. Vom: for cutting burning pain; feeling chilly and irritable, worse at night.

Aconite: for sudden onslaught of symptoms after exposure to cold.

Sarsaparilla: when pain is only felt after urinating.

Bladder Problems

Incontinence takes many forms. Constipation can aggravate bladder problems so include more fibre in your diet. Watch your calorie intake as being overweight puts pressure on the bladder. Exercise. Include in your general exercise, movements to tighten the abdominal and pelvic muscles. One simple method is to clench the muscles you use to cut off your urinary flow. Clench and release continuously for a period of two minutes then relax.

Bach Flower Remedies

The same as for cystitis problems.

Tissue Salts

Kali.Phos: for incontinence or retention of urine from nervous causes.

Nat. Mur: for incontinence where there is a liking for salty food.

Combination Remedy B.

Herbs

Yarrow: use loz (30g) of the herb to l pint of boiling water, leave for 15 minutes, strain, cool, and drink l or 2 cups daily for as long as necessary.

Black Cohosh can help by easing the water build up and stopping spasms. You can obtain a tincture and take as prescribed on the packaging.

If one of these is not sufficient then consult a herbalist for further, maybe stronger, combinations of astringent and diuretic herbs.

For contraindications of herbs, see appendix four.

Reflexology
Massage the following reflexes: *solar plexus, pituitary, adrenal glands, kidney, ureter, bladder*, and the *lymph nodes* in the groin and leg area.

Homeopathy
Allium Cepa: an excellent diuretic. For best results the tincture should be used.
Cinchona: Tones the bladder muscles and is advised as a tonic for the bladder.
Ruta Graveolens: if there is constant pressure on the bladder, constant urging, can hardly retain urine or cannot pass it.

The Kidneys
Always consult a professional practitioner about any kidney problems as it can become serious without attention. General guidelines to help the kidneys stay healthy. Drink up to 3 pints of quality water or boiled water a day. Dehydration concentrates the urine which increases the chance of cystitis and kidney stones. Answer the call of nature as soon as you hear it. The longer urine stays in the body the greater the chance for bacteria to breed or the minerals to crystalise into stones.

Kidney Stones
Kidney stones are small lumps of calcium and uric acid that crystalise in the kidneys or ureter. It is best to avoid foods high in oxalic acid such as spinach, rhubarb, beetroot, and chocolate until the stones are dispersed. Current research indicates that taking calcium supplements can increase the risk of stones as the body cannot absorb the artificial forms of calcium found in

supplements and has to flush it out of the system, adding stress to the kidneys. Research has also shown that a daily glass of red wine, or red grape juice if you do not drink alcohol, can be helpful in prevention. Eat foods which are rich in magnesium and vitamin B6 as they may help prevent calcium oxalate kidney stones (see appendix 5).

Bach Flower Remedies
The same as for **cystitis and bladder** problems.

Tissue Salts
Calc. Sulph: for kidney problems in general.
Mag. Phos: for pain associated with kidney stones.
Nat. Phos: to help prevent the formation of stones.
Nat. Sulph: for kidney upsets in general.

Herbs
We would not recommend that you treat yourself for kidney stones without first seeking the guidance of a herbalist. Kidney stones do respond very well to herbal treatment.

We can suggest a gentle herb combination of *Gravel root* and *Hydrangea root* added to fresh organic apple juice which can be used as a solvent for small stones or gravel. These herbs, and also *Wild carrot*, have a diuretic effect and should be taken together with a demulcent herb such as *Marshmallow root* to soothe the urinary tract.

For contraindications of herbs, see appendix four.

Reflexology
Massage the following reflexes: *solar plexus, parathyroid, pituitary gland, kidney* (work cautiously in this area as this is a most painful complaint, and only work on one side at a time) *ureter, bladder, adrenal glands*, and the *lymph node*s of the leg and groin area.

Homeopathy

Erbium: this remedy can tone up the kidneys when they are weak and inactive. It also helps to promote recovery from conditions of inflammation.

Ferrum Phos: for inflammation of the kidneys.

Belladonna: if there is high fever in addition to the local trouble take Bella. in preference to *Ferr-phos.*

Berberis Vulgaris: for kidney trouble associated with a liver disorder.

Pareira Brava: a general organ remedy for the kidneys.

End Note

The remedies suggested in this chapter are intended to treat symptoms. Read the information in chapter three to determine the most likely root cause of your problem. The remedies are suggested as a means of "buying time" whilst you deal with the root cause issues.

Study the full descriptions of the Bach Flower Remedies given in appendix two as these can help break the patterns which led to the problems arising in the first place.

Chapter Fifteen

The Second Chakra

As a general remedy for the second chakra ailments, the following Bach Flower Remedies can be taken either individually or in combinations of no more than six. These suggestions are based upon an intuitive use of the Bach rather than their original uses. These are for the chakra itself and not for specific conditions. For specific remedies, see throughout the text.

Chestnut Bud, Pine, Rock Water, Vine (particularly for men).

Female Bits

Prolapse

This is a condition where the ligaments supporting the womb, bladder, and rectum are weakened. A lump may be felt in the vagina and in severe cases the lump may protrude through the vaginal opening. The ligament weakness may affect the bladder, resulting in mild or severe incontinence.

Exercise and posture are important. Work specifically on the pelvic floor muscles. Try yoga. The Alexander Technique will help with posture. Avoid heavy work which could put strain on the lower abdomen.

In the herbal world, *Black cohosh* (not taken in pregnancy or heavy period) or *False Unicorn* root are helpful in preventing prolapse.

Menstrual Problems

The herbs mentioned below should not be taken if there is any possibility of pregnancy as they may stimulate the uterus. General health care will help with all menstrual problems. Frequent exercise, fibre, raw fruits and vegetables help to prevent constipation (a contributory factor to painful periods) and foods rich in iron, calcium, magnesium and vitamin B complex help the body to keep in balance. (See appendix 5 for the food sources.) Warm relaxing baths, lower back massage or gentle tummy massage, a hot water bottle - in general anything that relaxes and soothes the muscles.

Bach Flower Remedies
Holly. Hatred, envy, jealousy, suspicion.
Rock Water. Rigid minded, self denying.
Vine. Dominating/inflexible/tyrannical/autocratic/arrogant. Usually make good leaders.

Read the full descriptions in appendix two to determine the right remedy or combination for your circumstances (be totally honest with yourself).

Tissue Salts
Mag. phos: is a nerve and muscle fibre stimulant and can help with menstrual cramp. Dissolve 10 tablets in warm water and sip.
Kali.Phos: menstrual colic, spasms and cramp.
Combination Remedy N for menstrual pain.

Herbs
As calcium levels drop very low a week before menstruation begins, it may help to start taking a calcium tincture a week before (see Osteoporosis).

There are herbs to tonify the uterus and balance the hormones. An infusion of the following herbs may be of benefit: *Agnus Castus, False Unicorn, Motherwort, Squawvine.* Combine the herbs, infuse and drink 3 times a day for up to 4 weeks.

Painful periods can be soothed by an infusion of *Chamomile, Wild Yam, Black Cohosh, Fennel, Crampbark, Marigold, Passiflora* and *Raspberry*. Combine herbs, one dessertspoon per cup of boiling water and drink three times a day as required. The above herbal combinations will be available in tincture form from a herbalist or herbal supplier.

Fresh young *dandelion leaves* in salads, and *dandelion tea*, taken regularly will act on both water retention and cleansing the liver.

A hot infusion of *Chamomile* with a little fresh or dried *ginger* added is a simple, easily available way of soothing your system.

For contraindications of herbs, see appendix four.

Reflexology
Not to be given during a period but in between times. Massage to the *solar plexus* reflex will calm the whole system, then the following reflex points: *breast, thyroid, parathyroid, pituitary, kidney, adrenals, intestines*, the *spine*, and then, gently, the *ovaries* and *uterus*.

In all cases of reflexology treatment the reproductive system has to be treated with gentleness as over stimulation of these points can be harmful. Work on these reflexes should not be undertaken during pregnancy or menstruation by anyone other than a trained Reflexologist.

Pre-menstrual Syndrome (Tension) - (PMS)
Physical symptoms such as headaches, swollen breasts, spots, bloatedness are common and many women experience distressing psychological disturbances such as irritability, insomnia, lack of concentration, a decrease in their sex drive, tearfulness and sometimes depression. The hormonal changes effect body and emotions.

It helps to greatly reduce, if not cut out, your intake of tea and coffee as the caffeine reduces the body's ability to absorb nutrients. Replace them with herbal teas. Increase intake of salads, fresh fruit and vegetables, cut out sugar, and reduce red meat and salt (particularly in the week before the onset of the symptoms). Exercise, even if it is just walking, is beneficial. Relax with meditation, yoga, a warm bath or massage.

Bach Flower Remedies
Agrimony. Those who hide worries behind a brave face.
Cherry Plum. Uncontrolled, irrational thoughts.
Gorse. Pessimism, defeatism - "Oh what's the use!".
Olive. Fatigued - drained of energy.
Mustard. "Dark cloud" that descends, making one low and saddened for no known reason.
Sweet Chestnut. Utter dejection, bleak outlook.
Vervain. Over-enthusiasm - fanatical beliefs.

Read the full description in appendix two to determine which remedy or combination is right in your circumstances.

Tissue Salts
Nat.Mur: if there is sadness, irritability, fluid retention and swollen breasts.

Herbs
Start taking preventive measures. Use the following a day before you normally feel the symptoms of PMS. An infusion of *Chamomile* (one dessertspoon per cup of boiling water left to cool) three times a day as needed. Chamomile is calming and also acts as a diuretic which will help with some of the water retention.

Wild Yam, Agnus Castus, False Unicorn. Combine these herbs, use one tablespoon, place in a stainless steel or glass saucepan, add one pint of boiling water and simmer for 15 minutes. Strain, cool and drink two or three times a day. These herbs help to stabilise the hormones.

Evening Primrose oil can also be useful. Start about ten days before the period is due.

Wild Yam (on its own) is beneficial in relieving symptoms. Make an infusion of 3 grammes of the powdered herb in a pint of water and drink throughout the day, starting two days before your symptoms normally start. It can also be taken in capsule or tincture form, follow the directions on the packaging.

For contraindications of herbs, see appendix four.

Reflexology
As detailed above.

Thrush/Yeast Vaginitis (Candida infection)

Candida is a part of the body's normal flora, but when this fungus overgrows and infects the vagina, the result is a type of vaginitis called a yeast infection. The most common yeast infection symptoms include local irritation, a large amount of white cheesy discharge, and intense itching and burning. Include live yogurt or acidophulus and soured products in your diet as they contain microorganisms called lactobacilli, which are normally present in the bowel and vagina, and which actually destroy the fungus. Avoid refined starches, sugar, yeasts, sweets, vinegar, coffee, tea, citrus fruits, until the infection has healed. Fungus multiplies in a sugary environment. Include more vegetables, pulses and gluten free grains.

Another common cause of thrush is the overuse of antibiotics and the use of oral contraceptives. For vaginal thrush (vaginitis), both partners should be treated as it can be passed back and forth by infecting the foreskin. Grapefruit seed extract has been shown to be effective against yeast infections, used both internally (as a remedy) and externally (as a douche and disinfectant).

Bach Flower Remedies

Centaury. Weak willed; exploited or imposed upon.

Cerato. Those who doubt their own judgement, seeks confirmation of others.

Crab Apple. The "cleanser". Self disgust/detestation. Ashamed of ailments.

Gorse. Pessimism, defeatism - "Oh what's the use!"

Walnut. Assists in adjustment to transition or change.

Read the full descriptions in appendix two to determine the right remedy or combination to suit your circumstances.

Tissue Salts

Combination D: if there is white vaginal discharge.

Combination B: if the discharge is coloured.

Herbs - External

Vaginal douches cleanse the area of the overgrowth of infectious organisms. We have given a variety of douches as it is important to find the one that suits you. Be aware that excessive douching may actually promote infection.

Herbal douche - *Golden Seal, Lavender, Marigold, Myrrh, Thyme.* Infuse using equal parts. Use a dessertspoon of the mixture to a half pint of boiling water, leave to cool, use cotton-wool to bathe the affected area.

Try an organic apple cider vinegar and water (50ml vinegar/per litre of water) douche twice daily for a week.

Tea Tree oil is effective against fungal infection. Mix four drops of Tea Tree essential oil in a douche or six in a bath.

Herbs - Internal

Echinacea has antifungal properties and enhances the immune system. It can be taken internally or as a douche.

Fresh *Garlic* has an anti-microbial effect and therefore helps to suppress excess fungal growth and aids the digestive tract.

Acidopholus tablets and/or live yogurt can also help by restoring the body's natural microorganisms. A professional herbalist can offer eliminative and/or hormonal internal remedies to bring natural vaginal defences back on line.

For contraindications of herbs, see appendix four.

Homeopathy
Sulphur: for an itching vulva which is worse when hot or after bathing, with unpleasant odour.
Rhus.tox.: for itchy, red eruptions which are relieved by heat.

Oral Thrush
Tinctures of *Marigold* and *Myrrh* are recommended as a mouth wash. If cold sores on the lips accompanies oral thrush, Tissue Salt *Nat. Mur* is recommended.

Menopause
A great deal of research by alternative practitioners has produced successful alternatives to H.R.T (Hormone Replacement Therapy). There is a great deal of help now available. This is quite a specialised field so it is best to consult a homeopath, a herbalist or a specialist in alternatives to artificial HRT. For a list of practitioners, see appendices six and seven.

The following may be helpful as it provides general advice as well as specific suggestions. Remember, natural remedies work with the body to maintain as many natural processes as possible, as opposed to artificial treatments, such as HRT, which are designed to mask symptoms. The other problem with artificial HRT is that no matter how long you take it, once you stop, the body still has to go through all of the symptoms.

Natural alternatives for HRT

Besides just taking remedies for menopause symptoms, it is wise to be aware of other factors that effect the hormones in the female body, and by changing some lifestyle factors, one can often alleviate or eliminate the symptoms without remedies.

1. It is important to maintain healthy adrenal glands. These are the glands which help with progesterone and oestrogen production needed in the body after the menopause. When under stress (see appendix one for suggestions), these glands can underfunction in their production of hormones thus creating a great many symptoms from sore joints and weight gain to hot flushes. There are two herbs which have been found to stimulate the functions of the adrenal glands, and once the course of treatment is completed, their effects remain.

Chasteberry. This herb stimulates the pituitary gland which stimulates the adrenal glands to produce more progesterone. It also tends to have a normalizing effect on oestrogen, stimulates libido and energises the system, for spotting, flooding and irregular periods. Also helps to protect against breast and uterine cancers, helps reduce breast lumps and tenderness, oedema, endometriosis and fibroids, PMS, clears skin problems, vaginal dryness and most menopausal symptoms. Take 10 - 30 drops of the tincture 3 x daily in some water, favour the higher dose at first, dropping the dosage as the months go on, symptom dependent. As this herb takes 3 - 4 months to become effective within the system, it is recommended that it is taken for eighteen months for the effects to be permanent.

Liquorice can also be very beneficial as it promotes adrenal gland function. Take as a tincture, 1 - 4 teaspoons daily, in water, on an empty stomach. Take for seven days and then leave off for seven days. Start at the small dose first and gradually increase it. In small doses and for short periods (seven days) it has minimal contraindications (see appendix four) but as it would be necessary to take slightly higher doses and for longer periods it would be better taken under the supervision of an alternative HRT practitioner or a herbalist as it is a powerful herb. Care should be taken with liquorice if the adrenal glands are hyper functioning, and do not use if you retain water in body tissues.

2. Minimise xenoestrogen exposure. These potent "false" oestrogens are found in many chemical sources like HRT, the Pill and other medical drugs, organophosphate fertilizers and plastics, which mean that except for organic food, our foods contain xenoestrogens which leach in from plastic containers or get into the plant from the fertilized soil. The research results are not encouraging.

3. Exercise and Bone Health. It has been shown that 30 minutes of aerobic exercise increases the blood progesterone levels by 40 per cent. Although it is natural body oestrogen that slows down bone loss, progesterone is the hormone which lays down new bone. See also the comments under osteoporosis in chapter fourteen. There are at least 18 key bone-building essential nutrients for top bone health - including <u>balanced</u> amounts of *phosphorus, calcium, magnesium, manganese, zinc, copper, boron, silica, fluorine* (not fluoride), *vitamins A, C, D, B6, B12, K, folic acid* and *essential fatty acids* (see appendix five).

The body only uses minerals when they are in proper balance. For example, girls who consume diets high in meat, soft drinks and processed foods, which have high levels of phosphorous, have been found to have an alarming loss of bone mass. Whilst normal levels of phosphorous are necessary for bone health, too high a level of it in your diet, e.g. from a high intake of soft drinks, will draw calcium out of the bones to compensate for the imbalance.

4. Fresh and raw food. Raw food is full of enzymes, in quantities to greatly help in digestion. Most of these enzymes are removed if the food is cooked at temperatures of 118 degrees F (48°C) or above. When our body is having to expend a great deal of energy to produce lots of enzymes, it is taking energy away from somewhere else within the body. Try to avoid sugars and refined carbohydrates as they are nutrient-deficient foods.

5. Drink more water - at least two litres a day. Boiled water that has been left to cool or pure filtered are best - try to obtain a filter that removes heavy metals, pesticides, chlorine and bacteria. If you boil filtered water for 2 or 3 minutes, more of the toxins will be removed, you must then store the cooled water in glass bottles in the fridge. The water levels in the body are very important. In times of dehydration, the body will maintain blood fluid levels by taking 8% from the blood, 26% from the fluid around the cells and 66% from inside the cells. Every biochemical process in the body takes place in water, so we then compromise the efficient processes of removing wastes, bringing nutrients and producing all biological chemicals, including hormone production, in the cells.

Cells that are dehydrated are also short of oxygen, so providing a breeding ground for viruses, bacteria and fungi resulting in illnesses and degenerative diseases.

6. Avoid the following:
Alcohol - it dehydrates the body, and there can be a 25 per cent increase in risk of osteoporosis as alcohol can interfere with calcium uptake.
Smoking - it can reduce bone mass by 25 per cent (blood acidity draws calcium out of the bones to alkalinise the blood).
High meat and dairy intake, increases bone mass loss by raising blood acidity (as for smoking).
Tea and coffee as they stop the absorption of minerals.
Artificial sweeteners containing Aspartame - see chapter twenty one.

7. Flushes. Avoid hot foods (such as soup) and heating foods like curry spices, pepper, and chillies. Tea, coffee, sugar and alcohol tend to make the symptoms worse. Also, reduce consumption of meat and dairy products as they can make flushes worse. Substitute garlic or onion powder for salt when cooking as salt increases urinary excretion of calcium.

8. Other remedies. *Motherwort tincture*: - this herb has been known to calm, help to reduce the frequency of hot flushes, promote undisturbed sleep, act as a diuretic, ease vaginal dryness, ease the symptoms of PMS, reduce cramps and rejuvenate the tissues of the bladder, uterus and vagina. *Do not take if you are flooding.* Take up to 20 drops every two hours for a day or so to stabilise bad flushes, then go to 20 drops 4 x daily for two weeks, then to 30 drops 3 x daily for as long as necessary, slowly dropping the dose to nothing or to a low maintenance dose. For night sweats, take 20 drops in water before sleep, and the same if you wake in the night, this is in addition to the daytime dose.

If taking *Motherwort* with the *Chasteberry*, use 30 drops 3 x daily of *Motherwort* for about 3 months when the *Chasteberry* will start being felt, and then cut down the *Motherwort*.

Black Cohosh tincture has an oestrogenic effect and is an adaptogen (balances the body's systems). It can help with hot flushes, sleep disturbance and irritability and helps to prevent prolapse. *Not to be taken if you are flooding or are pregnant.* Take 10 - 30 drops over a whole day, in divided doses, eg 5 drops 2 x daily up to 10 drops 3 x daily, in water.

An infusion of *Sage* can help with hot flushes. Use 1 teaspoon of dried sage (3 teaspoons of fresh herb) in 1 cup of boiling water, leave to infuse for ten minutes, strain and drink 1 tablespoon 1 - 8 times daily. At night to help night sweats, make up half a teaspoon in half a cup of boiling water and let it stand for ten minutes then drink all of it. *Do not take if you have vaginal or mouth dryness. Do not use it continuously as it becomes ineffective.*

Dandelion tincture can help with water retention problems, 10 - 20 drops 3 x daily with meals. *Do not take if pregnant.*

Wild Yam. The wild yam has a phytohormone (a hormone derived from plants) in it called diosgenin which is the closest molecule to our body's natural progesterone found in nature. Ingested or applied transdermally, the diosgenin is not able to be converted to progesterone in the body as there is no biological pathway to make it happen. In fact diosgenin has an oestrogenic effect on the body. Diosgenin only becomes progesterone - a nature-identical molecule, meaning *exactly* like the one produced in our body - when it is moved through biochemical pathways, in a laboratory. This is then added to a transdermal cream where progesterone is taken up via the skin. This is a far more effective means of administering it - if given orally, the liver deactivates 80-90 per cent of the active ingredients, whereas through the skin between 50 and 80 per cent is available to the body.

It is not the same process used to produce the progesterone of HRT. These are chemically produced from wild yams into an "end product molecule" which does not break down in the body. The cream can also work by balancing the artificial oestrogen imbalance produced by the pill and plastics etc. If this cream is used whilst coming off HRT, it need not be for a long term course, especially if using other methods as well.

We have included Wild Yam progesterone cream as some women have found it useful to alleviate menopause symptoms, however, it should not be used for long periods as it may prevent the body from finding its own natural hormonal balance. The herbal suggestions work with the body and encourage it to find its own natural balance, if only wild yam progesterone cream is used, the body may become dependent upon the cream and not generate its own progesterone.

For vaginal itching, try using a *Vitamin E* cream (with no fragrance added) or open a *Vit E* capsule and use the oil directly on the itch. *Vit E* oil or *Aloe Vera* gel can also be used to lubricate the vagina if intercourse is painful.

Contraindications and properties for the above herbs are listed in appendix four.

Coming Off HRT

Follow the previous diet and lifestyle recommendations. Use *Motherwort tincture* as recommended to help stabilise the hormonal fluctuation reactions, like flushes. At the same time start the *Chasteberry tincture*, 12 - 18 month course (remember, this takes three to four months to be effective, but well worth persevering with).

You can also use a natural progesterone (*Wild yam*) cream for three to six months until all of the HRT is out of your system and the *Chasteberry* has taken over. You can try any of the other remedies if your symptoms persist - the *Black Cohosh* tincture is recommended.

If your breasts become tender, try eating *magnesium* rich foods, see appendix 5, and cut back on dairy foods.

If you genuinely have low oestrogen levels (this is extremely unlikely as most symptoms are caused by too much oestrogen), you can get natural phyto-oestrogens from some foods, especially soya based foods. The active ingredient is called soya isoflavone (**make sure that the soya has not come from a genetically modified source as GM soya can contain up to four times as much xenoestrogens as non GM and the body cannot absorb these as readily**). Soya isoflavones will be found in foods such as tofu, miso and soya beans. It is not often that phyto-oestrogens will be necessary, so try the other remedies first. Other foods and herbs containing phyto-oestrogen are: anise, celery, fennel, ginseng, alfalfa, red clover and liquorice.

If the breasts become tender using phyto-oestrogens, cut back or stop as this could be showing you that your body is producing its own again.

Cut down the HRT whilst using the above:

HRT pills - start using one on alternative days for about 3 - 4 days, then every 2nd day for 4 - 6 days, then every 3rd day. You can stop them at any time after completing this process, but if taking the above herbs and other recommendations, you should be able to cut them out within 10 - 14 days.

Patches. Replace one a week, then start cutting bits out of the next patch, eg cut it in half and let that last a week. You may not need any more - in fact try to stop them, if you are following the recommendations and herbs above (consult an alternative HRT specialist or a herbalist if you have any doubts).

Bach Flower Remedies
Gentian: Despondency.
Hornbeam: "Monday morning" feeling - procrastination.
Impatiens: Nervous irritability and impatience.
Olive. Fatigued - drained of energy.
Scleranthus Uncertainty/indecision/vacillation. Fluctuating moods.
Walnut: Assists in adjustments to transition or change.
Willow: Resentment, embitterment, "poor old me".

Read the full description given in appendix two to determine the right remedy or combination for your circumstances.

Tissue Salts
Silica: for connective tissues and calcium uptake.
Nat. Mur: helps with fluid retention.
Kali. Phos: to help with flushes.
Calc. Phos: to help with calcium distribution within the blood.

Reflexology
Massage the following reflexes: *pituitary gland, thyroid* and *parathyroid, ovary, uterus, adrenal.*

Homeopathy

Sepia A good all round remedy for menopausal symptoms. Take for no more than seven days and if symptoms persist, you should consult a homeopath.

Male Bits

The Prostate

When the prostate is inflamed or enlarged it can interfere with urination and intercourse. Prostatitis can cause pain in the back, lower abdomen, testicles and in the area between the scrotum and the anus. Prostatic fluid, if allowed to accumulate, can put pressure on the system and act as a growth medium for the bacteria infecting the gland. Self massage of the prostate by routinely clenching the muscles you use to stop the urine flow is helpful. Hold the position as long as is comfortable and then let go. Regular ejaculation prevents the build up of the prostatic fluid. Exercise is a preventative measure as this helps the lymph system, but avoid cycling as it can put pressure on the prostate.

It has been found that higher intakes of zinc are beneficial. Pumpkin seeds contain zinc as do sunflower seeds. A handful (1 - 4 ounces) of pumpkin seeds eaten each day would be appropriate. If you grind sunflower seeds and add hot water, they make a good alternative to tea or coffee which are considered to be an irritant to the prostate, as are alcohol and sugar. Avoid processed, spicy or junk foods. Increase intake of fresh fruits and vegetables. As dehydration can be a problem, keep up a good intake of quality water to flush the whole system (at least 2 litres a day).

The main male hormone is testosterone. However, the body manufactures this hormone from progesterone. Male progesterone is produced from the adrenal glands and converted to testosterone as the body requires. Prostate problems can very often arise because the body has absorbed too many xenoestrogens from the environment and it disrupts the body's natural flow of progesterone and, consequently, testosterone. As with so many women's problems, men are beginning to suffer oestrogen dominance. A growing body of research is suggesting that one of the best ways of treating prostate problems is to use a natural progesterone (*wild yam*) cream. It does not alter your sexual orientation nor does it make you grow breasts, but what it does do is to provide the body with the raw material to produce necessary hormones such as testosterone. It actually seems to have the opposite effect of feminising men by not only increasing their sense of well-being but also their sex drive!

The cream should be applied to the abdomen in small daily doses but, like female use of the cream, it will probably take a couple of months before the effects are fully appreciated. Once the prostate problems are no longer present, the cream can be stopped and only applied once a month as a maintenance dose.

Bach Flower Remedies

Agrimony. Those who hide worries behind a brave face.
Beech. Critical and intolerant of others.
Cherry Plum. Uncontrolled, irrational thoughts.
Chestnut Bud. Refuses to learn by experience - continually repeats same mistakes.
Chicory. Over possessive - (self centred) - clinging and over protective especially of loved ones.
Heather. Talkative, (obsessed with own troubles and experiences).
Rock Water. Rigid minded, self denying.
Vine. Dominating/inflexible/tyrannical/autocratic/arrogant. Usually good leaders.

Read the full description given in appendix two to determine the right remedy or combination for your circumstances (it is important to be as honest with yourself as possible - or ask your partner).

Tissue Salts
Nat. Sulph: when it is difficult to retain urine.
Kali. Phos: when there is a frequent need to urinate.
Mag. Phos: when the need to urinate is constant when walking or standing. When the prostate is enlarged.
Combination Remedy Q.

Herbs
Saw Palmetto is used to treat prostate enlargement and inflammation, painful ejaculation, difficult urination and enuresis (the inability to control urination) and can be taken regularly. It seems to inhibit the multiplication of prostate cells. It is readily available in health food stores. Take as prescribed on the packaging or as prescribed by a herbalist.

Panax Ginseng as a tonic can be of additional benefit.

If you do have prostate problems, it is best to consult a qualified herbalist as there are a number of herbs that act as diuretics and urinary tract tonics.

For contraindications of herbs, see appendix four.

Reflexology
Massage the following reflexes: *solar plexus, pituitary, the lymphatic system, prostate, testicle*, the *urethra*, the *bladder*, the *spine*, working particularly on the *lower spine*.

Homeopathy
Erigeron: relieves congestion and has some value in reducing the enlargement of the prostate gland.
Hydrangea: where there is great thirst with abdominal symptoms and enlarged prostate.
Sabal Serrulata: for enlarged and spongy prostate gland.
Thlaspi Bursa: can be very useful in prostate enlargement.

Just for interest's sake and to avoid harmful drugs, there are several herbs with *aphrodisiac* properties. *Damiana* and *Saw Palmetto* are two such herbs. Combine the herbs, use one teaspoon per cup of boiling water, stand for ten minutes and drink three times a day. Damiana has a testosterone-like effect and can also be very good for raising the female libido. These are also available as tinctures.

Siberian Ginseng (see appendix 4). Check packaging on Ginseng products as some products contain very little of the actual root.

For contraindications of herbs, see appendix four.

There are a number of herbal products on the market that help sexual potency. Check them out.

Oh, and don't forget about a creative pastime, it's better than anything else to give your spirits a lift!

End Note

The remedies suggested in this chapter are intended to treat symptoms. Read the information in chapter four to determine the most likely root cause of your problem. The remedies are suggested as a means of "buying time" whilst you deal with the root cause issues. Study the full descriptions of the Bach Flower Remedies given in appendix two as these can help break the patterns of behaviour which led to the problems arising in the first place.

Chapter Sixteen

The Third Chakra

As a general remedy for the third chakra ailments, the following Bach Flower Remedies can be taken either individually or in combinations of no more than six. These suggestions are based upon an intuitive use of the Bach rather than their original uses. These are for the chakra itself and not for specific conditions. For specific remedies, see throughout the text.

Agrimony, Aspen, Cherry Plum, Holly, Mimulus, Rock Rose, Star of Bethlehem, Walnut, Willow.

The Liver

Liver problems can be very serious and professional advice should be taken.

Problems with the liver can range from constipation, poor skin, sluggishness of the whole system, hormonal imbalance, headaches and irritability to cirrhosis, and hepatitis.

The following suggestions will be aided by a decrease in the consumption of fatty foods, soft drinks, spicy or fried food, coffee, alcohol, hydrogenated fats (margarines etc.), prescribed drugs (these have to be processed by the liver and put the system under severe strain) and increase your consumption of foods rich in potassium such as almonds, bananas, kelp, prunes, raisins, rice, wheat bran and seeds. Also increase your intake of fresh fruit and vegetables, and fresh vegetable juices. Natural juices help to cleanse the liver. Carrot, celery and beetroot juices (don't forget that beetroot juice turns your urine pink!)

are recommended. Over consumption of alcohol and stress take their toll on the liver.

Bach Flower Remedies
Agrimony. Those who hide worries behind a brave face.
Aspen. Apprehension for no known reason.
Beech. Critical and intolerant of others.
Centaury. Weak willed; exploited or imposed upon.
Cerato. Those who doubt their own judgement, seeks confirmation of others.
Gorse. Pessimism, defeatism - Oh whats the use!
Holly. Hatred, envy, jealousy, suspicion.
Larch. Lack of self confidence. Feels inferior. Fears failure.
Mimulus. Fear of known things. Shyness, timidity.
Oak. Normally strong/courageous, but no longer able to struggle bravely against illness and adversity.
Pine. Guilt complex - blames self even for the mistakes of others. Always apologising.
Rock Rose. Suddenly alarmed, scared, panicky.
Walnut. Assists in adjustment to transition and change.
Rescue Remedy for short term problems.

Read the full descriptions given in appendix two to determine the right remedy or combination for your circumstances.

Tissue Salts
Nat. Phos: if there is liverishness, acidity and poor digestion.
Nat. Sulph: if there is heaviness, sluggishness, bilious vomiting.
Combination Remedy B.
Combination Remedy D.

Herbs
To cleanse and tonify the liver: *Dandelion, Balmony, Burdock, Artichoke* and *Fennel*. Combine equal quantities, make an infusion using one teaspoon per cup of boiling water and drink two times a day for five days. Repeat as necessary.

An infusion of *Calendula* (made in the same way) aids digestion and promotes bile production.

Milk Thistle is a tonic herb well known for its ability to protect the liver and to cleanse it more deeply if it is very congested. The seeds contain Silymarin which helps stimulate cell growth and protects them from toxic injury. The product can be purchased either from a herbalist or from health food stores. *Milk Thistle* is especially useful if you are: in a toxic environment, taking large doses of pharmaceutical drugs that are hard on the liver, have chronic hepatitis or are undergoing harsh cancer treatments. (In those situations it would be advisable to see a qualified herbalist). The above herbs are also available as tinctures from a herbalist or herbal supplier.

Ginger helps remove toxins - add it fresh to your food and you can add it to the drink below..

A gentle liver and digestion cleanser drunk first thing in the morning (on an empty stomach) can be made from the following ingredients mixed in a blender, 8floz (200ml) freshly squeezed lemon juice with an equal amount of spring water, one clove of freshly crushed garlic mixed with one tablespoon of extra virgin olive oil will gently cleanse the liver. Take over a period of three to four days. The lemon juice emulsifies the olive oil making it taste better. If you really do not like the taste of lemon, you can substitute the same amount of organic apple juice and add a large sqeeze of fresh lemon juice. Follow this ten to fifteen minutes later with a herb tea and then eat mainly fruit and vegetables (both cooked and raw) for the rest of the day. Or, if you prefer, just drink plenty of water with fresh lemon juice.

It is advisable to try and drink a minimum of 2 litres of distilled/filtered/boiled water every day. *Please note that some herbs used to stimulate the liver can also stimulate the muscles of the uterus. Pregnant women should seek advice from a professional herbalist before using them.*

For contraindications of herbs, see Appendix four.

Reflexology
Massage the following reflexes: *solar plexus, thyroid* and *parathyroid, liver, gall bladder, spleen, kidneys*, and the *lymphatic system*. When working on a sluggish liver and tender reflex the reaction afterwards may be unpleasant with tiredness and possibly headaches as the liver cleanses the system and the blood stream carries away the extra toxins. Breathing exercises will help (see appendix one).

The Gall Bladder
Gall stones are solid particles that can range in size from microscopic crystals to rocks the size of a bantams egg (and hopefully no bigger). They precipitate out of the bile that has become too concentrated in the gall bladder. The function of the gall bladder is aided by eating a diet of at least 50 to 75 per cent raw foods, fresh vegetables and whole grains, and cutting out animal fats and proteins, alcohol, coffee and tea, and spicy/fried or processed foods.

Use extra virgin olive oil to cook with or on salads as the oil has been found to be beneficial in the prevention of gallstones. Hydrogenated oils and fats will increase the stresses on the gall bladder. To help cleanse the system drink as much fresh organic apple juice (this does not include cider!) as you can over a five day period. Drink more water to keep the water content of bile topped up.

Bach Flower Remedies
Chicory. Over possessive - (self centred) - clinging and over protective especially of loved ones.
Gentian. Despondency.
Larch. Lack of self confidence. Feels inferior. Fears failure.
Mimulus. Fear of known things. Shyness, timidity.
*Rock Water.*Rigid minded, self denying.
Willow. Resentment, embitterment, "poor old me".

252

Read the full descriptions in appendix two to determine the right remedy or combination to suit your circumstances.

Tissue Salts
Mag. Phos: is helpful particularly when dealing with colic from gallstones and wind.
Combination S: for biliousness and stomach upset.
Combination E: if there is flatulence, indigestion and colic.

Herbs
We would recommend seeking the advice of a herbalist if you have gallstones.

Reflexology
Massage the following reflexes: *Solar plexus, liver, gallbladder, pancreas, stomach, intestines, spleen, bladder.*

The Spleen
The spleen is an extremely important organ which can affect several of the body's systems. There are a large variety of remedies available from herbalists, homeopaths, etc. and we would recommend that you consult with a qualified practitioner to find the best advice for your particular circumstances.

Bach Flower Remedies
The same remedies as for the gall bladder.

Tissue Salts
Nat. Mur: as a general cleanser.
Nat. Phos.
Combination Remedy B.
Combination Remedy C.

Herbs
If you know that you have spleen problems, you should consult a herbalist.

Reflexology
Massage the following reflexes: *solar plexus, stomach, gall bladder, liver, pancreas, kidneys, spleen, lymphatic system.*

Homeopathy
There are a number of homeopathic remedies available for spleen conditions so it would be advisable to consult a homeopath.

The Pancreas

Diabetes Mellitus
This is a condition where the pancreas fails to produce enough insulin. Diabetes can be a serious condition. The best recommendation we can make is for you to approach a qualified practitioner, work with them but always inform your medical practitioner so that all improvements are noted and taken into account in your treatment.

We have recently come across various articles on Aspartame, a substance used in artificial sweeteners, processed foods, and soft drinks. There is much debate on its safety and some countries have not permitted its use. We mention it here as diabetics obviously consume large amounts of low sugar products. We would advise that you check labels and avoid this substance and stick to natural unprocessed foods. See Chapter 21 for further information.

Increase your intake of fibre rich food (believed to reduce the body's need for insulin) wholemeal bread, bran cereals, jacket potatoes, fresh vegetables, seeds, nuts, Brewers yeast, baked beans. Also eat foods rich in Vit C and E (Vit E acts as an antioxidant and is vital for maintaining healthy blood vessels and C aids resistance to infection), plenty of raw fruits and vegetables and fresh vegetable juices - basically healthy fresh foods eaten in small amounts regularly throughout the day. You will find that by eating healthily your weight will reach its correct level. Studies show that reduction in weight is one of the major factors leading to a decrease in the need for insulin. Deep breathing and plenty of exercise corresponding to your level of fitness is also very important. Exercise produces an insulin like effect in the body so maybe speak to your healthcare practitioner about the right approach for you.

Bach Flower Remedies
Agrimony. Those who hide worries behind a brave face.
Centaury. Weak willed; exploited or imposed upon.
Larch. Lack of self confidence. Feels inferior. Fears failure.
Mimulus. Fear of known things. Shyness, timidity.
Pine. Guilt complex - blames self even for the mistakes of others. Always apologising.
Scleranthus. Uncertainty/indecision/vacillation. Fluctuating moods.
Walnut. Assists in adjustment to transition or change.
Wild Rose. Resignation, apathy.
Willow Resentment, embitterment, "poor old me".

Read the full descriptions given in appendix two to determine the right remedy or combination for your circumstances.

Herbs
Bilberry leaves are a natural way of lowering blood sugar levels. Infuse a few of the leaves in hot water for thirty minutes and drink a cup of the resulting tea two or three times a day. It is recommended that a fresh infusion is used each time.

Raw *garlic* and *onions* are believed to help curb the increase of sugar in the blood and are always useful to help cleanse the system.

There are a number of excellent herbs which work well with diabetes mellitus. A herbalist will be able to help you find the right combination for your particular condition.

For contraindications of herbs, see appendix four.

Reflexology

Massage the following reflexes: *solar plexus, pituitary, liver, gall bladder, kidney, stomach, spleen, pancreas, colon, lymphatic system.*

The Stomach

Ulcers

Peptic ulcers - the symptoms are stomach pain, usually occurring after a meal, heartburn or nausea. Peptic ulcers may bleed and cause blood to appear in the vomit or may blacken the faeces. They can also rupture allowing bacteria into the abdomen causing peritonitis. Any severe abdominal pain should be referred immediately to a medical practitioner.

Eliminating stress, and learning relaxation techniques will help (see appendix one). Cut out refined foods (such as sugar), avoid highly seasoned or fried foods and cut out coffee, tea and alcohol and carbonated drinks. Eat plenty of vitamin K rich foods (which is needed for healing), such as dark green leafy vegetables, and vitamin C and E foods. It is advisable to cut out drinking cow's milk as the calcium and protein it contains stimulates the production of stomach acid. Goat's milk can be used as a substitute. Eat little and often. Drinking a large glass of water dilutes stomach acids and flushes them out, giving almost immediate relief of pain.

Avoid taking pain killers such as aspirin and the group known as NSAIDs (such as Ibuprofen) as they can severely irritate the lining of the stomach. NSAIDs have been shown to cause severe stomach problems (a number of studies) which are masked by the strength of the pain killer, the first sign of a problem can often be a perforated ulcer. Don't forget that an acid stomach can be caused by a back problem. If you have an acid stomach, it might be worth consulting a craniosacral therapist or an osteopath (see illustration number five).

The following remedies will help relieve the symptoms and root causes.

Bach Flower Remedies
Agrimony. Those who hide worries behind a brave face.
Star of Bethlehem. For all the effects of serious news, or fright following an accident etc..
Rescue Remedy for sudden shock.

Read the full descriptions given in appendix two to determine the right remedy or combination for your circumstances.

Herbs
Drink *Slippery Elm bark* (you can buy this ready made in powder form) and it will be even more effective, and maybe taste better, with *Liquorice root, Peppermint leaves, Chamomile flowers*, and *Marshmallow root*. These can also be made into a gruel or paste with fruit juice or water, or else mashed into a banana.

For contraindications of herbs, see appendix four.

Reflexology
Massage the following reflexes: *solar plexus, stomach, spleen, pancreas, adrenal glands, intestines, spine* and the *lymphatic system*.

Many studies now show that stomach ulcers are caused by the *helicobactor pilori* bacteria.

Recent research is showing some startling results with the treatment of a number of bacteria and infectious organisms with *Grapefruit Seed Extract*. The research has shown that this extract inactivates a whole range of these harmful organisms without affecting helpful bacteria etc..

The range of organisms claimed to be inactivated include: streptococci, straphylococci, salmonella, pseudomonas, giardia, lysteria, legonella, capylobactor jejuni and, for stomach ulcers, the helicobactor pilori bacteria.

Indigestion

If you are prone to indigestion, eat well balanced meals with plenty of fibre rich foods such as fresh fruits, vegetables and whole grains. Avoid citrus juices, fatty foods, fried foods, red meat, greasy snack foods such as crisps, refined carbohydrates, tomatoes, caffeine and salty or spicy foods.

Food combinations are important, make a note of foods that make the situation worse and eliminate them. Chew food thoroughly, don't wash food down with liquid, but drink a glass of water half an hour before eating, and avoid eating when upset or overtired. Exercise, such as brisk walking or stretching aids the digestive process.

Tissue Salts
Kali. Mur: White tongue, heavy feeling, indigestion after rich fatty foods.
Nat. Phos: for heartburn, acidity, liverish symptoms.
Combination Remedy E.

Herbs
Peppermint, Chamomile, Fennel, Aniseed, Ginger, can all be taken as hot teas about an hour after eating and, as needed, *Aniseed, Fennel* and *Cardamon* can be chewed in seed form to aid digestion after a meal.
For contraindications of herbs, see appendix four.

Reflexology
Massage the following reflexes: *solar plexus, stomach, spleen, pancreas, liver, gall bladder, intestines.*

Homeopathy
Nux.vomica is a good general remedy for indigestion.

The Large and Small Intestines
(The Bowel)

Constipation

This condition is extremely common in the western world, largely because of stress, eating highly refined, unnutritious foods, eating too fast and having too little exercise. Change your eating habits to include more fresh and dried fruit, green leafy vegetables, and other high fibre food such as brown rice, and other grains. Avoid foods that are difficult to digest and have little or no fibre, such as dairy products, soft drinks, white flour, highly processed foods, coffee, alcohol or sugar. Increase fluid intake by drinking up to 2 litres of water a day whether you feel thirsty or not (but only half an hour before meals or one hour after eating - not with the meal to wash it down). Exercise is important and work particularly on the stomach muscles as this stimulates the bowel action. It is best not to make a habit of taking laxatives as regular use of them increases the bowel's dependence upon them. There are herbs, however, which act more as a food than a laxative to cleanse and tone the bowel and get the peristaltic muscles working again. These are indicated under "Herbs".

Bach Flower Remedies

Chestnut Bud. Refuses to learn by experience - continually repeats the same mistake.

Chicory. Over possessive - (self centred) - clinging and over protective especially of loved ones.

Crab Apple. The "cleanser". Self disgust/detestation. Ashamed of ailments.

Honeysuckle. Living in the past - nostalgic. Home sickness.

Pine. Guilt complex - blames self even for the mistakes of others. Always apologising.

Rock Water. Rigid minded, self denying.

Water Violet. Proud, reserved, enjoys being alone.

Wild Rose. Resignation, apathy.

Read the full description given in appendix two to determine the right remedy or combination for your circumstances.

Tissue Salts
Nat. Mur: for dry stools
Combination Remedy S.

Herbs
For very mild constipation try *Liquorice root*. Chew the root or make a decoction by placing one teaspoon (5ml) in a cup of hot water and drink three times a day.
Linseed provides soothing bulk to the stomach. Place a tablespoon of the seeds in a cup of cold water and soak overnight and add to your cereal in the morning or use hot water and soak until they are soft, drink the juice and eat the seeds.
A successful formula for cleansing and toning the bowel consists of: *Cascara sagrada bark, Turkey Rhubarb root, Barberry root bark, Fennel seed, Liquorice root, Ginger root, Red Raspberry leaves, Lobelia herb*, and *Cayenne pepper*.

This formula originated from Dr. Christopher, a well known American herbalist. For people who have occasional constipation, these herbs can be taken in powdered form in capsules - 2 capsules 3 times a day - and can be ordered from various herbalists. If you have any history of irritable bowel syndrome, are pregnant or if you need anything stronger, consult a qualified herbalist.

For contraindications of herbs, see appendix four.

Reflexology
Massage the following reflexes: *solar plexus, stomach, liver, gallbladder, pancreas, small* and *large intestine, adrenal glands*, and *lower back*. When working on the large intestine, the colon, work clockwise up the ascending, along the transverse, and down the descending - working with the body's process rather than against. You can almost feel the hardness

of constipation when using this technique and some discomfort will be felt in the reflex.

Homeopathy
Alumina: for dry motions, with no urging or movement of the bowel for days.
Nux vomica: if there is a history of poor bowel movement linked to long usage of laxatives, or there is urging and no stool. A small stool may be passed with the feeling some is left behind.
Silica: the stool recedes when partly expelled.

Diarrhoea

As diarrhoea can be the body's way of cleansing itself of something toxic, it is best to allow nature to take its course. It is advisable to avoid food for twenty four hours and stick to a liquid diet to give the bowel a rest. Keep drinking plenty of quality water to avoid dehydration.

For acute diarrhoea, add two tablespoons of honey, one quarter teaspoon of sea salt, and one quarter teaspoon of bicarbonate of soda to one litre of water and mix well. Sip this mixture every five minutes for as long as possible. Diarrhoea in children is extremely serious and dehydration must be avoided at all costs. Consult your healthcare practitioner if your child has chronic diarrhoea.

If the symptoms persist for more than two days, there is blood in your stool, urination slows or stops or severe abdominal pain, you should consult a professional practitioner. If diarrhoea is recurrent or chronic, there may be an underlying problem, such as food allergy, or intestinal parasite. A kinesiologist can help with finding allergies, but a stool analysis may have to be done to find if there are parasites or infection.

Tissue Salts
Kali.Mur: diarrhoea due to fatty foods.
Combination S.

Herbs

Chamomile or Peppermint tea is calming.

An infusion of chopped *sage* (one dessertspoon per cup of boiling water) drunk when cool, after a light meal, will aid digestion and reduce diarrhoea.

Garlic once or twice a day for mild infection.

Ginger tea is good for cramps and abdominal pain.

Slippery Elm bark, taken in tea or extract form, is soothing to the digestive tract.

For contraindications of herbs, see appendix four.

Homeopathy

Arsenicum Album: diarrhoea with great prostration and burning thirst.

Colocynthis: agonizing pain in abdomen, causing to bend double which relieves the pain.

Dioscorea Villosa: pains radiate from abdomen to back, chest, arms etc. worse bending double and lying down.

Nux. Vomica: bruised soreness of abdominal walls with frequent ineffectual urging to stool. Diarrhoea after drinking too much alcohol.

When symptoms recede, start by eating very bland foods such as boiled rice and soups. Rice helps to form stools and supplies B vitamins. You can also drink the rice water, 3 cups a day is beneficial. Carob drinks and carrot juice can also be taken. Bananas are a rich source of nutrients and are easily digested by the body and are rich in a binding substance called pectin (remove the centre seed strip before eating the pulp). Grated organic apple may be used, or organic plain yoghurt with a small amount of fine grated ginger. For a child, cut up an organic apple and leave it to go a little brown before eating it (if you do not use organic apples, it must be peeled first to remove chemical residues - see chapter twenty one).

During the course of our research for this book, we came across several references to Grapefruit seed extract being used for bacterial and viral infections. The research on this substance is pretty amazing. Most harmful bacteria, many viruses and infectious organisms are killed off by this extract whilst leaving helpful bacteria in one piece. It has been shown to inactivate viruses, yeasts, fungi, parasites, worms and bacteria.

The extract comes in a highly concentrated, liquid form which needs to be diluted in water or fruit juice before it is drunk. It can also be used as a disinfectant for making surfaces, including foods, bacteria free without having any of the after tastes of normal disinfectants or even Tea Tree oil. It is also hypo-allergenic. It has also been found to be extremely effective in the treatment of holiday diarrhoea. Many eczema patients have found that, where their condition is yeast or fungus based, the extract has helped to clear up their skin.

It really does seem to be as effective and useful as the research implies and would seem to be able to replace a large number of domestic and medicinal chemicals and treatments.

End Note

The remedies suggested in this chapter are intended to treat symptoms. Read the information in chapter five to determine the most likely root cause of your problem. The remedies are suggested as a means of "buying time" whilst you deal with the root cause issues.

Study the full descriptions of the Bach Flower Remedies given in appendix two as these can help break the patterns of behaviour which led to the problems arising in the first place.

Chapter Seventeen
The Fourth Chakra

As a general remedy for the fourth chakra ailments, the following Bach Flower Remedies can be taken either individually or in combinations of no more than six. These suggestions are based upon an intuitive use of the Bach rather than their original uses. These are for the chakra itself and not for specific conditions. For specific remedies, see throughout the text.

Chicory, Gentian, Heather, Larch, Olive, Red Chestnut, Water Violet.

Heart, Blood and Circulation

The basics of heart care are well publicised and we would agree with the majority, except when it comes down to the fat, low fat, no butter part. Avoid all foods containing trans fatty acids (margarines, low fat spread, hydrogenated oils etc.) as they can cause heart disease - see Chapter 21. Exercise to keep the heart and lung muscles strong, avoid artificial stimulants such as colas, coffee, tea, alcohol, nicotine, highly spiced foods, processed foods and sugar. Increase your consumption of fresh fruits, vegetables and whole grains and add kelp and sea vegetables to your diet for necessary minerals. Garlic is equally good for high or low blood pressure so include it in your daily diet. Avoid late nights, overtiredness and worry. And to link into the heart chakra, stop having sex and make love instead. Relaxation, meditation and gentle exercises such as yoga will help bring down stress levels and calm the whole of the system. Hawthorn tea is useful as a heart tonic. Hawthorn tinctures can be obtained from herbal chemists. A dosage of ten drops in a little water before meals is recommended as a gentle cordial tonic. Bilberries are a good blood tonic and help with poor circulation.

Red wine has, for some time now, had a reputation for preventing heart disease. Research has now found that purple grape juice could be just as good. The presence of chemicals called flavonoids stop blood platelets from sticking together and forming clots. Grape seed extract is a source for oligomeric proanthocyanidins, OPCs, which are flavonols that have powerful antioxidant capabilities. They strengthen and repair connective tissue, including that of the cardiovascular system.

The uterus produces a hormone (prostacyclin) which helps to guard against heart disease. If your doctor has recommended a hysterectomy, explore every alternative avenue to treatment before agreeing to surgery as the hormone cannot be manufactured by any other organ.

Hígh Blooð Pressure

The advice above is equally good here. Eat more fruit, vegetables, whole grains such as brown rice, buckwheat, millet, oats, beans and Vitamin C and selenium rich foods. Drink herbal teas, fresh vegetable and fruit juices, including tomato juice, and filtered or boiled water and try coffee substitutes. Essential fatty acids are important for circulation and for helping to lower blood pressure. These are contained in blackcurrant seed oil, flaxseed oil, olive oil and primrose oil. Change your daily routine to include more relaxation, fun and games.

Follow a low salt diet. Read food labels - most labels do not give salt content but sodium (the chemical name for salt is sodium chloride, sometimes shown as Na). To understand how much salt is in a product, multiply the sodium content by $2^1/2$ and the answer is in grammes of salt. It is best to use products that are marked sodium or salt free.

The World Health Organisation, as well as most governmental advisory bodies, recommends that your blood pressure should be monitored for a minimum period of six months (before being prescribed medication) as your bp levels can vary considerably over any given period. Nobody knows what a correct bp level is - each person is an individual and their correct bp can only be established by monitoring over a prolonged period. The standard cuff bp reader used by most doctors is open to interpretation and the opinion of one doctor will vary from that of another. If your bp is measured by a cuff reading on your left arm, the cuff reading from your right arm will probably be very different. It can vary so much that one arm can show high bp whilst the other shows low bp. If you have been diagnosed as having high bp, you should have your bp measured regularly and frequently to ensure that you do actually require medication (source: WDDTY).

Bach Flower Remedies
Agrimony. Those who hide worries behind a brave face.
Beech. Critical and intolerant of others.
Elm. Overwhelmed by inadequacy and responsibility.
Holly. Hatred, envy, jealousy, suspicion.
Impatiens. Impatience, irritability.
Mimulus. Fear of known things. Shyness, timidity.
Oak. Normally strong/courageous, but no longer able to struggle bravely against illness and/or adversity.
Rock Water. Rigid minded, self denying.
Star of Bethlehem. For all the effects of serious news, or fright following an accident etc..
Vervain. Over enthusiasm - fanatical beliefs.
Vine. Dominating/inflexible/tyrannical/autocratic/arrogant.

Read the descriptions given in appendix two to determine the remedy or combination that is right for your condition.

Tissue Salts
Calc. Fluor: for the walls of the blood vessels.
Calc. Phos: for blood cell formation.

Kali. Sulph: for heart palpitations.
Nat. Mur. for circulation problems and anaemia.
Elasto. to help reinforce "elastic" tissues.

Herbs
If taking hypertension drugs, consult a qualified herbalist. For mild symptoms try *Hawthorn, Limeflower, Motherwort, Ginger* and *Yarrow.* Infuse a heaped teaspoon of the combined herbs in a cup of boiling water, leave to cool for ten minutes and then strain. Drink twice a day for up to six weeks. Research has shown that garlic is powerful in breaking down oxygenated cholesterol, the fatty substance which can cause furring of the arteries. Add plenty of fresh garlic to your food, in salad dressings etc. Chew fresh parsley to take away the taste, or smell, if it is not to your liking (see chapter twenty one for additional comments).

For contraindications of herbs, see appendix four.

Reflexology
Pay particular attention to the following reflexes, and then massage all the reflexes; *solar plexus, thyroid and parathyroid, heart, kidneys, adrenal glands*, and the *lungs.* Stress is a major factor in high blood pressure so a full, gentle, reflexology workout is required. Finish the work out with a massage of the whole foot with four drops of lavender oil in a small amount of carrier oil. When working on the heart reflex, take extra care to be soothing and gentle.

Low Blood Pressure
Symptoms are usually moments of dizziness, giddiness, or fainting on standing up quickly. This is due to a slower than normal response in changing position. Standing up slowly may relieve the symptoms. Eat regularly (don't skip breakfast) and avoid artificial stimulants such as colas, coffee, tea, alcohol, nicotine, and take gentle regular exercise combined with periods of rest.

Bach Flower Remedies
Clematis. Inattentive, dreamy, absent-minded, mental escapism.
Honeysuckle. Living in the past - nostalgic. Home sickness.
Olive. Fatigued - drained of energy.
Star of Bethlehem. For all the effects of serious news or fright following an accident etc..
Wild Rose. Resigned, apathy.
Willow. Resentment, embitterment, "poor old me".

For a full description of these remedies, read appendix two and choose the remedy or combination that suits your condition.

Tissue Salts
Same as for high blood pressure.

Herbs
Hawthorn tea or *ginger tea* can be beneficial.

Anaemia
Symptoms can be dizziness, tiredness, insomnia, disturbed vision, loss of appetite, headaches, swollen ankles, palpitations. Always consult a professional practitioner if you suspect anaemia.

Eat plenty of iron rich food such as, kelp, dark green leafy vegetables, dandelion leaves, parsley, nettles, dried apricots and figs, pumpkin seeds, strawberries, nuts - especially almonds, raisins, eggs, wheatgerm, Brewers yeast, pumpkin, red peppers, soya beans, lentils, beetroot. Molasses is especially good for building strong red blood cells. If possible eat Vit C rich food (oranges, blackcurrants, green peppers, potatoes, etc.) with your meal as this helps with iron absorption. Bananas are rich in iron phosphate (a form the body finds easy to absorb) and B6 which helps the body use iron. Carrots help the body to produce new red blood cells. If you are vegetarian, it would be advisable to eat more vitamin B12 foods (see appendix five).

Full-bodied red wines (especially organic), in moderation, may help as the red grape seeds contain a blood cleansing agent.

Bach Flower Remedies
Holly. Hatred, envy, jealousy, suspicion.
Olive. Fatigued - drained of energy.
Pine. Guilt complex - blames self even for the mistakes of others.

For a full description of these remedies, read appendix two and choose the remedy or combination that suits your condition.

Tissue Salts
Ferr. Phos. and *Kali. Sulph.* Take one dose of *Ferr.Phos* in the morning and one dose of *Kali.Sulph* at night for a period of three weeks. Combined in this way the salts enable the body to assimilate iron and use it more efficiently.
Combination B is aimed particularly towards anaemia.

Herbs
Alfalfa, Centaury, Thyme, Dandelion root, Nettle, Rosehip, Watercress, Yellow dock. Combine the herbs, use one teaspoon per cup of boiling water, cool and drink three times a day for up to 6 weeks.

For contraindications of herbs, see appendix four.

Reflexology
Massage the following reflexes: *solar plexus, thyroid and parathyroid, pituitary, liver, kidneys, spleen.*

Homeopathy
Bovista: a tonic in cases of anaemia.
Ferrum Metallicum: in low potencies helps the body assimilate iron.
China: when the anaemia is due to loss of vital fluids.

The Endocrine System

See the whole of this book!

The Immune System

There are a number of ways to strengthen or boost the immune system. Avoid stress and adopt a positive mental attitude when dealing with any illness or disease, from colds to cancer. Meditation using positive imagery is helpful (see appendix one). Avoid processed foods, sugar and soda. Vitamin E and Selenium (an antioxidant mineral) help to keep the immune system healthy. Yellow, green and orange vegetables are rich in antioxidants. Foods rich in Vit P (bioflavonoids which help the absorption of Vit C) and Vit C, help ward off infection (see appendix five). Add kelp to your diet (particularly brown kelp and giant red kelp) as it contains iodine, calcium, iron, carotine, protein, riboflavin and Vit C which are necessary for the immune system's functional integrity. Carrot juice with a small amount of fresh lemon juice boosts the immune system.

Another immune system problem relates to women, especially post menopausal women. A number of studies have shown that the thymus can shrink due to oestrogen dominance brought about by the artificial oestrogens contained within the pill and HRT. If the thymus shrinks, it will affect the body's immune function but also lead to an increased risk of breast cancer (see chapter six). Men are not excluded from this problem due to the massive increase in artificial oestrogens in the environment. The problems can be remedied, for women, by applying natural progesterone cream and coming off the pill or HRT (see chapter fifteen). Men can also be helped in this way, see chapter fifteen for details.

Bach Flower Remedies
Agrimony. Those who hide worries behind a brave face.
Cerato. Those who doubt their own judgement, seeks confirmation of others.

Clematis. Inattentive, dreamy, absent minded, mental escapism.

Elm. Overwhelmed by inadequacy and responsibility.

Gentian. Despondency.

Gorse. Pessimism, defeatism - "Oh what's the use!"

Heather. Talkative (obsessed with own troubles and experiences).

Impatiens. Impatience and irritability.

Larch. Lack of self confidence. Feels inferior. Fears failure.

Mimulus. Fear of known things. Shyness, timidity.

Oak. Normally strong/courageous, but no longer able to struggle bravely against illness and/or adversity.

Olive. Fatigued - drained of energy.

Star of Bethlehem. For all the effects of serious news, or fright following an accident etc..

Sweet Chestnut. Utter dejection, bleak outlook.

Walnut. Assists in adjustment to transition or change.

White Chestnut. Persistent unwanted thoughts. Preoccupation with some worry or episode. Mental arguments.

Wild Oat. Helps determine one's path in life.

Wild Rose. Resignation, apathy.

Willow. Resentment, embitterment, "poor old me".

Read the full descriptions given in appendix two to determine the right remedy or combination for your condition.

Tissue Salts
Silica: a good cleanser and conditioner.
Kali. Sulph: for "itis" type illnesses.
Nat. Sulph: for flu like symptoms.
Combination Remedy B
Combination Remedy L as a tonic.

Herbs
Echinacea is one of the major herbs to boost the immune system. Echinacea stimulates the immune system and has an anti-viral and antibacterial affect and is readily available in tincture form. Take as necessary and as directed on the

271

packaging. A good tincture should "fizz" on the tongue for a minute or two, and to get the most effect from the herb it is best to leave gaps for a week or ten days between periods of taking it daily for ten days.

Plentiful *Garlic* (one of the best, and easily available, natural antibiotics), is particularly helpful in warding off infection. *Propolis* is also helpful.

For contraindications of herbs, see appendix four.

Reflexology

Massage the *solar plexus, thymus, pituitary, sinus, the whole of the lymphatic system, breast, lungs, spleen.*

Homeopathy

General homeopathic treatment aims to improve the immune system. You need to consult a professional homeopath.

As the lymphatic system can become sluggish you can help by massaging the lymphs. Use a special glove or pad and brush your body firmly in a direction towards the thymus, in the upper part of the body, and towards the spleen in the lower part. The movement should be up the arms and across the chest or back, or up the legs and across the abdomen or back (see illustration number twelve for a drawing of the lymph system). It can initially be a little painful but persevere as it is effective and don't forget the armpits and neck. It is possible to obtain professional lymph drainage.

End Note

The remedies suggested in this chapter are intended to treat symptoms. Read the information in chapter six to determine the most likely root cause of your problem. The remedies are suggested as a means of "buying time" whilst you deal with the root cause issues.

Study the full descriptions of the Bach Flower Remedies given in appendix two as these can help break the patterns of behaviour which led to the problems arising in the first place.

Chapter Eighteen

The Fifth Chakra

As a general remedy for the fifth chakra ailments, the following Bach Flower Remedies can be taken either individually or in combinations of no more than six. These suggestions are based upon an intuitive use of the Bach rather than their original uses. These are for the chakra itself and not for specific conditions. For specific remedies, see throughout the text.

Hornbeam, Impatiens, Oak, Vervain.

The Lungs and Bronchials

Asthma

Symptoms include sudden breathlessness with a feeling of tightness in the chest or throat and a feeling of suffocation and difficulty in breathing out. There may be wheezing and coughing, sometimes with sticky sputum. The most common time for attacks is at night and especially early morning.

There are a number of different forms of asthma, all of which can be helped by developing relaxation techniques which help to regularise breathing patterns (see appendix one). The following can also help: the elimination of mucous-stimulating foods (which surprisingly includes bananas) is beneficial to all chest complaints. Dairy products often seem to aggravate asthma so try omitting them from your diet for a trial period and note the difference made. Goat or sheep products could be an alternative. Include fresh fruit and vegetables - especially garlic and onion as they are said to counteract the formation of mucous, and fresh vegetable juices such as carrot, celery, spinach. Asthma can very often be aggravated by allergies to certain foods, and food additives. Begin to change your diet by eliminating different food groups and see if it makes a difference to your symptoms. A visit to a kinesiologist might also help as they can test the body for allergies. Another common cause are household allergies such as dust mites etc.. We had a client who's asthma like symptoms were caused by being allergic to the residues caused by his cats' fleas.

Another common cause of asthma like symptoms is the regular use of drugs such as aspirin and the group of drugs known as NSAIDs (such as ibuprofen). Steroid preparations should only be used as emergency treatments, long term or regular usage can cause damage. Steroids do not actually treat anything, they just open up the airways and mask symptoms (WDDTY plus numerous other reports).

Some asthma sufferers have received great benefit from putting an ioniser in their room. See *Freedom from Asthma* by Alexander Stalmatski, published by Hale Clinic, London. Professor Buteyko, the Russian Scientist who trained Alexander Stalmatski, came to the conclusion that asthmatics actually breathe too much, and he then brought about a breathing technique to counteract this. Clinical trials of his technique have found that this is a very successful approach. Long term and chronic sufferers have either totally cut out their medication or significantly reduced it. Doctors who are not threatened by the success of an "alternative approach" have used this technique for their patients and one doctor, on prime time television, said he had reduced his drugs bill by one half.

Bach Flower Remedies
Aspen. Apprehension for no known reason.
Holly. Hatred, envy, jealousy, suspicion.
Impatiens. Impatience, irritability.
Mimulus. Fear of known things. Shyness, timidity.
Rock Water. Rigid minded, self denying.

Rescue Remedy will help alleviate fear and panic. Four drops in a cup of water sipped as required.

Read appendix two for a full description of the remedies and choose the remedy or combination to suit your circumstances.

Tissue Salts

Kali. Phos: for nervous asthma or a tight chest and difficulty in breathing. If there is thick white phlegm which is hard to move take *Kali. Phos.* and *Kali. Mur.* Alternate the salts throughout the day as required.

Mag. Phos: may help to relax spasms. One dose every two hours during an attack or, for a long term course, one dose three times a day for ten days.

Kali. Sulph: for asthma.

Calc. Phos: is a general remedy believed to be helpful for all types of asthma.

Combination remedy J can be used for coughs, colds and chestiness.

Herbs

Our advice would be to consult a qualified herbalist for all asthma conditions. In the meantime, the following may help.

Motherwort and *Scullcap:* combine and infuse one teaspoon per cup of boiling water, cool and drink a cupful every two hours for a soothing, and calming drink after a spasm attack.

Chamomile tea is soothing for stress, and is thought to have an anti-inflammatory action - drink as required.

For contraindications for herbs, see appendix four.

Reflexology

Massage the *solar plexus, pituitary gland, lungs, large* and *small intestine* (remembering to go round the intestine clockwise), *adrenal glands, cervical* and *thoracic* regions of the *spine.*

Homeopathy
Consult a professional homeopath for the best results but the following have been found to be helpful.

Arsenicum album: when there is difficulty in breathing, and the sufferer needs to bend forward to breathe, where there is restlessness and exhaustion and the symptoms are worse between midnight and two a.m.
Kali.carbonicum: the attack peaks between 3 and 5 a.m.
Aconite: if attacks occur after exposure to dry wind or the cold.

Bronchitis and Coughs
Symptoms (for bronchitis) are of a mild fever with a cough, discomfort or pain in the sternum and breathing is faster than normal. The following remedies may be used at the early stages of bronchitis. Children or those suffering from chronic bronchitis must seek professional help. General advice is as above, cut out dairy products and increase the intake of fresh salads, fruit and vegetables. Include fresh garlic as much as possible into your daily routine as it is a natural antibiotic. Drink plenty of fluids, water, herbal teas, fresh juices, etc..

Bach Flower Remedies
The same as for asthma.

Tissue Salts
Ferr. Phos: for the first stages of bronchitis.
If the situation worsens take *Kali. Mur.* with *Nat. Mur.*
These three salts are combined in *Combination Remedy J* which may be taken instead.

Herbs
Echinacea is excellent as the first line of treatment in upper respiratory problems.

Bronchitis

Aniseed, Coltsfoot, Elecampane, Hyssop, Iceland Moss, Wild Cherry Bark. These herbs, when combined, act as an expectorant and soothe the inflamed tissue. Combine, use one teaspoon of the mixture to one cup of boiling water, cool and drink three times a day as required.

Coughs

A simple cough remedy can be made from *honey, fresh lemon* and a few drops of *glycerine* in hot water.

Infusions of *Elderflower* or *Elecampane* for catarrhal coughs, *Wild Cherry Bark* for irritating coughs, *Mullein* for hard coughs. Use one teaspoon per cup of boiling water. Honey can be added.

For contraindications of herbs, see appendix four.

Reflexology

Massage the *solar plexus, pituitary gland, lungs, adrenal glands* and *lymphatic system, large intestine* (colon).

Homeopathy

Ipecae: with rattling of mucous in the bronchial tubes.
Phosphorus: with loss of voice or hoarseness.
Aconite: at the onset of feverishness.
Pulsatilla: if the cough is dry, or there is thick green discharge and the patient does not feel thirsty.
Kali.Bich: if the mucous is stringy, tough and thick with difficulty in coughing up.
Drosera: sudden violent attacks of coughing.
Sulphur: for those who take cold easily which often goes into the chest (chestiness).

For the best results Asthma and chronic bronchitis should be treated by a professional herbalist or homeopathic practitioner.

The Thyroid

For mild thyroid problems eat iodine rich foods such as kelp, sea vegetables, and other seaweeds, and in moderation, iodised table salt. See appendix five. Avoid using fluoridated toothpaste and water and chlorinated water as they can block the iodine receptors in the thyroid gland, reducing the production of thyroxin.

Bach Flower Remedies

Overactive Thyroid (hyperthyroidism)
Centaury. Weak willed; exploited or imposed upon.
Cerato. Those who doubt their own judgement, seeks confirmation of others.
Clematis. Inattentive, dreamy, absent minded, mental escapism.
Elm. Overwhelmed by inadequacy and responsibility.
Gorse. Pessimism, defeatism.
Larch. Lack of self confidence. Feels inferior. Fears failure.
Mimulus. Fear of known things. Shyness, timidity.
Pine. Guilt complex - blames self even for mistakes of others. Always apologising.
White Chestnut. Persistent unwanted thoughts. Preoccupation with some worry or episode. Mental arguments.
Wild Oat. Helps determine one's intended path in life.
Wild Rose. Resignation, apathy.
Willow. Resentment, embitterment, "poor old me".

Underactive Thyroid (hypothyroidism)
Beech. Critical and intolerant of others.
Chestnut Bud. Refuses to learn by experience - continually repeats the same mistake.
Heather. Talkative (obsessed with own troubles and experiences).
Impatiens. Impatience, irritability.
Vervain. Over enthusiasm, fanatical beliefs.
Vine. Dominating/inflexible/tyrannical/autocratic/arrogant.

Read appendix two to determine which remedy or combination suits your condition. Be totally honest with yourself!í

Tissue Salts
Ferr. Phos. for hypoactive thyroids.
Mag. Phos. for hyperactive thyroid.

Herbs
You should consult with a fully qualified herbalist for all thyroid problems.

Reflexology
Massage the following reflexes: *solar plexus, thyroid, parathyroid, pituitary, throat, liver, adrenal.*

Homeopathy
You should consult with a fully qualified homeopath for all thyroid problems.
The following remedies can be used in the short term:
Iodum: for an overactive thyroid.
Spongia: if the thyroid is swollen, feels hard, and there is constant clearing of the throat.

End Note
The remedies suggested in this chapter are intended to treat symptoms. Read the information in chapter seven to determine the most likely root cause of your problem. The remedies are suggested as a means of "buying time" whilst you deal with the root cause issues.

Study the full descriptions of the Bach Flower Remedies given in appendix two as these can help break the patterns of behaviour which led to the problems arising in the first place.

Chapter Nineteen
The Sixth Chakra

As a general remedy for the sixth chakra ailments, the following Bach Flower Remedies can be taken either individually or in combinations of no more than six. These suggestions are based upon an intuitive use of the Bach rather than their original uses. These are for the chakra itself and not for specific conditions. For specific remedies, see throughout the text.

Beech, Cerato, Cherry Plum, Clematis, Scleranthus, Wild Rose.

Central Nervous System

Meditation, yoga, massage, art, music and any relaxation technique which can bring about a calm state would be useful here. Aspartame (an ingredient of artificial sweeteners and low calorie foods, drinks, etc.) has been shown to adversely effect the central nervous system as have organo phosphates (see chapter twenty one). Central nervous system disorders, particularly ones which involve memory loss such as Alzheimers, can be helped by high doses of Vit E (over one gramme daily), a selenium supplement and only using virgin olive oil in cooking (Dr J Wallach). If you have been given a diagnosis of Alzheimers, it would be advisable to have your Vit B12 levels checked as a deficiency can produce similar symptoms. To correct this situation a visit to a nutritionist could prove beneficial. A general "brain tonic" can be made from an infusion of *Gingko* leaves or taking the tincture three times a day for short periods. The Gingko tree is not known as the "memory tree" for nothing!

Bach Flower Remedies

Centaury. Weak willed, exploited or imposed upon.

Chestnut Bud. Refuses to learn by experience - continually repeats the same mistake.

Clematis. Inattentive, dreamy, absent minded, mental escapism.

Crab Apple. The "cleanser". Self disgust/detestation. Ashamed of ailments.

Elm. Overwhelmed by inadequacy and responsibility.

Gentian. Despondency.

Gorse. Pessimism, defeatism - "Oh what's the use".

Honeysuckle. Living in the past - nostalgic. Home sickness.

Larch. Lack of self confidence. Feels inferior. Fears failure.

Mimulus. Fear of known things. Shyness, timidity.

Mustard. "Dark cloud" that descends, making one saddened and low for no known reason.

Oak. Normally strong/courageous, but no longer able to struggle bravely against illness and/or adversity.

Pine. Guilt complex - blames self even for mistakes of others. Always apologising.

Rock Rose. Suddenly alarmed, scared, panicky.

Sweet Chestnut. Utter dejection, bleak outlook.

Walnut. Assists in adjustment to transition or change.

Wild Oat. Helps determine one's intended path in life.

Willow. Resentment, embitterment, "poor old me".

Read appendix two to determine the right remedy or combination to suit your circumstances. Be totally honest with yourself.

Tissue Salts

Kali.Phos: Phosphorus is the chief nerve mineral.

Mag. Phos: for when there are cramps, twitching or nerve pain.

Combination Nervone.

Herbs

Infusions of *Peppermint* or *Lemon Balm* or *Chamomile* make gentle tonics. *Rosemary* and *Sage* can also be used in this way.

Oats, used both as a food and a medicine. Eat porridge. Soak in a bath containing a muslin bag of oats. Take half a teaspoon of oat tincture three times daily.

A tincture of *Scullcap, St. John's Wort, Lavender, Oat seed* and *Celery seed* could be taken. Half a teaspoon three times daily, for a maximum of a week at a time. The tinctures can be obtained from a herbalist or a herbal supplier.

For contraindications of herbs, see appendix four.

Reflexology

Give a general massage to all the reflex points.

Homeopathy

Arnica Montana: for all complaints that have their origin in trauma. Ideal remedy for mental and physical exhaustion and nervous collapse due to accidents.

Hypericum: for all conditions of contraction and spasm, spinal pain and lack of co-ordination between brain and body. By toning the spinal column itself and relaxing spinal muscles it helps the organism to adjust itself.

Chamomilla: it is soothing to all of a nervous disposition and who get mentally irritable.

The Eyes

Foods rich in Vit A, Vit B and Vit C, together with the minerals selenium and zinc help to promote good eyesight and help to fight free radicals (see below). These vitamins and minerals are all contained in fresh fruit and vegetables. Include in your diet; broccoli, raw cabbage, carrots, cauliflower, green vegetables - particularly spinach, sunflower seeds and watercress. Drugs which can affect eyesight include: aspirin, anticoagulants, some anti-depressants, corticosteroids, HRT, marijuana etc., check any medication you are taking for side effects. Eye muscles can be exercised and relaxed to improve their function. The Bates Method is very popular as an aid to improved eyesight, and life without glasses.

Avoid dairy produce, and any fats or oils that have been subject to heat, whether by chemical processing (hydrogenated) or cooking. These foods promote formation of free radicals which can damage the lens. Use virgin olive oil or cold pressed oils. Free radicals are freely moving atoms, or groups of atoms, which can break down the proteins and fats used by the body to manufacture the walls of body cells. Free radicals can be reduced by taking antioxidants (see appendix five). Grape seed extract is a powerful antioxidant.

Milk sugars (lactose) and refined white sugars have been shown to be a major contributor to cataract growth because of the body's inability to cope with food sugars (Science Magazine).

Eyestrain, injury, conjunctivitis.

Bach Flower Remedies
The same as for the nervous system.

Tissue salts
Nat. Mur. for tired eyes and eyestrain, and when there is also difficulty in reading in artificial light.

Herbs
Eyebright, is probably the most popular eye herb, it is good for any eye irritation or inflammation. Make an infusion, strain and cool and bathe the eye. An infusion of *Chamomile* can be used if the eye is inflamed and sore. Both can be used as a compress, leave on the eyes for 15 minutes.

Many of the microorganisms that cause conjunctivitis cannot tolerate heat, so use a hot compress several times a day. If pain or blurred vision occurs, or the condition does not clear within four days, consult a qualified practitioner.

For occasionally itchy or tired eyes, close your eyes and apply a cold compress for ten minutes (try cold, damp teabags).

Sliced cucumber, placed on the eyelid for about ten minutes is particularly helpful when the eye is inflamed.

For contraindications of herbs, see appendix four.

Reflexology
Massage the following reflexes; *solar plexus, eyes, ears, nose, sinuses, pituitary, thymus, spleen, liver, kidneys, the upper lymphs*, and *spine*. This treatment covers all eye problems.

Homeopathy
Euphrasia (Eyebright): when the eyes are inflamed, burning, watering, unable to bear bright light and for general infections of the eye.
Ruta Graveolens: eyestrain followed by headaches. Eyes red, hot and painful from sewing or reading too much. Follows *Arnica* for injury and bruising to the eye.

Styes
If you suffer from styes frequently, check you are eating enough vitamin A foods. See Appendix five. If you chop a fresh organic onion it makes the eye water and helps to wash out impurities.

Herbs
Try a herbal compress of *Plantain*. Infuse one teaspoon of the herb in a small amount of hot water, strain. Apply to the eye on a cotton wool pad or use as an eye wash.

Applying a hot compress to the area for ten minutes or so, four or five times throughout the day will help bring the stye to a head.

Homeopathy

Belladonna: when the stye is red and throbbing.
Hepar. Sulph.: when the stye starts to point, to ripen quicker.
Aconite: promotes healing once the pus has been discharged.
Staphysagria: recurrent styes. Margin of lids itch.

Ears

It is dangerous to attempt to relieve deafness yourself by poking about in the ear to remove wax as this can damage or perforate the ear-drum. A simple way to soften ear wax: use a few drops of almond oil or olive oil and lemon juice, heat the mixture by placing it in a small container and float in a cup of fairly warm water until it reaches body temperature. Using a dropper, apply a small amount of the oil two or three times a day. Take care not to poke the ear with the dropper. Do not use a cotton bud as this can compact the wax and make it harder to remove. Never insert foreign bodies into the ear. It is helpful to lower intake of mucous forming (such as dairy products) and refined foods, and increase Vit C rich foods.

Deafness

Deafness has many causes. The most obvious is exposure, especially long term, to loud noise. Food allergies, especially to dairy products and wheat, can be the cause for recurrent middle ear infection. Earwax buildup or impaction can cause hearing loss. An upper body lymph drainage massage would be beneficial as swollen or congested lymphs can put pressure in the ear.

Bach Flower Remedies

The same as for the central nervous system.

Tissue Salts

Kali.Sulph: for deafness caused by catarrh
Kali.Phos: for deafness accompanied by nervous exhaustion.

Herbs

Echinacea helps fight infection and helps reduce congestion. It can be taken in tincture form or capsule.

Ginkgo biloba helps to reduce dizziness and improve hearing loss related to reduced blood flow. It can be taken in tincture form and should be taken for at least two weeks for best results. It is also helpful in cases of tinnitus (ringing in the ear).

Earache or Infection

A variety of bacteria and viruses can cause middle ear infection but one common cause of ear infection in children is food allergies (a kinesiologist can help with this). Avoid the most common allergenic foods, such as wheat, dairy products, corn, oranges, peanut butter, sugar, fruits and fruit juices. It is possible then to reintroduce the foods gradually and watch for reactions. To reduce the development of food allergies, rotate your diet and do not repeat the same foods frequently.

Tissue salts

Ferr. Phos: use at the first sign of inflammation, when the ear feels hot and looks red.
Silica: where there is pus and offensive odour; pain and swelling around the ear.

Herbs

Garlic oil, Mullein oil: add a couple of drops of slightly warmed oil to clean cotton wool and place gently inside the outer ear. You can also put the drops directly in the ear and then block the ear with cotton wool. Mullein oil has anti-inflammatory properties and eases pain.

Keep the ear warm and rub a little lavender oil around the ear.

Chamomile, Echinacea, Golden Rod, Golden Seal: combine the herbs, make a decoction using one teaspoon of the herbs to one cup of water, simmer for ten minutes. Drink a cupful three times a day to reduce inflammation and prevent infection.

For contraindications of herbs, see appendix four.

Reflexology
This treatment covers all ear complaints and is excellent for tinnitus sufferers. Massage the following reflexes: *solar plexus, thymus, pituitary gland, lymphatic system, sinus, ears, eustachian tubes, liver, spleen, large intestine, spine.*

Homeopathy
Aconite: sudden attack of earache after exposure to draughts or cold wind.
Belladonna: Ear looks red and hot, throbbing in the ear, and is accompanied by a headache. There may be inflammation or boils.
Chamomilla: Earache in teething children. The child is irritable and fretful and one cheek is red.
Pulsatilla: indicated when earache follows a cold or has developed during a cold. Pains worse from warmth at night, better for open air. There may be a thick yellow discharge.
Carbo.Veg. For tinnitus with nausea and vertigo.

The Nose

Sinus Problems
Symptoms include pain above or below the eyes, cheeks and forehead which worsen when bending, lying down or coughing. There may be headaches, sometimes fever, sense of smell diminished, and discharge from the nostril. Cutting out mucous forming foods such as dairy products is advised. Increase your intake of raw foods and drink plenty of water, fresh vegetable and fruit juices, and hot drinks such as herbal teas to make the sinuses flow. Garlic is recommended for sinus problems, as well as for colds, chills, influenza, and bronchial complaints. Try to use fresh garlic daily. Ionisers are said to help mucous drain

more easily. Check for food allergies or allergies to house dust mites etc..

Tissue Salts
Kali. Sulph: when the nose is blocked and is worse in a warm room, there is yellowish catarrh.
Nat.Mur: if there is a loss of sense of smell.

Herbs
Blend *horseradish root* and *apple cider vinegar* into a pulp and chew one third of a teaspoon full (increasing up to one teaspoon full) three times a day. This acts as an effective blast to the sinuses *(note: horseradish can give some people indigestion and aggravate stomach ulcers)*.

Chop fresh onions, particularly organic as they are stronger, to help clear the sinuses.

Elderflower, Eyebright, Echinacea, Golden Rod, Golden Seal, Parsley root, Marshmallow. Combine the herbs and use one dessertspoon per cup of boiling water. Cool and drink twice a day. These herbs help release blocked mucous and soothe inflammation. *Ginger, Elderflower* and *Peppermint* can be used in the same way.

For contraindications for herbs, see appendix four.

Reflexology
Massage the following reflex points: *solar plexus, thymus, pituitary, lymphatic system, sinuses, nose, eyes, adrenal glands.*

Homeopathy
Kali.bich: when there is heavy congestion, with yellow, stringy catarrh, headache over the eyebrows.
Pulsatilla: when the area of pain changes, symptoms worse indoors, tendency to weep, yellow catarrh, and the nose is sometimes stuffed.

Merc. Sol: Infected catarrhal inflammation of frontal sinuses. Pain is worse at night, there is an offensive taste in the mouth.

If symptoms persist, you should consult a qualified practitioner.

The Mouth

Mouth ulcers can be taken as a sign of general debility or stress so it is important to check that your diet is well balanced and that you relax as much as possible. A more serious cause is the herpes virus so if the problem continues seek the help of a qualified practitioner. Change your toothpaste as some brands may irritate the gums, and try other toothpastes that contain myrrh, and medicinal herbs (these will be sold in healthfood shops and, very occasionally, in main stream shops). Try a mouthwash of pure, unsweetened cranberry juice as recent studies have shown that it can reduce bacteria and plaque.

Tissue salts
Nat. Phos. or *Combination C.*
Combination D. if the ulcers are on the corner of the mouth.

Herbs
Marigold, Myrrh, Thyme, Golden Seal: a mouthwash made from any of these herbs should help clear up the ulcers. Either infuse the herb, or use a tincture diluted in water. Tinctures can be purchased from herbalists or herbal suppliers. Use 5 drops in about half an inch of warm water. Honey can be added.
Chewing *Liquorice root* is soothing and healing. *Garlic* is, as always, helpful.

For temporary relief of tooth and/or gum pain. Rub a drop or two of *Clove oil* directly on the affected area. If the oil is too strong, you can dilute as required with a few drops of olive oil. Take *Echinacea* to boost the immune system.

For contraindications for herbs, see appendix four.

Reflexology
Massage the following reflexes: *solar plexus, thyroid, throat, liver, kidney, spleen, large intestine.*

Homeopathy
Mercsol: when there is increased salivation, bad breath, and pain is increased by heat or cold.

The Tongue

Lost sense of taste
Various studies have shown that an increased intake of zinc is helpful in restoring the sense of taste. Try it and see.

Tissue salts
Nat. Mur: can be taken on its own. Also use if there are blisters on the tongue.
Combination Remedy Q. covers these problems and is useful if the tongue is inflamed.
If the tongue is coated use *Nat.Phos.* or *Combination Remedy C.*

The Pituitary Gland

The pituitary gland works directly with the chakra. The pituitary secretes, or gives the signals to other organs to secrete, most of the body's hormones and is therefore mainly treatable through the other organs.

If you do have a pituitary gland problem, it is best to seek the advice of a qualified practitioner.

End Note

The remedies suggested in this chapter are intended to treat symptoms. Read the information in chapter eight to determine the most likely root cause of your problem. The remedies are suggested as a means of "buying time" whilst you deal with the root cause issues.

Study the full descriptions of the Bach Flower Remedies given in appendix two as these can help break the patterns of behaviour which led to the problems arising in the first place.

Chapter Twenty
The Seventh Chakra

The seventh chakra links in directly with the consciousness and is directly "answerable" to the soul. Problems associated with the seventh chakra are only treatable through the chakra's function - our link with our higher selves.

As a general remedy for the seventh chakra ailments, the following Bach Flower Remedies can be taken either individually or in combination. These suggestions are based upon an intuitive use of the Bach rather than their original uses. These are for the chakra itself and not for specific conditions. For specific remedies, see throughout the text.

Centaury, Gorse, Mustard, Wild Oat.

However, we do tend to suffer from certain problems in this region of the body, mainly headaches, and there are some suggestions which can be used for these conditions.

Headaches

Migraine
This is an excruciating, one sided pain which is normally accompanied by vision distortion, nausea, and sensitivity to light. Migraines occur for many reasons, stress, tension, hormonal cycles, digestive problems, allergic reaction. Food allergies are usually animal fats, cheese, ice cream, oranges, chocolate, fried foods, sugar and red wine. Try to discover if you have other food allergies or intolerance, perhaps visit a kinesiologist. Remove these foods from your daily diet and see

its effect on the frequency of migraine. A report in the Lancet found that when such foods were eliminated from the diets of sufferers, as many as 93% found relief from symptoms. Good bowel health is very important as constipation can lead to a buildup of toxins.

There is a tendency by migraine sufferers towards perfectionism and over activity, and to drive themselves too hard, this can put a strain on the whole system. The migraine often hits the moment they stop - usually on holiday. Time given to relaxation and more periods of pleasurable occupation would be beneficial. Find a relaxation technique that works for you and use it. Yoga and meditation are recommended (see appendix one). Frequent use of over-the-counter, and prescribed, painkillers may actually increase the likelihood of a migraine attack. You then start a cycle of tablet, pain, tablet. Headaches can also be caused by injuries to the neck or upper back.

If you have headaches which do not respond to treatment, try visiting a sacrocranial therapist, an osteopath, a consultant in Alexander Technique, or consult a kinesiologist or Irridologist for help in diagnosis.

If your migraines occur at, or about the time of your period, they could be the result of oestrogen dominance. Too much oestrogen in the body can cause a fluctuation in the hormone balance of the whole system, resulting in a lack of progesterone. This situation can best be alleviated by the use of natural progesterone creams applied several days before your period is to begin (see chapter fifteen).

Tissue salts
Nat. Mur: for throbbing, burning headaches preceded by misty vision or zig zag lights, or when there is numbness in the face which signals an attack.
Silica: pain beginning in the neck, coming over the head, and ending in one eye.
Combination Remedy F.

Herbs

Lemon Balm, Feverfew, Meadowsweet, Rosemary: make an infusion by using a dessertspoon of the combined herbs to one cup of boiling water. Drink up to 3 cups a day as necessary. Add *Scullcap* if nervous tension is also present.

A study carried out by the University of Nottingham showed that taking *feverfew* reduced the incidence of migraine and associated vomiting. *Do not take feverfew if pregnant.*

If the bowel is not working well, take two or three herbal bowel capsules with each meal for a while (see under Constipation).

Drink plenty of water with fresh lemon juice squeezed into it, throughout the day, to help cleanse the liver.

For contraindications for herbs, see appendix four.

Reflexology

Work on the *solar plexus, thyroid gland, pituitary gland*, the *neck* and *head* (all around the big toe), *eyes,* gently with the *liver* (too much toxin in the system will increase the headaches - breathing exercises are effective here), *colon, small intestines, kidneys* (may be sensitive), *spine* (paying special attention to the top).

Homeopathy

Kali. Bich when there is blurred vision before the headache.
Belladonna: intense, violent throbbing pain focused on the forehead, which is relieved by sitting down.
Bryonia: heavy crushing pain which may be accompanied by vomiting or nausea. Worse for movement but relieved by pressure.

Tension headaches

This occurs mainly at the back of the head and is usually relieved by laying down. They can be caused by stress, tension, digestive problems, allergies, PMT, injury, toxins such as tobacco and alcohol. If headaches are persistent then professional advice must be obtained as there are more serious causes for headaches. Poor posture, creating muscle tension, can be helped with the Alexander Technique.

Tissue Salts
Kali.Phos: with humming in the ears.
Combination F. for nervous headaches and migraine.

Herbs
When a headache hits, drink a cup of hot *peppermint tea* and rest for a while. Rub Lavender oil into the temples and breathe slowly and deeply and relax.
Lemon Balm, Meadowsweet, Peppermint, Rosemary and *Vervain:* combine the herbs, infuse one teaspoon per cup of boiling water and drink every few hours whilst symptoms persist.
For contraindications for herbs, see appendix four.

Homeopathy
Euphrasia: with painful, watering eyes and unable to bear bright light.
Hypericum: when the pain is lessened by bending the head backwards.

Massage. Headaches which tend to start from the back of the head are often relieved by firm effleurage on the back of the neck. Massage the neck and shoulder muscles to relieve stress and tension. Pay particular attention to the lymph nodes in the neck. Blocked lymphs can contribute to muscle tension around the neck (or in fact anywhere on the body). A face massage, concentrating on the forehead and temples, can be soothing.

It is possible that some headaches may occur from potassium deficiency, vitamin B2 deficiency and hypoglycemia (low blood sugar levels). Low blood sugar can cause migraine headaches. Eating regularly and not skipping breakfast can help keep the blood sugar levels balanced. Try one of the following and if there is no change move on to the next.

Potassium.

Isotonic drinks - glucose is directly absorbed into the system (some contain Aspartame so check the ingredients).

Carry with you *barley sugar* or *glucose sweets*. If you feel that a headache is about to begin, suck on a couple of the sweets.

Vitamin B2 (Riboflavin) found in apricots, milk, cheese, chicken, fish, eggs, Brewers yeast, wheatgerm.

Also try a herbal programme for a full system de-tox., consult a qualified herbalist for advice. There are other causes for a variety of head/neck and teeth pains which are associated with the current global and personal changes, see *The Fool's First Steps* by Chris Thomas.

Insomnia

Sleeplessness can arise for a variety of reasons and the following remedies will be helpful but if you are suffering from long term chronic insomnia, it is best to consult with a professional practitioner. Avoid stimulating foods and drinks at bedtime; try various relaxation techniques until you find one to suit you. Try to avoid sleeping pills as they can make the situation considerably worse.

Don't forget to do the giveaway!

Try to include one or more of the following in your evening meal as they contain tryptophan which promotes sleep: bananas, figs, dates, yogurt, milk, tuna, whole grain crackers, nut butter, turkey. Avoid the following as they contain tyramine which increases the release of norepinephrine, a brain stimulant: bacon, ham, sausage, cheese, chocolate, sugar, spinach, tomatoes, potatoes, eggplant, sauerkraut and wine close to bed time. Alcohol, in small quantities, can help to induce sleep, but it will disrupt deep sleep patterns later on. Avoid tobacco as nicotine is a neuro stimulant.

Bach Flower Remedy

Olive. Fatigued - drained of energy.

Vervain. Over enthusiasm - fanatical beliefs.

White Chestnut. Persistent unwanted thoughts. Preoccupation with some worry or episode. Mental arguments.

Read appendix two to determine the right remedy or combination to suit your circumstances.

Tissue Salts

Kali. Phos: where there is nervous tension and habitual sleeplessness.

Kali. Phos, Mag. Phos, and *Nat. Phos*: where there is stress and insomnia from being under strain.

Herbs

Lemon Balm, Chamomile, Lime Flowers, Orange Blossom and *Passiflora.* Infuse a dessertspoon of the combined herbs to make a soothing bedtime drink. *Vervaine* and *Skullcap* can be added if nervous tension is present.

Lavender, either fresh, or the oil on a handkerchief by the bed or pillow is very soothing.

Put four to six drops of *lavender oil* in your bath or have an *oat* bath, (put one or two cups of oatmeal/oatflakes into a muslin bag and into the bath as it runs) before bedtime.

Fit in an evening walk and, if you can, walk barefoot on the grass.

For contraindications for herbs, see appendix four.

Reflexology

It would be very soothing to rub the whole foot with *lavender oil* mixed with a little carrier oil just before going to bed. Pay particular attention to the *solar plexus*, the *brain reflex, pancreas, thyroid* and *parathyroid* and the *spine* reflex.

Homeopathy

Aconite: with much twisting and turning.

Arnica: overtiredness, body aches and the bed feels hard.

Coffea: when your mind will not rest, and you feel wide awake.

Nux Vomica: for 3 a.m. sleeplessness due to strain or over-indulgence of any kind, with irritability and waking up feeling unrefreshed.

Take a dose of the recommended remedy half an hour before going to bed and repeat half hourly as necessary, or follow the advice on the packaging.

The Pineal Gland

If you read the description of the pineal gland in chapter nine, you will see that the main health problem associated with this gland is ME. As this illness is directly associated with the higher elements of consciousness, through the seventh chakra, the only realistic solution is to re-evaluate the way in which you live your life and the directions that you have taken and if there are any alternative directions you feel you should be moving in.

Cancer

There are a number of alternative approaches to the treatment of cancer, however we are prevented from listing them here as the Cancer Act of 1939 prohibits the advertising of any such remedies. Publishing them here would constitute an advertisement and is, therefore, contrary to the law as it currently stands.

Britain has one of the worst cancer survival rates in the world.

We have written to the government asking that funding be made available for research into alternative treatments for cancer, but the reply we received stated that many more millions of pounds are to be channelled into orthodox treatments and the reply did not address the question of alternative treatments to any satisfactory degree.

Perhaps now is the time for this law to be repealed and the discussion on <u>all</u> treatments for cancer opened to full and informed public debate and choice.

We would recommend that you consult with a qualified health advisor to investigate the many alternative possibilities available.

We have formulated a herbal tincture which works on a chakra level and is in the process of being trialed. The combination of six herbs is formulated to help correct the near collapse of the affected chakra. This formula has been arrived at by the age old process of "scanning" a variety of herbs to arrive at the correct combination. This is a similar process to that used by tribal shaman to find the properties of the herbs and plants which grew in their locality and is the means by which herbs were originally named. If you wish to take part in this trial, please ask your chosen health advisor to contact us at the address at the back of this book.

End Note

The remedies suggested in this chapter are intended to treat symptoms. Read the information in chapter nine to determine the most likely root cause of your problem. The remedies are suggested as a means of "buying time" whilst you deal with the root cause issues.

Study the full descriptions of the Bach Flower Remedies given in appendix two as these can help break the patterns of behaviour which led to the problems arising in the first place.

Chapter Twenty One

Personal Comments

During the course of our research for this book, we have come across a huge volume of information about the food we eat, bacteria, calcium supplements, water supplies, drug side effects, etc., all of which affect us and our health. Most of this information is frightening and not widely available. It has been very difficult to limit this chapter as there is so much information. It has been very difficult to choose what to include and what to leave out, whilst at the same time not sounding like we are standing on a soap box.

We have, and continue to be, misinformed and deliberately misled by our governments, pharmaceutical companies and food and water suppliers. Essentially, we are being rapidly poisoned by our daily diets. All of our food is produced and processed by chemical treatments. All of our water is produced with little regard to what actually comes out of the tap. There is such a high level of xenoestrogens in water, processed foods and our environment from plastics and artificial hormones that men are rapidly becoming sterile. Even the fish in our rivers are having difficulty producing male genes. We have been misled to a point which is criminal and all for the sake of profit. The conclusion we have reached is that if it is not organic, if it has undergone a chemical process, if it is promoted by a pharmaceutical company (for example, an article in the December edition of "The Big Issue" stated that "Quorn" is manufactured by the biotech company Zeneca (the company that introduced GM tomatoes to Britain) - we telephoned Quorn, on their information line, and they refused to confirm or deny this link), if it contains any kind of chemical treatment, essentially, if it is not "natural", do not put it in your mouth. It is that simple.

Everything that is marketed, promoted or prescribed by food or drug companies contains chemicals which do not produce any positive benefits. The only medical advance made in the last one hundred years, that is beneficial, is antibiotics and even these have become dangerous from overuse. We live in a dangerous world which is increasingly poisoning us.

The only choice that we have is to drink boiled water and to eat organic foods - anything else is dangerous to our health. This is not an overstatement of the problem - people die from their medication, people die from food additives, people die from the chemicals in our food and water.

We are constantly under threat, and all for the sake of short term profit. Enough is enough. We must retake control of our lives or, very shortly, humanity will no longer exist. This is our choice - we quietly accept or we fight back. We have no other choice available. Insist on organic, non-chemically, non-genetically modified food or we perish as a race. It is that serious and that immediate.

One of the most insidious and serious threats we are faced with is genetically modified (GM) food. In the last couple of years new technology has arisen which allows the chemists to place the genes of one organism into the genetic structure of another. Throughout the whole of human history, we have genetically altered our food. The strengths of one plant have been added to other plants of the same species which were not so strong, but had other characteristics which were useful. In this way we produced plants which had high crop yields and were hardy to frost or disease. What they are now proposing to do is to add the genes of one species into the genes of another. This is not the same as selective breeding.

Our traditional farming methods have only added the genes of one species into the genes of a sub-species. Wheat is a good example of this kind of cross breeding. Hardy species of wheat were crossed with species that had high crop yields. This worked very well and no side effects were built into our foods. All we ended up with were species of wheat which could feed us and survive our winters.

What genetically modified foods do is different. They are modified by introducing the genes of one species into a totally different species. Instead of crossing wheat with wheat, we are now attempting to cross pigs with wheat or fish with tomatoes. This might not sound like too much of a problem, perhaps even beneficial. This is the view that the biotech companies would like us to believe and is an extremely contorted view of the reality of the situation which does not even begin to explain the horrors of their stated ultimate aims.

Everything on the planet contains DNA. DNA is deoxyribonucleic acid and is the basic building blocks of all living things. The DNA is comprised of billions of coding sequences which tell each body cell what its function is. This DNA contains short sequences of information that are called genes. DNA is so complex that our scientists only know, by their own admission, what less than ten percent of it does. Despite this, they believe that they can isolate a particular DNA sequence (gene) which performs certain functions within an animal's body. This function could be something like an ability to withstand extreme cold, for example. This function would be useful in crops such as tomatoes so that crops could be picked earlier or later in the season and remain fresh on the supermarket's shelves for longer. These are commercial decisions, not health decisions.

The way in which foods are modified is this. A likely gene (DNA sequence) is isolated. The gene is then separated from the host animal. This gene sequence is then introduced into a carrier organism (known as a vector). These vectors are made from organisms which have the ability to invade tissue cells, such as viruses and bacteria. The choice of vector depends upon its life span and stability etc. and its ability to reproduce rapidly. The vector most experimented with are bacteria as they are present in all organisms. The bacteria usually chosen for these experiments is the E. Coli bacteria, the one that causes death through food poisoning (many forms of the E. Coli bacteria exist, but the one commonly used is a genetically modifed strain, E. Coli: 0157. This is the strain which caused the food poisoning outbreak in Scotland in 1998 which killed twenty people).

Once the genetic material is added to the bacteria, it is injected into the seeds of a plant. The bacteria then multiply within the body of the seed and transfer the animal genetic material into the genetic material of the plant. The bacteria stays within the plant or transfers into the soil around the plant (the latest research shows that these types of bacteria can stay in the soil for up to two years - see Dr Mae-Wan Ho). This means that GM plants not only contain the genetic structures of animals but also bacteria which can kill by food poisoning. As we eat the plants, we are at risk both from food poisoning and taking on the new genetic material, into our own genetic structures, with unknown consequences.

Once the modified bacteria has been introduced into the soil, it can remain until the next crop is planted. If the next crop is a food crop, the bacteria and genetic material could transfer itself into the new crop. If grass is planted, the bacteria may transfer into whatever animal grazes on the grass. As the animal grazes, the E.Coli is added into its digestive system, either causing the animal to suffer food poisoning or is transferred to us as we eat the animal. The genetic material could also be transferred into the animal's genes, again, with unknown consequences. The bacteria in the soil could also interact with other organisms, animals, birds, worms, insects, other bacteria, trees, flowers, fungus, etc., and transfer the mutated genetic material onto them. The current bacteria vectors are aimed at specific crops, specific plants or specific animals. The latest developments are an attempt to produce vectors which can cross the genetic barriers of any species. This process has the potential to wipe out all life on the planet as the effects of these mutated genetic strands within the environment is totally unknown and the indications from laboratory tests is definitely not encouraging.

One example of this was where a gene from a snowdrop was added into a potato to make it resistant to greenfly. It did make the potato resistant to greenfly, but it also killed ladybirds. Fortunately, the experiment was stopped (source: The Soil Association).

So, eating GM foods has two most likely outcomes. The first is that we take on the genetic structures of an animal and introduce them into our own genetic make up with unknown affects. Secondly, we ingest bacteria from plants which has previously only been found in animals. This bacteria has the capability of killing us.

Current research is showing that the Darwinian view, that the human geno is inviolate, is totally wrong and a strong enough vector could transfer genetic material from any species into humans, again with unknown consequences.

The biotech companies assertions that transgenic foods are totally safe are not fully justified. Adding a gene from brazil nuts into soya beans caused an allergic reaction in people sensitive to eating nuts and the development was stopped. In 1989, the genetic alteration of the bacteria used to produce the food supplement, Tryptophan, resulted in the deaths of 37 people and the permanent disabling of 1500 people in the USA (source - The Soil Association).

Other evidence is slowly beginning to emerge about GM foods. Soybeans have been genetically modified for some years. Due to a lack of effective labelling laws, many foods now contain GM soya. The biotech companies state that it is not possible to segregate GM soya from non GM soya before the beans are used in foods. So, if the lable says that a product contains soya or soya lecithin, it will contain a percentage of GM soya unless it is clearly labelled as coming from non GM sources. GM soya contains increased amounts of phytoestrogens which have been linked to reproductive abnormalities in children (Dr Mae-Wan Ho).

The only people who can possibly gain from GM foods are the companies that produce it by increasing their profits. Why have governments approved genetically modified plant trials for human consumption and then banned the produce from their own restaurants?

The problem does not end there. Animals are now being genetically modified to suit particular market trends or higher profit margins. A trial was carried out on a dairy herd a couple of years ago. The cows were injected with a genetically modified version of cows' growth hormone. This was done in order to make the cows grow bigger and faster and produce a considerably increased quantity of milk. The outcome was that the milk was totally undrinkable. Whilst this might not seem to be a major problem, especially as the same thing was not tried again, it reflects how little the people who are carrying out these experiments actually know about genetic structures or the final outcome of those experiments.

The long term effects of genetically modified plants and animals is totally unknown. Even the short term effects can be very unexpected, as demonstrated by the cows. Basically, the scientists do not know what effects the introduction of GM foods into the human food chain will have. Neither do they know what effects there will be on the environment or the knock on effect on other animals (think how honey is made and what potential effects there could be on the bees as they collect pollen from these plants and what effects there could be on other plants as the bees travel from plant to plant carrying genetically modified pollen with them).

The current argument being used by these biotech companies is that GM crops are being developed and trialed in third world countries in order to feed the starving millions in those countries. There are very many reasons why these populations are starving, most of which are to do with western capital loans and the conditions imposed in granting those loans (such as growing cash crops which provide us in the west with cheap food but which cannot feed the local population). However, a major contributing factor is the activities of the biotech companies which also includes providing loans to third world banks and organisations to promote the biotech company's aims in those countries.

Many regions of the world have plants growing naturally which help the indigenous population to live in the region by providing natural protection against local diseases. You eat the plant as part of your natural diet and it builds up resistance against disease. As these plants have these properties, the biotech companies have patented the active ingredients for future pharmaceutical uses. As these patented plants now become the property of these companies, the local people cannot plant these crops without paying royalties to the biotech companies. The local people cannot afford to do this and they have to change their diet or move to another region where they do not need the natural protection provided by these plants.

These kinds of situations are used by the biotech companies to argue that their GM crops can be trialed in these areas with the promise that they will be able to feed the starving. So far, all of these trials have failed. The crop yield has been considerably lower than non GM crops and they have required a higher percentage of agro chemicals to make them grow.

Again, we have a situation where the advertising does not reflect the truth.

What does work is a system known as "Sustainable Farming". This is a process where the local people grow their own local food from traditional crops and sell any surplus, an organic process which works with and within the total environment. A traditional method which does not involve using any GM crops. The people are fed, a profit is made and the environment is not harmed in any way.

Another problem with our food is the amount of chemicals used to produce them. These are normal food crops and *not* genetically modified ones. With plants, the sequence of events is, essentially, this: the fallow ground is sprayed with chemicals to fertilise. The seed is sprayed with a cocktail of chemicals which prevent mould growth, promote growth and deter pests. The seeds are then sown into the chemically prepared and fertilised ground. As the crops begin to grow, there are again sprayed to inhibit growth to suit market trends and to deter pests. Various chemicals are sprayed onto the crops as they grow for similar reasons or to promote growth. Just before the crop is harvested, it is sprayed again to promote rapid growth. Once it is harvested, it is sprayed again to enhance its appearance and to deter mould growth during storage. If the plant is to be included in the ingredients of pre-prepared meals, it then goes through further processes (processed foods) each stage of which adds further chemicals.

We do not eat vegetables any more, we eat chemicals in a vegetable shape. To top things off, most processed foods are designed to be microwaved. Many tests have shown that microwaved foods are stripped of any remaining minerals and vitamins. The final outcome? - food that is totally devoid of any nutrition or energy. Dead stodge which does not feed the body in any way but puts it under severe stress as the chemicals are toxic. As the body fights this toxicity it does not have the resources to fight any other health problem.

We have only one answer - eat organic vegetables and meats. The production of these crops is growing as more and more people demand them. They are expensive at the moment, but the more people insist that their local supermarket stocks them, the cheaper they will become and the more they will be readily available. The supermarkets have tremendous power to control the food production cycle, but they cannot sell their food if nobody wants it. Insist on organic and the supermarkets will force their suppliers to produce it and the price will come down. We do not have any alternative choice. We either start to eat organic or the body continues to become so full of toxins that we cannot physically survive. According to the World Health Organisation, every year a minimum of twenty thousand people are killed and three million people are injured worldwide by pesticide poisoning.

Another report we came across was from Australia (BBC Ceefax - December 1998). Australia has a large population of fruit bats. These mammals traditionally feed upon wild fruits that grow in the forests. As their natural habitats are being increasingly destroyed to produce larger acres of farming land, the bats are turning to fruit cultivated by farmers. This fruit is chemically sprayed for similar reasons to those given above. It has now been found that fruit bats are increasingly being born with genetic birth defects. These defects include problems such as smaller wings, making them unable to fly, extra fingers or a lower number of fingers making it difficult for them to roost and, the most worrying of all, their heads are considerably larger than normal and they die. They might only be fruit bats, but we eat the same fruit and the same chemicals.

A report published in September 1998 by the Ministry of Agriculture on pesticide residues shows some of the problems that are beginning to arise. The report marks out apples, both home grown and imported, as the fruit most contaminated by pesticides. This report stated that 90% of all apples contained chemical residues, especially insecticides and fungicides. To make matters worse, 70% of the tested sample contained the residue of more than one chemical. The report also points out that all of the research that has been carried out into chemicals and food has been into the effects of individual chemicals, there has been no research into the effects on human health of eating foods with chemicals mixed in these ways. In the government's Food Safety Bulletin 7, March 1997, the government's medical advisors recommend that all fruit should be washed before eating and "whilst peeling fruit is a matter of choice, it is a sensible additional precaution when preparing fruit for small children" (source Friends of the Earth, Earthmatters - winter 1998). What that actually says, in government speak, is that before giving your child an apple to eat it must be peeled or it will poison. What could these chemicals do to our children? As yet, nobody knows, but the evidence is not encouraging.

Traditionally, farming methods followed a similar pattern of rotation. An average farm would have a number of fields, let's say six. These fields were fairly small and divided by hedges. During any one year, the farmer would plant five fields whilst the sixth field was left "fallow". Fallow means that the field was not planted, but left to recover its nutrients for the next season's crops. Very often, natural manures were added to the fallow field so that there was a large build up of natural nutrients for the next crop. The next year, they would still plant five fields but another one would be left fallow. This is, basically, how organic crops are produced.

Following the second world war, a huge number of people needed to be fed and so a new farming policy was formulated to increase production during the immediate post-war period. Hedges were removed and fields were made bigger in order to allow for more intensive farming methods. This is when chemicals began to be introduced. These new methods gave farmers bigger profits and higher yields with their crops. As the population grew, these higher yield crops were needed to feed the population. A number of years ago we reached a point where we were producing a surplus so massive that crops could not be sold and "mountains" of food began to appear. This brought about a change of policy. This new policy meant that farmers were paid to leave fields uncultivated. They were still paid to pour chemicals over the rest of their crops, to produce a high yield, but fields had to be taken out of production. So, on one side farmers were paid to leave fields empty whilst at the same time were paid to produce high yield chemically produced crops on the rest of their land. This sounds as though it is a return to traditional farming methods, where some fields were left fallow, but this is not the case. These fallow fields could not be used for any purpose and could not be fertilised. Also, because these fields were still counted as a part of the farmer's land, they could not be turned into wildlife areas. There then followed a further series of subsidies which allowed the farmers to use these fallow fields for other production purposes.

So, let's recap. Farmers were paid to put chemicals onto the crops to produce a higher yield. Farmers were then paid to leave certain fields empty whilst, at the same time, being paid to produce chemically fed, high yield crops on the rest of their land. And we still have mountains of surplus. If we returned to more traditional methods of farming, that is non chemical, we would have several benefits. Firstly, vegetables would be organically produced. Secondly, the farmers would not have the costs involved in having to use chemicals and, therefore, their profits would increase. Thirdly, we would not be poisoning ourselves with chemicals. We currently have too much productive land in the west, all we need to do is to stop using chemicals and use the land available to produce the organic food that we need. Several "Third World Countries" are adopting a form of food production called "sustainable farming". This is similar to the traditional methods employed by organic farmers. The results of these techniques has shown that people can be adequately fed, the farmers make a larger profit than they did with chemical farming and the environment is not destroyed.

The same applies to animal farming. Our food animals are now so full of chemicals, especially antibiotics and hormones, that our bodies are no longer able to fight off infection (antibiotics are used as a growth stimulant to make animals grow bigger and faster to increase the producer's profit; hormones, particularly oestrogen, are injected or fed into animals to promote fat and water retention, making them heavier). Infections are caused by bacteria and viruses. The more antibiotics we inject into our animals the more the bacteria and viruses become immune to them. We now have strains of bacteria which are totally resistant to any antibiotic. This means that our doctors do not have any drugs they can give us to help the body fight off infections and people die because of it. The oestrogen usage means that we are adding to male sterility and to many of the health problems experienced by women.

The biggest food scare over recent years has been with BSE. The official line is that BSE is caused by contaminated animal feed. We have treated several farmers for BSE type symptoms within our healing practice. BSE is a disease which attacks the central nervous system. In cows it is called BSE, in sheep it is called scrapies, in humans it is called CJD. These farmers have all had damage to their central nervous systems and all of them have had high concentrations of organo phosphates (OPs) within their central nervous systems. Based upon our researches, we can state with certainty that BSE and CJD are not caused by contaminated feed but by OP poisoning. Organo phosphates are used for a number of purposes on farms. This is the chemical used, until recently, for sheep dip and is still used to treat a number of parasites in cows. All of the farmers we have spoken to have noticed that their cows will show symptoms of BSE immediately following treatment by OPs. There is a growing body of evidence to support our view that OPs are to blame for these diseases (including studies carried out by the Ministry of Agriculture between 1997 and 1998). All of the instances of human CJD are clustered around factories which produce OPs. All of the herds or flocks that have demonstrated these symptoms have been treated by OPs (up until recently, all sheep had to be "dipped" against parasites every year and the only approved sheep dip was organo phosphate). The BBC recently aired a story of a herd of caribou in Canada which has BSE. They have not received any kind of contaminated feed as they live in the wild, several miles from any farms. But, where they do live is several miles down wind from a chemical plant which produces organo phosphates. How many coincidences do our governments need?

Drinking Water

Fluoride

Another problem concerns our drinking water. In the UK, a number of water authorities now add fluoride to the water supply. In America, 50% of all water supplies are fluoridated. The argument is that fluoride helps to build and protect tooth enamel. The idea has caught on so much that toothpaste manufacturers also include fluoride in their products. Fluoride is a poison.

There are three sources from which the fluoride in water or in toothpastes is taken. The fluoride added to water is usually one of two chemicals (the one mainly used in toothpastes is also sometimes used in water, which resulted in the water poisoning incident in Cornwall). These are hydrofluorosilicic acid and silico fluoride. These chemicals are waste products from the fertiliser (organophosphate production is the main source - see above for the effects of this), brick and glass industries. The fluoride added to dental products is sodium fluoride, it is actually aluminium oxide which is a waste product of aluminium smelting and is an active ingredient in pesticides, fungicides, rodenticides, anaesthetics, tranquillisers and the nerve gas, Sarin (source - articles in *Kindred Spirit* Autumn '98 and Winter '98).

There has been a huge amount of research carried out into the effects of fluoride on the teeth and on the body in general. The consensus of opinion is that fluoride *can* help to build stronger teeth in *some* children but, for other children and adults, fluoride actually rots teeth and causes a number of side effects which can very seriously affect health. All of these chemicals, especially the aluminium, strip the body of calcium and are toxic chemicals.

Yet another clever marketing ploy by the industrialists who now get paid for using their toxic waste.

312

There are a growing number of non fluoride toothpastes available from health food shops which clean your teeth just as well as fluoridated toothpastes.

Unfortunately, fluoride is not the only chemical problem. Large quantities of chemicals are now found in surface water (such as streams, ponds and oceans), groundwater (water found in natural underground aquifers and reservoirs) and in drinking water as it comes out of the tap. The source of these chemicals is pharmaceutical drugs. These are the drugs which we take in vast quantities every day and flush down the toilet as we dispose of bodily waste. Antibiotics, artificial oestrogens and other hormones, strong painkillers, tranquillisers, cancer chemotherapy chemicals etc., are all flushed into the water courses and our sewage filtering systems cannot extract them. The chemicals added to animals are also added to the land in the form of manure, sometimes, even untreated human waste is used in this way, these chemical residues run off the land in rainwater and build up in streams and rivers etc. or underground reservoirs.

Drinking water is extracted from these sources and the current treatment methods are unable to remove these substances before they arrive at the tap.

The first study to highlight the problem was carried out in Kansas City in the USA in 1976. The results of the study were ignored until a German study was begun in 1992 to investigate herbicides in water. The German study found that in any given water sample, between thirty and sixty different drugs can be identified (*Science News* March 1998). The concentrations of drugs were comparable to the levels of herbicides found in rivers from agricultural run off.

A large percentage of all drugs manufactured between 1992 and 1995 were designed to be soluble in fat but not in water. They act in this way so that they can break down the walls of body cells and act within the cell structure. This means that these types of drugs are extremely slow in breaking down within the environment. Of all drugs, between 50% and 90% are not absorbed by the body. The residues of these drugs pass through the body's digestive system and are excreted from the body. As they pass through the body, their chemical composition changes and are concentrated so they are stronger on leaving the body than they were on the way in (source Nexus December 1998).

Nobody knows what effect drinking these concentrations of chemicals in water every day has on the body. Neither does anybody know how these chemicals react with each other.

Some of these toxins can be removed from drinking water by home filters or boiling your drinking water in an open saucepan or a kettle with its lid off prior to drinking.

An ideal home water preparation set up would be this: water is directly filtered as it comes through the tap and fed into a glass or stainless steel tank which has a gas heater. The boiled water is then passed through a condenser (which produces distilled water) and finally through a glass spiral to "re-energise" the water. Once it has passed through the spiral, the water can be used for drinking or cooking. A very expensive set up, but one which we are all going to have to consider if the chemicals are not removed at source.

If you do not wish to use a fluoride toothpaste but are concerned about your teeth or are prone to tooth decay, we would recommend taking the tissue salt Calc. Fluor. for a ten day course once a year. This actually does strengthen tooth enamel.

Drugs
Before we go on to look at the issues surrounding medicinal drugs, ask yourself two questions.

1. If a drug is developed which does not cure a condition but suppresses the symptoms and that in order to keep suppressing the symptoms the patient has to take the drug for the rest of their lives, who benefits?

2. If a drug is developed which can "cure" an ailment with a single dosage, who has the most to lose?

The answer to both questions is - the drug companies.

The drug industry is currently worth trillions of pounds per year (that is £10,000,000,000,000), each pound of those trillions is another reason not to find a cure for anything.

We are now in a culture where we need to take a drug to counter the side effects of a drug given to treat a symptom. How far away from health can we actually go before we say STOP? The whole purpose of this book has been to give the real reasons why ill health occurs. We do not need any kind of medication to cure our ills and yet we have accepted the drug companies' propaganda and swallow millions of pills a day which fill our bodies with an unbelievable number of toxic chemicals. If we put these chemicals together with the ones in our food and water we arrive at the point where most physical symptoms of illness are caused by chemicals.

This does not go against the truth of the first half of this book. If we live our lives as our souls want us to, the chakras spin with a light which is blinding in intensity and makes us invulnerable to illness. The body is designed to deal with any natural antigen. If the chakras are spinning correctly then they will, literally, throw off any potential body pollutant from any source. If we go against the needs of the soul, we set up ripples and wobbles within the chakras which leave us open to illness. Even then, if our diet is healthy, the soul will help us to remedy the situations which brought about the chakra's wobble. Drug company propaganda has generated such an atmosphere of fear within our society that we are actively prevented from seeking out the underlying truth of the soul and almost forced into a situation where the only remedy is a little bundle of chemicals.

During the course of our researches for the second half of this book we have come across reports which make a mockery of most of our accepted understanding of illness and the need for surgery or drugs. All of this information is written by doctors and their findings and reports have been deliberately suppressed in order to promote drug usage and surgical procedures. Books such as *"What Doctors Don't Tell You"* are packed with medical reports and investigations which totally contradict the advice given by most doctors. Magazines such as Nexus are also full of evidence of deliberately misleading medical statistics and advice.

Which would you prefer, a healthy body brought about by your own efforts or surgery due to chemical overload. This is the choice we have.

During the course of our work as psychic surgeons, we treat many clients who have been taking prescribed drugs for a number of years. Their bodies contain huge residues of these drugs as the body is not always able to flush them fully out of the system. Another problem is that of drug dependency. Think about that word, dependency, for a moment, it is a word coined by the medical profession which means that the body cannot function without the drug being present - in other words, they are addicted to the drug. The word was coined to imply that dependency is not the same as addiction.

The way in which dependency comes about is that some of the ingredients of these drugs are able to break down the defences of the body's cells and combine with sections of the body's DNA. This means that the drug effectively becomes a part of the patient's physical make up. In other words, the patient's body is fooled into believing that the drug is necessary to live. Most of the time, the drugs tend to invade sections of DNA which are not passed on to our children but some drugs, such as

Thalidomide, can be passed on to future generations with disastrous consequences. We have direct experience of treating a client who's mother had taken Thalidomide and the daughter's cell and DNA structures were altered by the drug and had the capacity of being passed on to her children - a minimum of three generations.

Whilst on the subject of drugs. There are many substances in common usage which are termed "recreational drugs". These are drugs such as marijuana and ecstacy. With both of these drugs we have found side effects which are not commonly known. When we have treated clients who have used these drugs, there have been side effects. With marijuana, the blood vessels into and around the brain become coated with a sticky, tar like residue which can restrict blood flow to the brain. Ecstacy has the ability to invade cell structures. It does not seem to affect DNA but the body's cells all contain the drug and it appears to take an extremely long time for the drug to clear out of the system.

Aspartame

Aspartame is an artificial sweetener up to 200 times sweeter than sugar. This sweetener took the place of saccharine which became unpopular when studies showed a link with bladder cancer in laboratory animals. Saccharine is still on sale in the U.K.. Aspartame is included in thousands of food products, such as diet soda, fruit drinks, instant breakfasts, chewing gum, mints, cocoa and other instant drinks etc. Some countries have actually banned its use but it is still widely available in some 90 other countries. It is actually known, through research, that aspartame causes a blockage of the formation of serotonin in the brain, which would cause insomnia and psychiatric disorders like depression. Ironically, it has also been found that aspartame can actually cause you to *gain* weight because it increases your appetite for carbohydrates and sugar. Migraine, headaches, nausea, bloating, abdominal pain and diarrhoea are just a few of the listed side effects, which also includes death!

Diabetics consume large amounts of diet foods, and once again research has produced the information that aspartame can actually throw off insulin control. It is also claimed that the side effects of artificial sweeteners tend to be exacerbated in children, and these risks multiply in diabetic children who are more likely to consume chemical soda and sweets.

The list of doctors, professors and medical institutes who have carried out research into the side effects of aspartame is quite impressive. Dr. H.J. Roberts, a diabetic specialist, has written a book on his research called "*Aspartame (NutraSweet): Is it safe?* (Philadelphia, The Charles Press.) It would appear from his research that aspartame began life as a drug for peptic ulcers, was found to be sweet and the rest is history. As far as we can see, artificial sweeteners, in any form, only benefit the drug companies, is detrimental to not only our physical but also our mental health and should be avoided at all costs.

Osteoporosis

Why are we all aware of osteoporosis? Basically because it has been rammed down every women's throat that at menopause she will automatically fall foul of this supposedly dreadful disease, end up with fractures, broken hips, and a dowager's hump.

Single handedly, women are supporting the pharmaceutical industry, the medical profession and the dairy farmers. Men, even though they can also suffer from osteoporosis, were not targeted because it was oestrogen that needed to be remarketed after the original oestrogen/breast cancer scare ruined sales.

There is a substantial amount of evidence out there which comes to the same conclusions as we do that synthetic hormonal drugs (HRT), dairy products and calcium supplements actually *weaken* the bones and have other harmful effects on the body. Calcium supplements have been shown to increase the risk of kidney stones, calcification of the bones, "sand in the muscles", etc. In combination, all of these treatments have been medically linked to just about every major illness suffered by western women.

Once again we are in a position where the prescribed medication has caused greater harm than the original symptoms. On a more ironic note, recent research indicates that it is a lack of progesterone and not oestrogen that is the root of the problem and that most of the problems experienced by women are due to oestrogen dominance.

If you suffer from a reduction in bone density which is in the range of 5 to 15 per cent then this will be caused by a natural process that exists within the body. As mentioned in chapter 6, the brain uses blood born calcium to transmit messages throughout the body. The body sees blood calcium as a higher priority than calcium in the bones. Deficiencies of these percentages actually fall within the body's natural range. If your reduction in density is greater than fifteen per cent then it probably has a menopausal link, however, an alteration to diet and exercise can correct even this deficiency. In our experience a reduction in bone density of up to 25 per cent can be easily rectified using these methods. See chapter fifteen for dietary and other suggestions.

During our research we have come across a plethora of information which can be summed up in this paragraph from the author of *"Hormone Heresy: What Women MUST Know About Their Hormones"*, Sherrill Sellman:

"Osteoporosis is not an ageing disease or an oestrogen or calcium deficiency but a degenerative disease of western culture. We have brought it upon ourselves through poor dietary habits and lifestyle factors, and exposure to pharmaceutical drugs. It is our ignorance that has made us vulnerable to the vested interests that have intentionally distorted the facts and willingly sacrificed the health of millions of women at the altar of profit and greed. It is only by our willingness to take responsibility for

our bodies and make the commitment to return to a healthy, balanced way of life that we'll be able to walk tall and strong for the rest of our lives."

Cholesterol

Everybody knows that cholesterol is bad for you. It blocks the arteries, causes heart disease, kidney failure and about four hundred other life threatening diseases.

Wrong.

The whole of the cholesterol/fat/health issue arose in the USA in the 1950's. Since the beginning of this century, the number of deaths from heart disease and myocardial infarction (a large blood clot blocking a main artery usually resulting in a heart attack) had risen from virtually zero to accounting for more than 30% of all deaths in the USA.

High levels of blood cholesterol was assumed to be the problem and a campaign was started to persuade people away from foods containing animal fats.

Many studies were carried out (funded by the vegetable oil/margarine industry) to try to establish a link between these deaths and cholesterol levels in the blood. Some of these studies were very large involving up to 37 000 people and one lasted for forty years. All of these studies failed to find the link they were looking for. What did become clear from these studies was that blood cholesterol levels made no difference to the incidence of heart disease or heart attack unless your cholesterol levels were too low!

Cholesterol is manufactured by the body for use as a building block for a number of useful substances. These include: corticosteroids (these are hormones that help us cope with stress and protect the body against heart disease and cancer); the production of the sex hormones for both sexes; it helps in the production of Vit. D which is a fat soluble vitamin needed for bone growth, nerve health, mineral absorption, muscle health, insulin production and a healthy immune system function; the production of digestive bile. Cholesterol is also an antioxidant.

Cholesterol levels are measured in milligrammes per decilitre of blood (mg/dL). The average amount of blood cholesterol is between 200 and 240 mg/dL. People with levels below 160 mg/dL have been shown to have a greater incidence of cancer, heart disease, accidents, infectious diseases, kidney failure and depression. There does not appear to be an upper limit for blood cholesterol which causes automatic health problems, there was, apparently, a perfectly healthy person whose level was measured at 1,300 mg/dL.

The body can only build cholesterol from saturated fats. These are found in butter, full milk, eggs, hard cheeses, lard, palm oil, coconut oil, olive oil, etc.. The body does not build cholesterol from any other type of source.

Since the 1950's health drive began, the processed foods advertising campaign has been operating in overdrive. Despite every indication to the contrary, they have consistently maintained a campaign advertising the assumed benefits of margarines and vegetable oils. None of these substances contain saturated fats. This means that these substances have no positive benefit to the body. We have to become a little technical here to explain what we mean by this, but bear with us.

Saturated fats produce long straight molecules which bind together very easily. This means that these fats can solidify at room temperature (as in butter - for example). Most vegetable "fats" produce non straight molecules (known as polyunsaturated fats) which means that they remain liquid at room temperature. The advertising slogan beloved by margarine companies that their products are high in polyunsaturated fats actually means that they have a high vegetable oil content. To produce a solid form (margarine - for example) or to produce an oil which can be heated (soya oil - for example), these vegetable "fats" have to go through a chemical process known as hydrogenation. This process alters the molecular structure by rearranging the hydrogen atoms in the molecule. This process "straightens" the molecule and helps them to produce a solid form.

The hydrogenation process produces a substance known as trans fatty acids (a form of free radical). These trans fats (as they are known) cannot be used by the body to produce cholesterol. What trans fats do is reduce the body's supply of antioxidants, increase the risk of cancer, increase the risk of heart disease and myocardial infarction, increase body weight, damage the reproductive system, damage the lungs and interfere with the production of prostaglandins (prostaglandins are a group of hormones which perform a number of functions throughout the body). Prostaglandin deficiency can lead to PMS problems, autoimmune disease and myocardial infarctions (amongst others). Basically, the rise in use of vegetable oils, margarines and low fat foods have led to no positive health benefits. The claims made by the processed food manufacturers have no basis in fact. Trans fats would appear to be directly responsible for the astronomical rise in a number of serious health problems.

Foods such as butter, meats, eggs, cheese, etc. actually help the body. Many of the above health problems have arisen since we began to change from these substances to polyunsaturated fats. The low fat, polyunsaturated campaign is one of the largest and longest lasting cons that we unsuspecting consumers have ever been subjected to. All of the research backing up this campaign has been paid for by the food industry to boost their incomes. Most of the medical reports that expose the lie have been suppressed. Many scientists cannot publish the truth as their research funding would be removed.

(Although the information contained within this section has been derived from a number of articles, reports and books, it is a precis based upon an article which appeared in *Nexus* magazine Vol. 6 Nos 1&2: Dec 1998 - March 1999, written by Dr Mary Enig and Sally Fallon, as their article succinctly pulls all of the research and information together).

Just as we were completing this book, the following item appeared on the Sci-Tech pages of BBC Ceefax on the 9th March 1999 under the heading: *"Heart Drugs Benefit More Say Studies"*.

"Even those not suffering from the symptoms of heart disease could benefit from taking cholesterol lowering drugs experts say.

Studies from around the world presented at a conference in New Orleans show people with only average levels of cholesterol can benefit from drugs.

Although exercise and diet can avert heart attacks and angina, experts think preventative prescriptions can help. Cholesterol lowering drugs cause only minimal side effects but are costly."

This is exactly how the news item was worded. Note the use of the word "expert" and the final sentence which says that the new drugs have only minimal side effects. This is a news item which says that even if you are perfectly healthy, you need to take cholesterol lowering drugs.

We telephoned the BBC to ask for clarification of the article. Apparently the item was taken from a report by the international news company, Reuters. The conference was for the American College of Cardiology and the above advice was presented by a Dr Antonia Gotto of Cornell University after carrying out a study on a new drug called "Ivostatin", to be marketed under the name of "Meracor". Both the study and the conference was sponsored by the drug company Merck. Another

323

example of advertising by the drug companies being presented as scientific fact.

In Conclusion

During the course of writing this chapter, we have carried out a large amount of research into prescribed drugs, food additives, food processes and marketing ploys. We have sifted through many reports, articles, books, etc. and read many millions of words. We could not hope to provide all of the information available as that would take several volumes as opposed to one chapter, however, the information is available to anyone who cares to go and look.

From our investigations, several things have become very clear.

1. Most TV and magazine advertisments only give a very limited, biased view and only reflect the aspect the advertiser is trying to promote (especially in food advertising). Most of the claims made in these advertisements should be treated with extreme caution.

2. Most medical and scientific studies are biased towards the companies who paid for those studies to be carried out. Even government licencing agencies are not immune from this kind of bias. Aspartame and the FDA is a good example of this.

3. Many publicly accepted "facts" are no more than "urban myths" about products or treatments and are more to do with advertising hype than reality.

4. Pre 1900, very few of our current life threatening diseases existed. Illnesses such as cancer, heart disease, heart attack, etc. were virtually unheard of. It is only since we began to use chemicals, artificially produced foods and mass pharmaceuticals that our problems began.

The life threatening infectious diseases, that killed huge numbers of people before 1900, have mainly been eradicated by improvements in sanitation, an understanding of disease transmission and the discovery of the antibiotic properties of certain moulds (penicillin).

5. Our definition of a cure is where symptoms no longer exist and the patient has not had surgery nor are they taking any kind of medication or remedy.

The medical definition of a cure is where the original symptoms no longer exist, whatever the condition of the patient. A cure is still claimed even if the patient died of the treatment, just as long as they did not die of the original symptoms.

6. We have found no evidence whatsoever that *any* drug has cured any illness - to our definition - except for antibiotics or headache pills.

7. We still consult our doctors for health and lifestyle advice when the average age of death of all doctors is 54 (mainly from heart disease and heart attacks - see chapter six).

In writing this chapter, we have attempted to highlight some of the many unhealthy ingredients we all encounter in our everyday diets and lifestyles. Try not to take it all to heart or to panic, but try to see them in context. All of the items covered in this chapter contribute to health problems by working against the body and putting the immune system under stress. Try to begin altering your diet and/or lifestyle to cut out as many of these substances as possible. As you begin to let go of these substances, your body will respond in a positive way.

All of our illnesses and diseases are caused by our not paying enough attention to our soul. We do not have any doubt about this. In the world in which we live, it is difficult to fulfil our full potential. We are always pulled between what we know we should be doing and what we have to do to survive. Within this conflict we generate symptoms of illness, it is almost inevitable. The only chance that we have for survival is that we eat foods which work with the body and help to sustain us. We are what we eat, or at least, so the old saying goes.

There is an Answer to All of These Problems

It is very simple.

Express your feelings; express your thoughts; be creative.

Eat naturally produced foods (include naturally produced meats if you are not vegetarian); eat organic vegetables; drink natural water, drink organic wines and take moderate exercise.

Laugh as much as possible and try not to take life quite so seriously.

This way we will all avoid ill health and fulfill the body's potential for a lifetime of 160 years (at least!).

We are more than human.
We are more than we ever dreamed possible.
It is time to live.
It is time to regain control.

Appendix One

Meditations

Meditations are an extremely useful way of bringing about a state of relaxation and to re-energise the body.

Unfortunately, not everyone is able to meditate and many are not comfortable with the idea. One of the problems is that during the Sixties and the Seventies, a form of meditation was introduced into the west from Asian countries where there is a tradition of using meditations. This form of meditation was called Transcendental Meditation (TM) and involved many hours of practice to clear the brain of all thoughts and the meditator then sat for long periods trying to keep the mind clear whilst concentrating on a single word or sound (called a mantra).

Most people found this kind of meditation extremely difficult, if not impossible and sometimes, very silly. The main reason for this is that our minds are always active and reacting to both internal and external stimuli. Our brains are not actually capable of concentrated thought for longer than seven minutes before it begins to start wandering into thoughts about the kids, the shopping, the boss, sex, etc.. To achieve the aims of TM, a clearance of all thoughts, takes many years of concerted effort and its benefits seem to be limited to relaxation, not that that is a bad thing. For those who have mastered the technique, they have received great benefits. But for the rest of us, the idea of sitting somewhere for several hours trying to empty our minds whilst humming softly does not seem very relaxing.

Our description is probably a little unfair to those who do practice TM as it obviously works, and works well, for them. For the rest of us though, this is how most people think of meditation.

Fortunately, this is not what we mean by meditation. Meditation can have many uses and many benefits and can be used to exercise the mind to achieve predetermined goals that allow the mind to roam and to experience. Quite a lot of medical research has been carried out into meditation and what happens when the mind enters a meditative state. These researches show that the bio-electrical wave emissions given off by the brain alter, the blood pressure drops and muscle activity reduces to virtually zero.

Many people use meditation to help their health problems and also just for recreation, whilst for some, they form part of their religious practices. Most religions promote the idea of a periodic "retreat". These retreats are usually in places where quiet contemplation is encouraged and this is a form of meditation.

Most health problems can be helped by meditation. We would see meditation as falling into two types. The first is to relax and the second is to carry out some kind of mental exercise. Relaxation type meditations are very beneficial, in terms of health, and these are the ones most commonly practised.

The techniques used for these meditations are quite simple to learn and to use and most people are able to master them quite quickly. Many people learn these techniques as part of a group. There are very many meditation groups run by a variety of kinds of people. Some are run by hospitals as part of their pain management clinics, some are run by local councils and are available through adult education classes and some are run by private individuals.

All of these groups are run by people who are experienced in meditating and teaching meditation. What they do is to help you to understand the meditative process and how to calm down the body and mind to reach a state where relaxation is possible.

Relaxation in this way has been medically shown to have a number of benefits. A large amount of research has been carried out which shows that meditations to relax can considerably reduce many chronic symptoms.

High Blood Pressure

It has been shown that people who meditate for ten to twenty minutes per day have been able to cut down or even stop their medication for high blood pressure. Relaxation type meditations slow down heart rate and muscle activity and help the body to better deal with stresses and tensions that are built up during our daily lives that bring about an increase in blood pressure.

Circulation Problems

For similar reasons to those given for blood pressure problems, people with circulation problems have also been shown to benefit. Although the heart rate and pulse slows during meditation, the increased sense of relaxation helps the blood to flow much more efficiently and therefore increase the circulation of blood to all regions of the body.

Chronic Pain

For most people who suffer pain from causes such as injury or back problems, the relaxed state and increased blood circulation allows the body to relax and remove tensions out of muscles. As the muscles relax, pressures on the nerves also reduces and can generate a situation where pain is relieved and, sometimes, even eliminated.

Insomnia

Insomnia is often caused by pain, anxiety, stress, etc. and so learning to relax can help to relieve these causes. As the body relaxes, tensions disappear and anxieties diminish allowing the body to achieve sleep. Meditation will not remove the causes of the stresses and tensions, but it will help the body to deal with them more efficiently and comfortably helping the sufferer to break the sleeplessness patterns.

Chest Problems

As the body relaxes into a meditation, the breathing becomes much easier and deeper. This change of breathing patterns, together with the benefits listed above, allow the lungs to relax and breath more efficiently, especially as the body now requires less oxygen to keep it working. The combination of slower, deeper breathing, reduced oxygen requirement and muscle relaxation is especially helpful for asthma.

How to Relax (Breathing Exercise)

The simplest way to relax is to use a breathing exercise. Just learning how to breath fully can have several of the benefits listed above and is, in itself, a simple form of meditation. If you can master this technique, the following meditation exercises can become very much easier to achieve.

You can carry out this exercise virtually anywhere and at virtually any time, but it works best if you are sitting or lying down. Begin by thinking about the process you are about to start. This helps to clear the mind and to relax your system. Begin to breath deeply through the nose, using the diaphragm to pull the air deeply into your lungs.

As you become used to breathing in this way, start to count. Count 1-2-3-4 to breath in, hold the breath for a count of 1-2-3-4, then breath out for a count of 1-2-3-4. The distance between the numbers will probably be quite short to begin with but, as you relax and become more practiced at it, the count will automatically lengthen.

Continue breathing in this way for a few minutes or until you are feeling relaxed, calm and more energised. You can use this exercise virtually any where and at virtually any time. If you are in pain, have panic attacks, asthma, headaches, heart problems, in other words, any condition where there is pain or stress, this exercise can be used to calm and relax whenever you have the need.

If you have not meditated before, and would like to give it a try, begin by using this exercise and, once you are relaxed, you can continue on with one of the exercises detailed below.

How to Meditate.

For some people, they prefer to meditate by themselves, whilst for others, they prefer to be a part of a group where they are led through the process. If you prefer to meditate by yourself, then following the procedure given below can help to start you into a more relaxed way of life. Most meditation teachers will follow a similar routine in their classes.

It is best not to eat or drink for a half an hour before you begin. Find a quiet room where you can relax and remain undisturbed. You can sit or lie down, it is your choice for the most comfortable position. You can either close your eyes or keep them open. The only warning there is here is that if you are most comfortable in a lying position with your eyes closed, you may fall asleep. Depending on your aims for a meditation, this may or may not be a good thing. If you wish to fall asleep, then it is a good thing, but if you wish to reach a state of relaxation during your day, then it is probably not so good.

Once you are sitting/lying comfortably, begin to concentrate on your breath. The aim is to fill your mind by concentrating on something specific and, as you are (hopefully) breathing in any way, its a good place to start. Feel the breath enter your nostrils and filling your lungs. Breath in as deeply as you can, following the breath as closely as possible. Hold the breath briefly and then breathe slowly out. It is better to take the same time breathing out as it did to breathe in. To help in this, it might be useful to count. Count as you breathe in and then take the same count to breathe out (a slow count of four is recommended). Empty your lungs as fully as you can. It can take a little practice to achieve an equal time for breathing in and out, but it is something which is worth practising until you can manage it as it helps to regulate oxygen flow and aids relaxation.

Keep concentrating on your breath for a couple of minutes until it is regular and you feel your body relaxing. It is important to breathe in by using the diaphragm and not the chest muscles as this draws the breath further into the lungs and helps to fill them more efficiently.

As you begin to relax, start to think of something which you find relaxing. It does not matter what this something is. It can be a photograph or a painting you have which you find relaxing. It can be a favourite place such as the sea shore or a woodland walk. Most people find the image of a garden the most useful and easiest to conjure up in their minds. Whatever or wherever the place or scene is, hold it in your mind, you can just sit there or, if you are practised at these things, you can walk through it experiencing the sounds and smells as well as the sights. The important thing is that you are in a place which you find comfortable and relaxing.

Inevitably, you will find thoughts of your normal life entering into your mind. It will always happen and there is very little that can be done to stop them. What you can do is to work with them. Acknowledge that the thoughts are there and that you will deal with them later. That is all that you need to do, just place them to one side and keep your attention on your favourite, relaxing, image.

Another use that this type of meditation can be be put to is to help fight your health problem. If you are suffering from an illness or disease, even cancer, once you become practised at visualising your favourite scene, or find that visualisation comes easily to you, you can turn your attention inwards.

Instead of being in your favourite and relaxing place you can travel through your body to the site of the organ or region affected. Imagine that you are filling the region with things that can help to destroy or remove your problem. We know of someone who imagined that their cancer was being eaten away by crocodiles, and it worked, the cancer went. You can travel into the thymus and stimulate it into producing "killer" cells which can help fight the infection etc.. You can also imagine the affected area is being flooded by light of a colour that matches the chakra corresponding to the affected area or better still, with golden light as this colour corresponds to a very high frequency of energy.

Keep up this exercise for a period of between ten and twenty minutes. In order to receive the most benefit, you will need to carry out this meditation every day. It has been found that daily use of these kinds of exercises can bring about relief for most health problems. It does not deal with the root causes of your problem (although you can use meditation to work on those), but it does help to push them aside for the time that the meditation lasts, giving you a more relaxed condition from where it is easier to deal with them.

As you finish the meditation, it is best to remain in position and move your muscles around for a couple of minutes. This is to stimulate the blood flow and get the heart beating a little faster. The meditations are intended to relax you and so your heart rate will have slowed, if you get up immediately, you might feel a little light headed whilst your blood flow catches up with your movement.

If you do decide to meditate, then you have to make time and space within your day, every day, to receive maximum benefit, at least until the time that you have dealt with the root causes of your illness.

Some people find it easier to carry out these exercises if there is relaxing music playing softly in the background and this is fine. Others find it useful to have a voice leading them through the various stages. You can put your own audio tape together for this purpose. You can record your own voice, or get a friend to record theirs for you, and create a tape of the right length for you. Once you are in the room you use for meditation and are in a comfortable position, you can switch on the tape and just relax into it.

Once you are practised at the technique, it is possible to use it virtually anywhere. This could be during your lunch break at work, commuting on the train, as soon as the children have gone to bed, etc.. Obviously, you should not try to meditate if you are driving or using tools of any kind, but other than those situations, meditation can be used at any time to help you to relax and it does not cause any problems with medication or any other form of treatment.

Other Meditations

The type of meditation described above is primarily intended to be relaxing. If you can use the other visualisation exercise to help fight your illness then it can be even more beneficial. However, you can use meditation to exercise the mind to carry out all sorts of tasks and journeys.

These are usually called guided meditations and serve specific functions. They are called guided because they are usually carried out to a taped voice guiding you into a chosen situation or exercise and then back out again.

The types of journeys or exercises you can undergo in this way is limitless. There are a huge selection of guided meditation tapes available from health food shops and specialist bookshops that range from helping to give up smoking to swimming with dolphins and just about anything else you can think of.

Some of these exercises can be very beneficial in easing health problems and some of the tapes are designed to do just that.

As part of the healing work that we do, we teach healing to beginners and already practising healers. As part of our courses, we have developed meditations to carry out specific functions. These have been developed to maximise the energy potential contained within the bodily chakras. The meditations are available on audio tape.

The tape contains four meditations. The first is designed to fully energise and balance the chakras. As one of the authors is able to "see" energies, this meditation has been produced to help to bring the energies of the chakras to as high a level as possible. As they can see the results of the meditation, they know that it works very well. The second meditation is intended to take you off to meet your spirit guide /angel. It is very easy to follow and is, again, very effective. The third exercise is designed to make the connection between the "higher self" and the self much stronger. For those who have difficulty with visualisation, the fourth meditation is of didgeridoo music which does the job of the first meditation, energises and balances the chakras. This takes the whole of the second side of the tape and lasts for approximately thirty minutes. Feed back we have received from the people who have used the didg side say that animals and children love it. If you wish to order a copy of the tape, an order form is printed at the back of the book.

If you find that you enjoy meditation exercises, there is one which can work extremely well and can also be very beneficial. Once you have reached a state of relaxation by using the breathing exercise, take yourself off to a garden. It does not matter what kind of garden you conjure up in your mind, cottage, formal, woodland, etc. as long as there is a house as a part of this landscape. You can spend as long as you like in the garden but you should, eventually, make your way towards the house. The house needs to be huge. Longleat or The White House proportions seem to work very well.

Slowly make your way through the garden and towards the front door of the house. As you arrive at the front door, just push it open and enter the hall. On the far left hand corner of the hall is a doorway. Walk down the hall and push open the door. What is in front of you is a library. This library is huge, there are books everywhere, on the floor, all around the walls, in stacks in the middle of the room, everywhere. This is why the image of the house needs to be so big, you could not get this library into anything smaller.

There are three ways to use the library. First, you can ask the library a specific question, it does not matter what kind of question it is, the library will present you with a book from which you can read the answer. Secondly, you can ask the library for something which will be of interest to you and a book will be presented. Thirdly, you can wander around the shelves and pick a book that catches your interest, open it and begin to read. There are probably many other ways in which the library can be used, we have suggested these three to get you started. You can access the library for just about any information of any kind - just use as you wish. The only warning there is, is that it can be very tempting to spend a great deal of time in the library and you need to set yourself a time limit before you enter it. Your mind will remember and bring you out at the appropriate moment.

Meditations can be used for many things and in many ways, most of which are extremely beneficial. If you have never tried to meditate before, give it a try and see what happens. There is nothing to lose and, possibly, much to gain.

Appendix Two

The Bach Flower Remedies® Described

As mentioned in chapter twelve, there are thirty eight Bach Flower Remedies. Each are intended to treat specific states of mind and aid in the healing process by alleviating many of the attitudes of mind which are a part of the underlying causes to an illness. These remedies should not be seen as something which *might* help, but are primary treatments which will begin to work on the root causes as soon as they are taken.

The use of the remedies is suggested in two ways throughout chapters fourteen to twenty. The first is a general treatment for each chakra and is based upon our intuitive use of the remedies. These suggestions have been arrived at by the remedies being "scanned" and the energies of the remedy being matched to the energy frequency range contained within the appropriate chakra.

This is an approach which will be new to most people. They are suggested from a viewpoint of being an overall energy enhancer for the chakras and can be taken as a general booster to the individual chakra. This method will not be found in any of the standard literature about the remedies.

The second method is as originally described by Dr Bach. Each condition has a specific remedy and they are suggested as being the best remedy for each ailment.

The descriptions of the remedies given here are in Dr Bach's own words and are reproduced from Dr Bach's book *"The*

Twelve Healers" by kind permission of The Dr Edward Bach Healing Centre and Trust whose copyright is maintained.

The remedies are separated into seven headings, each of which deals with particular conditions of mind. Although we have suggested particular remedies for specific chakras and ailments, you can choose your own to suit your specific condition. In order to choose a remedy for yourself, it would be best if you asked a close friend to choose it for you as the choice requires total honesty and most of us are not very honest with ourselves. The botanical name of the plants used is given in brackets.

For Those Who Have Fear

Rock Rose (*Heliathemum nummularium*)
The remedy of emergency for cases where there even appears no hope. In accidents or sudden illness, or where the patient is very frightened or terrified or if the condition is serious enough to cause great fear to those around. If the patient is not conscious the lips may be moistened with the remedy. Other remedies in addition may also be required, as, for example, if there is unconsciousness, which is a deep, sleepy state, Clematis; if there is torture, Agrimony, and so on.
Summary: suddenly alarmed, scared, panicky.

Mimulus (*Mimulus guttatus*)
Fear of worldly things, illness, pain, accidents, poverty, of dark, of being alone, of misfortune. The fears of everyday life. These people quietly and secretly bear their dread, they do not freely speak of it to others.
Summary: fear of *known* things. Shyness, timidity.

Cherry Plum (*Prunus cerasifera*)
Fear of the mind being over-strained, of reason giving way, of doing fearful and dreaded things, not wished and known wrong, yet there comes the thought and impulse to do them.

Summary: uncontrolled, irrational thoughts.

Aspen (*Populus tremula*)
Vague unknown fears, for which there can be given no explanation, no reason. Yet the patient may be terrified of something terrible going to happen, they know not what. These vague unexplainable fears may haunt by night or day. Sufferers are often afraid to tell their trouble to others.
Summary: apprehension for no known reason.

Red Chestnut (*AEsculus carnea*)
For those who find it difficult not to be anxious for other people. Often they have ceased to worry about themselves, but for those of whom they are fond they may suffer much, frequently anticipating that some unfortunate thing may happen to them.
Summary: obsessed by care and concern for others.

For Those Who Suffer Uncertainty

Cerato (*Ceratostigma willmottiana*)
Those who have not sufficient confidence in themselves to make their own decisions. They constantly seek advice from others, and are often misguided.
Summary: Those who doubt their own judgement, seeks confirmation of others.

Scleranthus (*Scleranthus annuus*)
Those who suffer much from being unable to decide between two things, first one seeming right then the other. They are usually quiet people, and bear their difficulties alone, as they are not inclined to discuss it with others.
Summary: uncertainty/indecision/vacillation. Fluctuating moods.

Gentian (*Gentiana amarella*)
Those who are easily discouraged. They may be progressing well in illness or in the affairs of their daily life, but any small

delay or hindrance to progress causes doubt and soon disheartens them.
Summary: despondency.

Gorse (*Ulex europoeus*)
Very great hopelessness, they have given up belief that more can be done for them. Under persuasion or to please others they may try different treatments, at the same time assuring those around that there is so little hope of relief.
Summary: pessimism, defeatism - "Oh what's the use!".

Hornbeam (*Carpinus betulus*)
For those who feel that they have not sufficient strength, mentally or physically, to carry the burden of life placed upon them; the affairs of every day seem too much for them to accomplish, though they generally succeed in fulfilling their task. For those who believe that some part, of mind or body, needs to be strengthened before they can easily fulfil their work.
Summary: "Monday morning" feeling - procrastination.

Wild Oat (*Bromus ramosus*)
Those who have ambitions to do something of prominence in life, who wish to have much experience, and to enjoy all that which is possible for them, to take life to the full. Their difficulty is to determine what occupation to follow; as although their ambitions are strong, they have no calling which appeals to them above all others. This may cause delay and dissatisfaction.
Summary: helps determine one's intended path in life.

Not Sufficient Interest in Present Circumstances

Clematis (*Clematis vitalba*)
Those who are dreamy, drowsy, not fully awake, no great interest in life. Quiet people, not really happy in their present

circumstances, living more in the future than in the present; living in hopes of happier times, when their ideals may come true. In illness some make little or no effort to get well, and in certain cases may even look forward to death, in the hope of better times; or maybe, meeting again some beloved one whom they have lost.

Summary: inattentive, dreamy, absent-minded, mental escapism.

Honeysuckle (*Lonicera caprifolium*)

Those who live much in the past, perhaps a time of great happiness, or memories of a lost friend, or ambitions which have not come true. They do not expect further happiness such as they have had.

Summary: living in the past - nostalgic. Home-sickness.

Wild Rose (*Rosa canina*)

Those who are without apparently sufficient reason become resigned to all that happens, and just glide through life, take it as it is, without any effort to improve things and find some joy. They have surrendered to the struggle of life without complaint.

Summary: resignation, apathy.

Olive (*Olea europoea*)

Those who have suffered much mentally or physically and are so exhausted and weary that they feel they have no more strength to make any effort. Daily life is hard work for them, without pleasure.

Summary: fatigued - drained of energy.

White Chestnut (*AEsculus hippocastunum*)

For those who cannot prevent thoughts, ideas, arguments which they do not desire from entering their minds. Usually at such times when the interest of the moment is not strong enough to keep the mind full. Thoughts which worry and will remain, or if for a time thrown out, will return. They seem to circle round and round and cause mental torture. The presence

of such unpleasant thoughts drives out peace and interferes with being able to think only of the work or pleasure of the day.
Summary: persistent unwanted thoughts. Pre-occupation with some worry or episode. Mental arguments.

Mustard (*Sinapis arvensis*)
Those who are liable to times of gloom, or even despair, as though a cold dark cloud overshadowed them and hid the light and the joy of life. It may not be possible to give any reason or explanation for such attacks. Under these conditions it is almost impossible to appear happy or cheerful.
Summary: "dark cloud" that descends, making one saddened and low for no known reason.

Chestnut Bud (*AEsculus hippocastanum*)
For those who do not take full advantage of observation and experience, and who take a longer time than others to learn the lessons of daily life. Whereas one experience would be enough for some, such people find it necessary to have more, sometimes several, before the lesson is learnt. Therefore, to their regret, they find themselves having to make the same error on different occasions when once would have been enough, or observation of others could have spared them even that one fault.
Summary: refuses to learn by experience - continually repeats the same mistakes.

Loneliness

Water Violet (*Hottonia palustris*)
For those who in illness or health like to be alone. Very quiet people, who move without noise, speak little, and then gently. Very independent, capable and self-reliant. Almost free of the opinions of others. They are aloof, leave people alone and go their own way. Often clever and talented. Their peace and calmness is a blessing to those around them.
Summary: proud, reserved, enjoys being alone.

Impatiens (*Impatiens glandulifera*)
Those who are quick in thought and action and who wish all things to be done without hesitation or delay. When ill they are anxious for a hasty recovery. They find it very difficult to be patient with people who are slow, as they consider it wrong and a waste of time, and they will endeavour to make such people quicker in all ways. They often prefer to work and think alone, so that they can do everything at their own speed.
Summary: impatience, irritability.

Heather (*Calluna vulgaris*)
Those who are always seeking the companionship of anyone who may be available, as they find it necessary to discuss their own affairs with others, no matter whom it may be. They are very unhappy if they have been alone for any length of time.
Summary: talkative (obsessed with their own troubles and experiences).

Over Sensitive to Influences and Ideas

Agrimony (*Agrimonia eupatoria*)
The jovial, cheerful, humorous people who love peace and are distressed by argument or quarrel, to avoid which they will agree to give up much. Though generally they have troubles and are tormented and restless and worried in mind or in body, they hide their cares behind their humour and jesting and are considered very good friends to know. They often take alcohol or drugs in excess, to stimulate themselves and help themselves bear their trials with cheerfulness.
Summary: those who hide worries behind a brave face.

Centaury (*Centaurium umbellatum*)
Kind, quiet, gentle people who are over-anxious to serve others. They overtax their strength in their endeavours. Their wish so grows upon them that they become more servants than willing helpers. Their good nature leads them to do more than their own share of work, and in so doing they may neglect their own

particular mission in life.
Summary: weak willed; exploited or imposed upon.

Walnut (*Juglans regia*)

For those who have definite ideals and ambitions in life and are fulfilling them, but on rare occasions are tempted to be led away from their own ideas, aims and work by the enthusiasm, convictions or strong opinions of others. The remedy gives constancy and protection from outside influences.
Summary: assists in adjustment to transition or change, eg puberty, menopause, divorce, new surroundings.

Holly (*Ilex aquifolium*)

For those who are sometimes attacked by thoughts of such kind as jealousy, envy, revenge, suspicion. For the different forms of vexation. Within themselves they may suffer much, often when there is no real cause for their unhappiness.
Summary: hatred, envy, jealousy, suspicion.

For Despondency or Despair

Larch (*Larix decidua*)

For those who do not consider themselves as good or as capable as those around them, who expect failure, who feel that they will never be a success, and so do not venture or make a strong enough effort to succeed.
Summary: lack of self-confidence. Feels inferior. Fears failure.

Pine (*Pinus sylvestris*)

For those who blame themselves. Even when successful they think they could have done better, and are never content with their efforts or the results. They are hard working and suffer much from the faults they attach to themselves. Sometimes if there is any mistake it is due to another, but they will claim responsibility even for that.
Summary: guilt complex - blames self even for mistakes of others. Always apologising.

Elm (*Ulmus procera*)

Those who are doing good work, are following the calling of their life and who hope to do something of importance, and this is often for the benefit of humanity. At times there may be periods of depression when they feel that the task they have undertaken is too difficult, and not within the power of a human being.

Summary: overwhelmed by inadequacy and responsibility.

Sweet Chestnut (*Castanea sativa*)

For those moments which happen to some people when the anguish is so great as to seem to be unbearable. When the mind or body feels as if it had borne to the uttermost limit of its endurance, and that now it must give way. When it seems there is nothing but destruction and annihilation left to face.

Summary: utter dejection, bleak outlook.

Star of Bethlehem (*Ornithogalum umbetelatum*)

For those in great distress under conditions which for a time produce great unhappiness. The shock of serious news, the loss of someone dear, the fright following an accident and such like. For those who for a time refuse to be consoled, this remedy brings comfort.

Summary: for all the effects of serious news, or fright following an accident, etc.

Willow (*Salix vitellina*)

For those who have suffered adversity or misfortune and find these difficult to accept, without complaint or resentment, as they judge life much by the success which it brings. They feel that they have not deserved so great a trial, that it was unjust, and they become embittered. They often take less interest and are less active in those things of life which they had previously enjoyed.

Summary: resentment, embitterment, "poor old me!".

Oak (*Quercus robur*)

For those who are struggling and fighting strongly to get well, or in connection with the affairs of their daily life. They will go on trying one thing after another, though their case may seem hopeless. They will fight on. They are discontented with themselves if illness interferes with their duties or helping others. They are brave people, fighting against great difficulties, without loss of hope or effort.

Summary: normally strong/courageous, but no longer able to struggle bravely against illness and/or adversity.

Crab Apple (*Malus pumila*)

This is the remedy of cleansing. For those who feel as if they have had something not quite clean about themselves. Often it is something of apparently little importance: in others there may be more serious disease which is almost disregarded compared to the one thing on which they concentrate. In both types they are anxious to be free from the one particular thing which is greatest in their minds and which seems so essential to them that it should be cured. They become despondent if treatment fails.

Being a cleanser, this remedy purifies wounds if the patient has reason to believe that some poison has entered which must be drawn out.

Summary: the "cleanser". Self disgust/detestation. Ashamed of ailments.

Over-care for the Welfare of Others

Chicory (*Cichorium intybus*)

Those who are mindful of the needs of others they tend to be over-full of care of children, relatives, friends, always finding something that should be put right. They are continually correcting what they consider wrong, and enjoy doing so. They desire that those for whom they care should be near them.

Summary: over possessive - (self-centered) - clinging and over protective especially of loved ones.

Vervain (*Verbena officinalis*)
Those with fixed principles and ideas, which they are confident
are right, and which they very rarely change. They have a great
wish to convert all around them to their own views of life. They
are strong of will and have much courage when they are
convinced of those things that they wish to teach. In illness
they struggle on long after many would have given up their
duties.
Summary: over enthusiasm - fanatical beliefs.

Vine (*Vitis vinifera*)
Very capable people, certain of their own ability, confident of
success. Being so assured, they think it would be for the benefit
of others if they could be persuaded to do things as they
themselves do, or as they are certain is right. Even in illness
they will direct their attendants. They may be of great value in
emergency.
Summary: dominating/ inflexible/ tyrannical/ autocratic/
arrogant. Usually good leaders.

Beech (*Fagus sylvatica*)
For those who need to see more good and beauty in all that
surrounds them. And, although much appears to be wrong, to
have the ability to see the good growing within. So as to be able
to be more tolerant, lenient and understanding of the different
way each individual and all things are working to their own
final perfection.
Summary: critical and intolerant of others.

Rock Water (*Aqua petra*)
Those who are very strict in their way of living; they deny
themselves many of the joys and pleasures of life because they
consider it might interfere with their work. They are hard
masters to themselves. They wish to be well and strong and
active, and will do anything which they believe will keep them
so. They hope to be examples which will appeal to others who
may then follow their ideas and be better as a result.
Summary: rigid minded, self denying.

Dosages

The stock concentrates sold by shops and practitioners (10ml bottles) will keep indefinitely. They can be taken by people of all ages, there is no danger of overdose or side effects, and if the wrong remedy is taken, there will be no harmful repercussions. They will not be influenced by, nor will they affect, any form of prescribed medication or alternative remedy.

First, determine your personality and temperament (it might be useful to ask a close friend to help you with this, or you can consult a Bach practitioner), your fears, worries, emotional upsets and your outlook and attitudes. More than one remedy can be taken at a time, but should be limited to no more than six.

Take two drops from each chosen stock bottle in a cup of water, fruit juice, or any beverage, and sip fairly frequently. Replenish the cup to continue treatment if need be. Hold the dose a moment or so in the mouth before swallowing to gain the full effect.

Alternatively, you can put the drops in a bottle (preferably a glass bottle) of approximately 1 fl.oz. (30ml) capacity and fill up with natural spring water (non-gas) and take four drops directly on the tongue from the bottle. Take as often as needed, but at least four times a day, especially first thing in the morning and last thing at night. Hold the dose a moment or so in the mouth before swallowing to gain the full effect. Such a prepared dosage bottle will remain fresh for about three weeks if stored in a cool place. Dosage drops can also be added to a baby's bottle or taken in a spoonful of water.

The Composite Rescue Remedy®

Dr Bach combined five specific remedies from the thirty eight to formulate an emergency composite that he chose to call "Rescue Remedy"®.

Its purpose is to treat the pre or post emotional effect that a sufferer may experience through shock, great fear or terror, panic, severe mental stress and tension, a feeling of desperation or a numbed, bemused state of mind.

To nullify the sufferer's shock and fear is of the utmost importance in helping the natural healing process of one's own being to proceed without hindrance. Shock, terror and panic can manifest in minor traumas as well as in the more serious states of emergency. A brief definition of "emergency" would be eg. when in mental or physical shock, terror and panic, various emotional upsets (bereavement, stage fright, visiting the dentist, general nervous debility, trauma etc.). Even severe bites and stings create the effects of shock and panic.

Rescue Remedy can be taken along with any of the other thirty eight remedies if required.

Note: it has to be remembered that each of the five remedies used in this composite can be equally efficient when taken as a separate entity as and when required.

Rescue Remedy can be included along with the others when needed, but use four drops instead of two as indicated for other remedies, and also count it as a single stock remedy rather than the five from which it is composed. When required for immediate or emergency use as a separate remedy, take four drops in a cup of water and sip at intervals. If the sufferer is unable to swallow, or in a comatose state, then the lips, behind the ears and the wrists should be moistened with the remedy.

Note: If liquid is totally unavailable, then drops can be taken from the stock concentrate, but it must be emphasised for the benefit of abstainers, that this would mean a direct intake of brandy.

Note: it does not take the place of medical attention.

External Application. For burns, scalds, stings, sprains etc. - apply a couple of drops direct from the Rescue Remedy stock bottle immediately to the affected area.

There is also available *Rescue Remedy Cream* (non-lanolin, Homeopathically prepared base) for ulcers, lacerations, burns, scalds, sprains, massage and many other needs.

Treatment of Animals

One can sometimes assess a particular personality trait or definite temperamental attitude in animals (aggressiveness, possessiveness, lethargy, timidity, jealous etc.) and so they, as with humans, can be treated accordingly with one or more of the thirty eight remedies. The Rescue Remedy, although not being considered a panacea for all ills as far as humans are concerned, does act as an excellent all purpose basic remedy for animals, who react very favourably to this remedy irrespective of the state or cause of suffering.

Dosage: four drops of the Rescue Remedy stock concentrate (plus two drops from any other chosen remedy) in the animal's drink. A dilution can also be sprinkled over its food. For larger creatures needing to drink out of a bucket, the dosage would be in proportion to approximately ten drops per gallon. Four drops on a cube of sugar might be appropriate with some animals.

Appendix Three

The Mineral Tissue Salts Described

The tissue salts were developed by Dr Wilhelm Heinrich Schuessler in 1873. He was a medical doctor and a Homeopath. He began investigating the structure of the body's cells and noticed that when his patients were ill, their cells were deficient in certain minerals. These minerals exist in minute, but measurable, quantities and Dr Scheussler's researches led him to the conclusion that by re-introducing these minerals, the body's cells would return to normal and the illness eased. Over many years of experimentation and observation of his patients, his theories were proved to be largely correct. In recent years, other researches into body cell construction are leading doctors to the conclusion that trace minerals do play a major roll in the body's health. In this way, Dr Schuessler was very much ahead of his time.

The Tissue Salts (also sometimes known as Schuessler's Salts or cell-salts) are included here because they help the body to recover from illness at a much faster rate than would normally be the case from prescribed medication or even alternative remedies.

The Salts are prepared in exactly the same way as Homeopathic medicines and are contained within a lactose based carrier.

Note: if you have a milk allergy or are sensitive to milk products, then these salts should be taken with care and stopped if you have an adverse reaction.

The salts should also be taken in the same way as Homeopathic remedies, they should not be touched with the fingers but "tapped" into the lid of the container and placed into the mouth from the lid.

There are twelve single tissue salts and eighteen combination tissue salts, each of which are taken for specific conditions. As with Bach Flower Remedies, they can be taken by virtually anyone and either by themselves or in combination with any other remedy or medication. You cannot overdose on these salts as they are natural components of the body's make up. If you take too many, the body rejects what it doesn't need and it passes out of the body in urine.

The body contains many substances which help it to function normally, most of these occur in minute quantities but can play a major role in the body's wellbeing. Altogether, there are about twenty minerals which the body needs and which are not synthesized by the body itself but are extracted from our food and drink. Plants, animals, etc. take their nourishment directly from the earth, these nutrients and minerals are then stored within their cells which become unlocked in our digestive system, allowing the body to extract the minerals it needs.

The Tissue Salts are listed below in the order in which Dr Schuessler listed them. Each are numbered and then named. The first name is the name by which the salts are normally known. The second name is the salt's full latin name from which the abbreviated name is taken. The third is the mineral name and, finally, its chemical formula eg. 6 (number). *Kali. Phos.* (normal name); *Kali phosphoricum* (full latin name); *Potassium phosphate* (mineral name); K_2SO_4 (chemical formula).

The Single Mineral Tissue Salts

1. Calc. Fluor.; Calcerea fluorica; Calcium fluoride; CaF_2

In nature this occurs, as do all other minerals, in the earth and in the rocks. In the body it occurs in the bones, the teeth, the walls of blood vessels and all connective "holding" tissues. Deficiency of this salt leads to upset of the above body components. These can, of course, lead to many body upsets if neglected. Therefore, more than one salt may be needed to be taken in a particular case, but Calc. Fluor. is for maintaining tissue elasticity. The main indicators for Calc. Fluor. deficiency are: varicose veins, varicose ulcers, piles (haemorrhoids), over relaxed tissues, flabbiness (or giving way and sagging of tissues, such as hernias and prolapse), poor teeth, late development of teeth in infants and children, deficient tooth enamel.

2. Calc. Phos.; Calcarea phosphorica; Calcium phosphate; $Ca_3(PO_4)_2$

This mineral occurs in bones and teeth and also in soft tissue but is mainly concerned with bony structures in general. Deficiency of this salt is seen in the following conditions: slow healing of fractures, bony deformities, delay in teething and general teething problems, some types of anaemia (calcium is important for the proper formation of blood), poor nutrition and digestion, coldness, cramps, chilblains, liability to colds and catarrh, children outgrowing their strength, chronic tonsillitis, some skin diseases (catarrhal types), polypus (growths of polyps within the body), coccydynia (persistent pain in the tail region of the spine, usually following the fracture of the small bones of the coccyx), hypochondriasis (when you always think you have a serious illness which is not the case).

In several of the above, other salts should also be taken (see combinations below). With a Calc. Phos. deficiency state, patients are usually made worse by coldness, coffee, tobacco and excessive self contemplation of the symptoms. Hypochondriasis is due to the fact that the phosphorous balance is essential for the proper functioning of the nervous system. Calc. Phos. deficiency sufferers are usually helped by dry, sunny weather and by bed rest.

3. Calc. Sulph.; Calcarea sulphurica; Calcium sulphate; $CaSO_4$

In the body, this mineral occurs in connective tissue, as a blood constituent and also in the liver cells (this is in connection with the liver function of removing worn out blood cells). A Calc. Sulph. deficiency impairs the blood cleansing function and other connected disorders can arise as well as disorders of connective tissues (this is the name given to material which holds other tissues together. It is found in organs, cartilege, bone, tooth dentine, lymphoid tissue, etc.) The following conditions occur with a Calc. Sulph deficiency: pimples during adolescence, boils, skin eruptions, skin slow to heal, catarrh, dandruff, falling hair, vertigo with nausea, sore lips, gum boils, neuralgia, frontal headaches (especially in elderly people), pancreatic upsets, liver upsets, kidney upsets.

4. Ferr. Phos.; Ferrum phosphoricum; Iron phosphate; $Fe_3(PO_4)_2$

This salt is found in all of the tissues of the body, but mainly the red blood cells. The iron is concerned with the oxygen carrying capacity of the blood. Its use in the muscles of the blood vessels is apparent when there is a deficiency as the walls relax leading to congestion and inflammation. Ferr. Phos. is used for all cases of inflammation, that is conditions ending in "itis" eg. bronchitis. It will be helpful in the first stages of these conditions and in more advanced stages, should be used in combination with N°5 - Kali. Mur..

Ferr. Phos. is a good childrens remedy. It is helpful in healing many of their illnesses and can frequently put them right before an orthodox diagnosis is necessary - however, if there is the slightest doubt about a condition you should seek medical assistance.

Ferr. Phos. is used for the following conditions: all minor respiratory disorders, childhood illnesses (measles, scarlet fever, etc.), the first stages of all inflammations and fevers, congestions, haemorrhage, nose bleed, excessive periods, throbbing, congested headaches, inflammatory rheumatism, coughs and colds, chills and feverishness, chestiness (alternate with Kali. Mur.), constipation or diahorrea (especially in children).

Ferr. Phos. is the most commonly used of the tissue salts. The tablets can also be crushed to a powder and applied directly onto small cuts to promote a more rapid healing.

5. Kali. Mur.; Kali muriaticum; Potassium chloride; KC_l

A deficiency in this salt affects the lower layer of the skin. This is the layer which exudes pus into pimples etc.. Kali. Mur. is used for second stage inflammatory illnesses. The salt is used for the following conditions: second stage of inflammation of all "itis" illnesses, minor respiratory disorders, coughs, cold symptoms and wheeziness, chestiness (in alternation with Ferr. Phos. for children's feverish colds), prior to vaccination to help eliminate side effects, chickenpox, scarlet fever, mumps, measles, white/grey coating of tongue, catarrh, eczema - especially infantile, warts, acne, constipation (in liverish states and in pregnancy), diarrhoea due to fatty foods, piles, menorrhagia (abnormally heavy and prolonged periods. Although this condition can be treated with this salt, you should always consult your doctor or a qualified therapist), leucorrhoea (a whitish vaginal discharge of mucous), shingles, burns and scalds.

A good indicator of a deficiency in this salt is that conditions are usually made worse by eating fatty foods.

6. Kali. Phos.; Kali phosphoricum; Potassium phosphate; K_2HPO_4

Kali. Phos. is the remedy for the nervous system and is the great nerve soother - phosphorus being the chief nerve mineral.

It is used for all nervous disorders and those that are so often called "neurotic" illnesses. From the presence of Kali. Phos. in other tissues of the body come its uses in the following conditions: all temporary nerviness, melancholia, hysteria, highly strung, fearfulness, despair, timidity and shyness, loss of mental and nerve power, nervous debility, emotional strain, excessive blushing, neuritis (inflammation of a nerve or nerves), incontinence or retention of urine from nervous causes, nightmares - all "unjustified" fears, inability to sleep, nervous indigestion, nervous diahorrea, nervous headache, alopecia (hair loss leading to baldness), nervous asthma, menstrual colic (spasms, cramps, etc.), ineffectual labour pains from anxiety, impotence and frigidity.

Patients requiring this remedy are usually made worse by noises and moving about, when left alone too long, or when they become over excited. They are helped by soothing company and conversation on uncontroversial topics. The remedy is useful at some stage in an illness both for the patient and for their loved ones.

7. Kali. Sulph.; Kali sulphuricum; Potassium sulphate; K_2SO_4

This tissue salt is found in the external layers of epithelial membranes (these are the outer layers of cells for virtually all of the surfaces of the body. This is a non-stick layer which allows for the free passage of liquids etc.. It is also the outer layer of the skin). The shedding of this layer causes yellow catarrh and the shedding of the outer layers of the skin. It is connected with the third stage of "itis" diseases.

It is also concerned with oxygen distribution within the body. Kali. Sulph. is used for the following conditions: the third stage of all inflammations, bronchitis, yellow coating of the tongue, thick yellow mucous catarrh, whooping cough, gastric catarrh, intestinal catarrh, asthma, colic (if the response to Mag. Phos. is poor), menstrual disorders, to help maintain healthy hair, dandruff, foul breath, measles, eczema, psoriasis, brittle nails, minor skin eruptions with scaling or sticky deposits, flashes of heat and chilliness, giddiness of inflammatory type, palpitations, headaches.

Patients requiring Kali. Sulph. are usually worse in hot weather.

8. Mag. Phos.; Magnesia phosphorica; Magnesium phosphate; $MgHPO_4.7H_2O$.

Mag. Phos. is found in similar tissues to Calc. Phos. ie. bones, teeth and nerve tissue, as well as in blood vessels and muscles, but basically it is a soft tissue salt. Deficiency of this salt leads to cramp-like conditions and collicky states and so it is known as the anti-spasmodic tissue salt. It is used for the following conditions: muscle cramps and spasms, minor occasional pain, hiccups, spasmodic shivers and twitching, intermittent retention of urine and bladder spasm, enlarged prostate, writer's cramp and similar conditions, stuttering, crampy labour pains, painful menstruation, ovarian neuralgia, gallstone colic, kidney stone colic, teething in infants, flatulence, intercostal neuralgia (pain around the rib cage), headaches, toothache where pains are sharp, shooting and boring, rheumatic pains, neuralgia generally. Mag. Phos. patients are often lean, nervous people. Pains are usually made worse from cold and touch and helped by warmth, pressure and bending.

9. Nat. Mur.; Natrum muriaticum; Sodium chloride; NaCl

Nat. Mur. is based upon a mineral called sodium chloride, or common table salt. We need one gramme of the crude salt per day but the average intake is ten grammes daily. This excessive intake creates havoc with many people and Nat. Mur. helps to put right this imbalance. Nat. Mur. occurs in all tissue fluids in the body and is often regarded as the most important of the twelve salts. It is a distributor and controller of water throughout the body. It is used in the following conditions: circulation problems, shock, watery vomiting, diarrhoea, minor haemorrhage, anaemia (you should always seek professional help for this condition), watery colds with flow of tears and runny nose, loss of smell, loss of taste, prolapse (with Calc. Fluor.) eg. shingles, herpes and blisters, insect stings and bites generally, thin watery milk in breast feeding, excessive size of breasts in pregnancy, hydrocoele (fluid around the testicles), excessive tears, excessive salivation, teething with excessive salivation, water brash (sudden, unexpected secretion of a quantity of saliva into the mouth), sneezing, hay fever, influenza, asthma, constipation (dry stools), headaches (early morning type), hysteria, sterility, nettle rash, chronic eczema, acne, greasy skin, ulcer of the gums, gout, sciatica, sunstroke.

10. Nat. Phos.; Natrum phosphoricum; Sodium phosphate; $Na_2HPO_4.2H_2O$.

This salt occurs in the fluid between cells and in the body tissues. It has two main types of action within the body: it controls acid generally (sometimes called the acid neutraliser) and it helps deal with fatty acids. Its first action is to deal with uric acid and lactic acid etc. helping to treat or deal with acid states. Its second usage is to help in dyspepsia (indigestion) due to excessive intake of fatty foods. It is used for the following conditions: all acid states of the bloodstream (uric acid dialysis), rheumatism of joints, rheumatic arthritis, gout, acid taste, to help prevention of gallstones, sick headaches, giddiness, conjunctivitis, itching of the nose, red, blotchy face, sea sickness (with Kali. Phos.), sour breath, grinding of teeth during sleep, yellow coated tongue, catarrh and thick yellow mucous, heartburn, nausea, morning sickness of pregnancy, gastric indigestion, sour flatulence, loss of appetite, constipation, diarrhoea, acidity, incontinence from acidity, sterility from acidity, leucorrhoea - sour smelling, sleeplessness from itching in acid states, rheumatic pain tendency.

Patients requiring Nat. Phos. are made worse by fats and sugars (sweets in children). Reducing their intake is usually helpful.

11. Nat. Sulph.; Natrum sulphuricum; Sodium sulphate; Na$_2$SO$_4$.10H$_2$O.

This salt mainly occurs in the spaces between the cells, but in a different way to Nat. Mur.. Nat. Sulph. appears to eliminate water and helps in removing dead cells. Nat. Sulph. is used for the following conditions: to help with the body's water balance, biliousness of a watery nature, vomiting in pregnancy, diarrhoea, constipation, grey or greenish/brown tongue, bitter taste in the mouth, liver upsets, gall bladder upsets, kidney upsets, pancreatic upsets, rheumatism in "watery" patients, gout in "watery" patients, asthma of a watery nature, bronchial catarrh, flu symptoms, hay fever, warts, ear noise and earache from fluid retention, flatulence and colic, distended stomach, queasiness, digestive upsets, hydrocoele. Patients needing Nat. Sulph. are usually worse in damp weather and feel better in dry conditions, hot or cold.

12. Silica; Silicea; Silicon Dioxide; SiO$_2$.

This salt occurs in the connective tissues and disturbance of its balance affects the nervous system from its presence in the coverings of nerve fibres. Disturbance of the silica content of the body usually ends in the formation of pus (note that Calc. Sulph. has a rather different action). Silica can be thought of as a conditioner and cleanser.

It is also a preventative in premature ageing - a lack of this salt causes atrophy of tissues. In food, silica is found in wholemeal bread and can be thought of as the "grit" of our diet. Silica is used in the following conditions: lack of stamina - both physical and mental, absent-mindedness, poor memory (see also Kali. Phos.), sweaty feet, all sweats of an unpleasant nature, alcoholic intolerance, falling out of hair, brittle nails (can be taken in alternation with Kali. Sulph.), eye strain, asthma from dust, pimples and spots, styes, fissures, boils, chronic bronchitis, coccydynia, alopecia, whitlows (an inflammation and infection of the fleshy part of the finger tips also a herpes type infection around the finger nails), ingrowing toe nails, premature ageing. Patients needing Silica are usually worse at night and suffer from the feet becoming cold. They are usually helped by a warm atmosphere and hot baths.

These are the twelve tissue salts. They are readily available from health food shops, just follow the instructions on the container. The salts can be taken with any other remedy or medication and it is impossible to overdose. The containers will carry a potency strength which is usually 6x, this refers to the number of times that the salts have been triturationed. This is a Homeopathic term and is explained in detail under the description of Homeopathic remedies.

The Combination Mineral Tissue Salts

Combination Remedy A
This remedy contains the tissue salts Ferr. Phos., Kali. Phos. and Mag. Phos.. It is used for sciatica, neuralgia and neuritis.

Combination Remedy B
This remedy contains the tissue salts Calc. Phos., Kali. Phos. and Ferr. Phos.. It is used for general debility, edginess, nervous exhaustion and convalescence.

Combination Remedy C
This remedy contains the tissue salts Mag. Phos., Nat. Phos., Nat. Sulph. and Silica. It is used for acidity, heartburn and dyspepsia.

Combination Remedy D
This remedy contains the tissue salts Kali. Mur., Kali. Sulph., Calc. Sulph. and Silica. It is used for minor skin ailments, scalp eruptions, eczema, acne and scaling of the skin.

Combination Remedy E
This remedy contains the tissue salts Calc. Phos., Mag. Phos., Nat. Phos. and Nat. Sulph.. It is used for flatulence, colicky pains and indigestion.

Combination Remedy F

This remedy contains the tissue salts Kali. Phos., Nat. Mur. and Silica. It is used for nervous headaches and migraine.

Combination Remedy G

This remedy contains the tissue salts Calc. Fluor., Calc. Phos., Kali. Phos. and Nat. Mur.. It is used for backache, lumbago and piles.

Combination Remedy H

This remedy contains the tissue salts Mag. Phos., Nat. Mur. and Silica. It is used for hayfever and allied conditions.

Combination Remedy I

This remedy contains the tissue salts Ferr. Phos., Kali. Sulph. and Mag. Phos.. It is used for fibrositis and muscular pain.

Combination Remedy J

This remedy contains the tissue salts Ferr. Phos., Kali. Mur. and Nat. Mur.. It is used for coughs, colds and chestiness and is the autumn and winter seasonal remedy.

Combination Remedy K

This remedy contains the tissue salts Kali. Sulph., Nat. Mur. and Silica. It is used for brittle nails and falling hair.

Combination Remedy L

This remedy contains the tissue salts Calc. Fluor., Ferr. Phos. and Nat. Mur.. It is used for sedentary lifestyle, toning the tissues and is a natural tonic.

Combination Remedy M

This remedy contains the tissue salts Calc. Phos., Kali. Mur., Nat. Phos. and Nat. Sulph.. It is used for rheumatic pains.

Combination Remedy N

This remedy contains the tissue salts Calc. Phos., Kali. Mur., Kali. Phos. and Mag. Phos.. It is used for menstrual pain.

Combination Remedy P
This remedy contains the tissue salts Calc. Fluor., Calc. Phos., Kali. Phos. and Mag. Phos.. It is used for aching feet and legs.

Combination Remedy Q
This remedy contains the tissue salts Ferr. Phos., Kali. Mur., Kali. Sulph. and Nat. Mur.. It is used for catarrh and sinus disorders.

Combination Remedy R
This remedy contains the tissue salts Calc. Fluor., Calc. Phos., Ferr. Phos., Mag. Phos. and Silica. It is used for infants teething pains.

Combination Remedy S
This remedy contains the tissue salts Kali. Mur., Nat. Phos. and Nat. Sulph.. It is used for stomach upsets, biliousness, queasiness, sick headaches and is the summer seasonal remedy.

Special Combinations
There are some further special combinations that have been formulated for particularly troublesome conditions. Again, these are very readily available and may be extremely helpful if you suffer from the particular problem at which they are aimed.

Elasto
This contains Calc. Fluor., Calc. Phos., Ferr. Phos. and Mag. Phos.. This has a very large following from people who suffer from troublesome problems with the legs, in particular tired and aching legs or varicose veins. It derives its name from its benefits to the elastic tissues in the body.

Nervone
This contains Calc. Phos., Kali. Mur., Kali. Phos., Mag. Phos. and Nat. Phos.. The formulation may be used for nerve pains and for nervous disability. It is a safe and reliable remedy for a whole range of "nerve troubles" and allied ailments.

Zief

This contains Ferr. Phos., Nat. Phos., Nat. Sulph. and Silica. It is an effective remedy for rheumatic conditions.

Appendix Four

The Herbs Described

Throughout chapters fourteen to twenty, we have recommended a number of herbs. Set out below is a list of the herbs used and a description of their properties.

Herbs are much more gentle in their effects than manufactured drugs but this does not mean that they are harmless, read the cautions and use the recommended dosage. The remedies described here are primarily home remedies which will be most effective if used at the earliest possible onset of a problem, in combination with the nutritional recommendations.

When ordering your herbs, it is best to quote the full latin name as some herbs belong to a large family and have many sub-species which deal with a variety of complaints.

If you have any doubts at all, or fit into any of the following categories, you should consult with a qualified herbalist:

1. If you are pregnant.

2. If you are taking prescribed medication.

3. If you have a chronic (long term) condition.

4. If an acute (short term) condition does not remit (ease off) within a sensible time or worsens.

Herbs are available in a variety of forms. These are fresh, dried, tincture, cream, ointment, oil, capsules, tablets, powders or extracts. Although we have generally suggested herbal teas throughout the remedy section, all of the herbs can be taken in tincture form. Many people find it easier to take a tincture in water than to make up an infusion from dried herbs. Most herbalists or herbal suppliers will be able to make up a tincture combining any combination of herbs. Try to find a herbal supplier who is as organic as possible as many commercially produced herbs are subjected to the same kinds of chemicals and treatments as other commercially produced crops.

Agnus-castus (*Vitex agnus-castus* - chaste tree berry)
Parts used: fruits, fresh or dried in decoctions, tinctures or powders.
Properties: A pungent, mildly astringent, relaxant herb which affects the hormonal balance both in men and women; promotes lactation and relieves spasms and pain. **Caution: not suitable for pregnant women.**

Alfalfa (*Medicago sativa*)
Parts used: herbage (dried for infusions), leaves (used fresh), seeds (are germinated for 3-6 days for eating raw - sprouted).
Properties: an astringent, cooling, diuretic herb that cleanses toxins from the tissues, controls bleeding, and promotes absorption of nutrients. It works mainly on the circulatory and urinary systems and influences hormones. Contains chlorophyll, alpha and beta-carotene, B-complex vitamins, vitamins A, C, D, E, and K (fresh raw form to obtain vitamins - sprouts are especially effective) and minerals such as calcium, potassium, magnesium, zinc, phosphorus, sulphur, copper and iron.

Aniseed (*Pimpinella anisum*)
Parts used: leaves (used fresh), fruits/seeds (either distilled for oil, used whole, ground or distilled in water, infusions and spirit).
Properties: A sweet, spicy, stimulant herb which benefits the liver and circulation; improves digestion; clears mucous from air passages (expectorant), fights infection, and is helpful for menopausal problems. It can also be used as a culinary herb.

Artichoke (*Cynara scolymus*)
Parts used: leaves and root which are used fresh or dried in liquid extracts, syrup and tablets. The flower heads are used as vegetables.
Properties: a bitter, slightly salty herb that detoxifies and regenerates liver tissue and stimulates the gall bladder.

Balmony (*Chelone glabra*)
Parts used: herbage, which is dried for infusions, tincture, powder, and liquid extracts.
Properties: a bitter herb that acts mainly as a tonic for the liver and digestive system. It also has a laxative effect.

Bearberry (*Arctostaphylos uva-ursi*)
Parts used: leaves, which are dried for infusions, tablets, liquid extracts, and medicinal teabags.
Properties: an astringent herb that is anti-bacterial and an effective urinary antiseptic (useful for treating cystitis/bladder infection). Helps disorders of the spleen, liver, pancreas, and small intestines. **Caution: not to be taken by pregnant women, or children, or patients with kidney disease.**

Bilberries (*Vaccinum myrtillus*)
Parts used: leaves (dried for decoctions), fruits (dried for decoctions and liquid extract, and culinary use).
Properties: an astringent, cooling diuretic herb that has a tonic effect on the blood; helps to control insulin levels and strengthen connective tissue; acts as a diuretic and urinary tract antiseptic; useful for some eye problems. **Caution: do not use leaves for more than three weeks at a time.**

Black Cohosh (*Cimicifuga racemosa*)
Parts used: rhizomes, roots, which are best used fresh in tinctures, and are also dried for use in decoctions, liquid extracts and tinctures.
Properties: a bitter herb that controls coughing (reduces mucous production), lowers fever, soothes aches and pains, and stimulates the uterus, tones pelvic muscles, and helps

digestion. Useful for bronchial infections, menstrual and menopausal problems, labour and post partum pains, arthritis and rheumatic diseases. **Caution: not to be taken during pregnancy until birth is imminent or whilst breast feeding, or if you have flooding.**

Boneset (*Eupatorium perfoliatum*)
Parts used: whole plant, which is dried for infusions, liquid extracts, and tinctures.
Properties: a bitter herb that lowers fever, relieves bronchial congestion, loosens phlegm, acts as a laxative, has anti-inflammatory properties, and stimulates the immune system.

Buchu (*Agathosma betulina*)
Parts used: leaves, dried for infusions, liquid extracts, tablets and tinctures.
Properties: an aromatic herb that cleanses and stimulates the urinary system. The active ingredient is diosphenol, which is a potent antiseptic and diuretic. Used internally for urinary tract infections (especially prostatitis and cystitis), digestive problems, fluid retention, coughs and colds, rheumatism. **Caution: do not use for long periods without supervision.**

Burdock (*Arctium lappa*)
Parts used: stems (used as a vegetable), roots (as a vegetable or dried for decoctions, liquid extracts, tablets or tinctures), seeds (decoctions).
Properties: a herb that purifies the blood, reduces inflammation, controls bacterial infection, stimulates the immune system; helps liver and gall bladder function; helpful for skin disorder.

Cardamom (*Elettaria cardamomum*)
Parts used: seeds (dried for oil extraction, liquid extracts, powders, tinctures). The seeds are also used for culinary purposes.
Properties: a warm, pungent herb that has stimulating, tonic

effects, especially on the lungs and kidneys. It is helpful for flatulence, nausea and vomiting, headaches. It improves digestion and relaxes spasms.

Cascara sagrada (*Rhamnus purshiana*)
Parts used: bark, which is dried for one or two years before use in decoctions, liquid extracts, powders, and tablets.
Properties: a bitter, astringent herb that has a tonic effect on the liver and digestive system; acts as a colon cleanser, toner and laxative; also useful for parasitic infestation.

Cayenne (*Capsicum annuum var. annuum* - red pepper, sweet pepper, chili pepper)
Parts used: berries, used fresh, or dried for condiments, decoctions, ointments, powders, tinctures and tablets.
Properties: has tonic and antiseptic effects; aids digestion; stops bleeding from ulcers; improves circulation; good for the heart, kidneys, lungs, spleen and stomach; good for sinus problems; used as a poultice, it is good for localised pain relief. Acts as a catalyst for other herbs.

Celery (*Apium graveolens* - wild)
Parts used: herbage (liquidized to extract juice), roots (used fresh or dried for tinctures), seeds - make sure seeds are free from fungicide (dried for infusions, liquid extract, powders or distilled for oil).
Properties: a bitter, tonic herb that relieves indigestion, reduces blood pressure, has diuretic and anti-inflammatory effects and stimulates the uterus. Good for arthritis, rheumatoid arthritis, gout, and inflammation of the urinary tract. Acts as an antioxidant and sedative. Contains Vitamins B-Complex, A and C. **Caution: do not use in large amounts during pregnancy**.

Centaury (*Erythraea Centaurium*)
Parts used: herbage, which is dried for infusions and liquid extracts.
Properties: a very bitter herb which stimulates the secretions

and peristalsis of the intestinal tract; stimulates the appetite promotes digestion, and lowers fever. It contains bitter glycosides that stimulate the gall bladder and liver, increasing bile flow and improving digestion. **Caution: not to be taken by pregnant women.**

Chamomile (*Matricaria Chamomilla*)
Parts used: flowers, when fresh are distilled for oil, when dried, used for infusions, liquid extracts, and creams.
Properties: a bitter, aromatic herb that has an anti-inflammatory effect; has sedative qualities that act on the intestinal tract; an appetite stimulant; a nerve tonic. Chamomile tea is probably one of the most popular tisanes for its calming, soothing effect, particularly on restless children. **Caution; should not be used for long periods at a time as this may lead to ragweed allergy; do not use if allergic to ragweed.**

Chickweed (*Stellaria media*)
Parts used: herbage, used fresh as juice or poultices, fresh or dried as infusions, liquid extract, medicated oils, ointments, tinctures.
Properties: a soothing, cooling and slightly saline herb that relieves itching, promotes healing. It is useful for bronchitis and circulatory problems and has anti-rheumatic effects. Externally, very useful for skin diseases such as eczema, psoriasis, ulcers, boils, abscesses and for vaginitis. Can be used in salads or cooked as a vegetable. The leaves contain Vitamin C, B6, Bl2 and D as well as minerals such as choline, copper, biotin and phosphorus.

Cinnamon
Parts used: dried inner bark (infusions, tinctures, powders), branches and leafy twigs (distilled for oil).
Properties: a pungent, sweet, hot herb that aids the peripheral circulation of the blood; counteracts congestion; improves digestion, relieves spasms and vomiting; helps control infection - fights fungal infection, and is useful for yeast infections;

370

relieves diarrhoea and nausea. **Caution: not to be taken during pregnancy or when nursing.**

Cleavers (*Galium aparine* - goosegrass)
Parts used: whole plant, seeds, which are dried for infusions, liquid extract or tablets.
Properties: a bitter, cooling herb that has a diuretic, mild laxative and astringent effect and acts as a tonic for the lymphatic system (particularly useful for breast lumps/swollen lymph glands); promotes healing.

Coltsfoot (*Tussilago farfara*).
Parts used: leaves (fresh or dried for herbal tobaccos, liquid and solid extracts, and tinctures), flowers (fresh or dried in decoctions, liquid extracts, syrups and tinctures).
Properties: a bitter-sweet, expectorant herb. Controls coughing, soothes irritated tissue, relaxes spasms, reduces inflammation, and stimulates the immune system.

Comfrey (*Symphytum officinale*)
Parts used: leaves (dried for infusions, liquid extracts and poultices) root (dried for decoctions, liquid extracts and ointments).
Properties: a sweet, cooling, mucilaginous herb that has expectorant, astringent, healing and soothing effects; controls bleeding and reduces inflammation. Speeds healing of wounds and skin conditions. Comfrey contains allantoin, which promotes cell proliferation. **Caution: Comfrey root is subject to restriction in some countries. Comfrey leaf teas, and preparations for external use are considered safe but, there is advice against self medication of some comfrey products. Not to be taken during pregnancy.**

Cornsilk (*Zea mays* - maize)
Parts used: the silky tassel on the top of the corn (dried for use in decoctions, infusions, liquid extract and syrups).
Properties: a sweet, soothing herb, that is diuretic and stimulates bile flow; aids the kidneys, bladder and small

intestine. Good for premenstrual syndrome, cystitis, urinary tract and prostate problems.

Couchgrass (*Agropyron repens*)
Parts used: rhizomes (used fresh in homeopathic preparations or dried for decoctions, liquid extracts, and tinctures).
Properties: a soothing herb that improves excretion from kidneys and bowels; helps clear infection. Used internally for kidney and bladder complaints, cystitis, gout, and rheumatism. It is quite a strong diuretic.

Crampbark (*Viburnum opulus*)
Parts used: bark (dried for decoctions, liquid extracts and tinctures).
Properties: an astringent, sedative herb that regulates uterine function and relaxes spasms. Useful for painful menstruation, post partum and ovarian pain, hypertension, nervous constipation and muscular cramps. Contains Scopoletin, a coumarin that has a sedative effect on the uterus.

Damiana (*Turnera diffusa var. aphrodisiaca*)
Parts used: herbage, which is dried for use in compound mixtures, infusions, liquid extracts and tablets.
Properties: a pungent, bitter, warming herb. It helps regulates hormone function and stimulates the genito-urinary tract; improves digestion, calms the nerves, lifts the spirits, and rejuvenates kidney energy.

Dandelion (*Taraxacum officinale*)
Parts used: leaves/tops (fresh as a vegetable, juiced, or dried for infusions, tinctures and liquid extracts), roots (juiced, roasted or dried for decoctions, infusions, tinctures).
Properties: a bitter-sweet cooling herb with laxative, anti-rheumatic and diuretic effects.Cleanses the blood stream, stimulates liver function and improves digestion, the function of the stomach, pancreas, spleen and kidneys; reduces swelling and inflammation. It is are rich in antioxidant vitamins A and C, and minerals. The roots and leaves have culinary uses.

Devil's Claw (*Harpagophytum procumbens*)
Parts used: tubers (dried for decoctions, powders, ointments, tinctures).
Properties: a bitter, astringent, sedative and pain-killing herb that stimulates the digestive and lymphatic system, and reduces inflammation. Used internally for arthritis, rheumatoid arthritis, neuralgia, digestive problems involving the gall bladder and pancreas. **Caution: not given to people with gastric or duodenal ulcers, or during pregnancy.**

Echinacea (*angustifolia or purpurea*)
Both varieties have similar constituents and can be used interchangeably
Parts used: roots and rhizomes (dried for use in decoctions, infusions, powders, tablets, tinctures, liquid extract).
Properties: a bitter, alterative herb that stimulates the immune system and lymphatic system; has anti-bacterial and anti-viral effects and promotes healing. Useful for skin diseases, fungal infection, slow healing wounds, upper respiratory tract infections, the list is endless. Recommended as a boost to the immune system at the beginning of each season, particularly winter. Echinacea is more effective if it is taken for ten days at a time with a week off in between.

Elderberry/flower (*Sambucus nigra*)
Parts used: leaves (used fresh), bark (dried for decoctions), flowers (dried for infusions, floral water, ointments, tinctures), fruits (dried for decoctions, syrups, and tinctures).
Properties: a pungent, bitter, cooling herb that has anti-catarrhal, alterative, and diuretic effects and also reduces inflammation, soothes irritation, lowers fever, builds the blood, cleanses the system; enhances immune function and has powerful antioxidant properties.

Elecampane (*Inula helenium*)
Parts used: roots (used fresh to make extracts and syrup, dried for decoctions, powders and tinctures), flowers (dried for decoctions, infusions and powders).

Properties: a pungent, bitter, aromatic herb that is expectorant, diuretic, reduces inflammation, relaxes spasms and increases perspiration. It is effective against fungal and bacterial infections and acts as an alterative herb which cleanses toxins and stimulates the digestive and immune system. **Caution: not to be taken by pregnant women.**

Euphorbia pilulifera (asthma weed, pill-bearing spurge)

Parts used: herbage, which is dried for use in infusions, and tinctures.
Properties: an acrid, antiseptic herb that relieves spasms, wheezing and expels phlegm.

Evening Primrose (*Oenothera biennis*)

Parts used: oil. Ripe seeds are collected and pressed for the oil content.
Properties: an alterative herb, that regulates the hormonal system. Useful for skin disorders, such as eczema and acne, rheumatoid arthritis, coronary artery disease, premenstrual and menopausal syndromes and many other disorders. **Caution: should not be taken by pregnant women.**

Eyebright (Euphrasia officinalis - eyebright)

Parts used: herbage, which is dried for infusions, tinctures and homeopathic preparations.
Properties: an astringent herb that reduces inflammation. Particularly useful as an eyewash; relieves discomfort from eye strain or minor injury, irritation or allergy; also helpful for hayfever and upper respiratory tract problems.

False unicorn (*Chamaelirium luteum* - Fairy wand, Devil's bit)

Parts used: rhizomes, root (dried for infusions, tinctures and liquid extract).
Properties: an astringent, diuretic herb that acts mainly as a uterine and ovarian tonic. Balances sex hormones. Useful for treatment of menstrual and menopausal complaints, fibroids, infertility and prostate disorders.

Fennel (*Foeniculum vulgare*)
Parts used: leaves, bulb, seeds, stems are used for culinary purposes as well as medicinal. It is used in the form of an infusion, or in herbal teas and syrups. The seeds can be chewed to aid digestion and constipation.
Properties: a sweet, diuretic herb that relieves digestive problems, (acid, wind, colic) relaxes spasms, reduces inflammation, and increases milk flow. Promotes the functioning of the kidneys, liver, and spleen. It is recommended for use after chemotherapy or radiation treatment for cancer.

Feverfew (*Tanacetum parthenium*)
Parts used: whole plant, leaves (dried for infusions, powders, liquid extracts and tinctures).
Properties: a bitter, cooling, pungent, tonic herb that has laxative effects, improves digestion, relieves pain, relaxes spasms, lowers fever, dilates blood vessels, and stimulates the uterus. Useful for minor feverish illnesses, digestive and menstrual complaints. Feverfew has undergone a great deal of research and has proved to be an effective and relatively safe remedy in many cases of migraine and arthritis/rheumatism.
Caution: not to be taken by pregnant women.

Fumitory (*Fumaria officinalis* - earth smoke, wax dolls)
Parts used: flowering plant, which is dried for infusions, liquid extracts, tinctures and pills.
Properties: a bitter, tonic herb with mild diuretic and laxative effects, that improves liver and gall bladder function and helps reduce inflammation. Good for skin problems, including eczema and dermatitis and as a general liver cleanser.

Garlic (*Allium sativum*)
Parts used: bulbs. Fresh bulbs (crushed or as juice), or alcoholic extracts whose alliinase has been destroyed so that the preparation is odourless. It is available as a syrup, tinctures, or capsules.
Properties: a pungent herb that lowers fevers by increasing perspiration, improves circulation, regulates blood pressure so

that it treats both high and low blood pressure. Detoxifies the body and protects against infection by enhancing/boosting the immune system. Raw garlic contains a natural antibiotic and when crushed or chewed it releases the antibiotic chemical. Garlic has recently been found to reduce glucose metabolism in diabetes, slow the development of arteriosclerosis, and lower the risk of further heart attacks in myocardial infarction patients. It is good for virtually any disease or infection, ranging from a cold to cancer, a list too long to include here. Contains vitamins A, B1, B2, and C and many minerals including sulphur, germanium, iron, magnesium, manganese, phosphorus, potassium, selenium, zinc, copper, and calcium.

This herb has amazing properties and is a must in everyday use. Our recommendation, for the most benefit, is to eat it crushed, raw, in a drink or salad dressing. Chewing a few aniseed or fennel seeds, or fresh parsley, can eliminate garlic breath.

Ginger (*Zingiber officianale*)

Parts used: roots, rhizomes.

Properties: a strong antioxidant and antimicrobial agent for sores and wounds. It improves digestion, controls nausea, cleanses the colon, improves liver function, controls vomiting and coughing, stimulates circulation, relaxes spasms, and relieves pain. Useful for bowel disorders, colds, coughs, influenza, morning sickness, motion sickness, peripheral circulatory problems. **Caution: can cause stomach distress if taken in large quantities or if you already have a "hot" condition.**

Ginseng (*Panax*)

Ginseng is cultivated commercially in Korea, China, Russia and the USA. *Parts used:* the root.

P.ginseng (Asian or Oriental Ginseng)

Properties: a sweet, tonic herb that both relaxes and stimulates the nervous system, encourages secretion of hormones, lowers blood sugar and cholesterol levels, improves stamina and increases resistance to disease. **Caution: this herb is not usually prescribed for pregnant women, or patients under 40 years old, or with depression, anxiety, sleeplessness, or acute inflammatory disease. (After three weeks of use, it is best to take a break of a week or two).**

P.quinquefolius (American ginseng)
One of the best tonic herbs with similar properties to P.ginseng, but less stimulating and less strongly hormonal. Mainly prescribed for patients with yin energy deficiency, whereas Panax Ginseng is a yang tonic.

P.pseudo-ginseng
The flowers are sometimes used.
Properties: a sweet, slightly bitter, warming herb that reduces inflammation, improves circulation, relieves pain, has anti-bacterial effects, and helps control bleeding. **Caution: not to be taken if pregnant.**
Brazilian ginseng or Suma is the root of *Pfaffia paniculata*. It has long been used by native people as a cure-all and as an aphrodisiac. The ground root is taken as a tonic and is particularly useful during the menopause.
Siberian ginseng is the root of Eleutherococcus senticosus. It has similar, though stronger, active constituents to Panax species and is considered to be less heating than *P.ginseng*. **Caution: should not be given to children, taken longer than three weeks at a time, or if you have high blood pressure. Contra-indicated with caffeine.**

Golden Rod (Solidago virgaurea)
Parts used: herbage, which is dried for infusions, tinctures, powders, ointments and liquid extract.
Properties: a bitter, astringent, cooling herb that is a urinary antiseptic, dries up nasal discharges e.g. sinusitis, rhinitis. It nourishes the kidneys, reduces inflammation, promotes healing and improves digestion.

Golden Seal (*Hydrastis canadensis*)
Parts used: rhizomes, roots, which are dried for use in decoctions, tablets, tinctures and liquid extract.
Properties: a bitter, alterative herb that reduces inflammation, is effective against bacterial and amoebic infection, improves assimilation and digestion and acts as a mild laxative. It is also a decongestant, stimulates bile flow and uterine contractions, and checks bleeding. **Caution: Not to be taken by pregnant women, diabetics, or people with high blood pressure or glaucoma. Should not be used for prolonged periods or on a daily basis for longer than 7 days at a time.**

Populations of this plant in the wild are becoming depleted and the rhizomes are becoming increasingly expensive. Be prepared to pay a high price (we can only hope that it contributes to growing more of the plant). Golden Seal contains isoquinoline alkaloides, including berberine (as found in *Berberis vulgaris* - common Barberry). Although there is no real substitute for all the functions of Golden Seal, Berberis comes close.

Note: We have no wish to further endanger a species so would suggest that when writing off for your herbs you ask for advice, whether the plant is still endangered and, if so, would they like to suggest an alternative.

ary *Grindelia camporum* **(gumplant, gumweed, tarweed)**
Parts used: herbage, which is dried for use in infusions, liquid extracts, tinctures and is used fresh in poultices.
Properties: a bitter, pungent, aromatic herb that relaxes spasms, has sedative effects, and is an expectorant and anti-inflammatory. **Caution: excess may irritate the kidneys, but used with other herbs or in occasional small doses it is fine.**

Gravel Root (*Eupatorium purpureum* - Joe Pye weed, queen of the meadow)
Parts used: rhizomes and roots, which are dried for decoctions and tinctures.

Properties: a slightly bitter, restorative, cleansing herb that acts especially on the genito-urinary organs and uterus.

Hawthorn (*Crataegus oxyacantha* - known also as May after its time of flowering)

Parts used: fruits, which are used raw or cooked, or dried whole for use in decoctions, tinctures and liquid extracts. The juice can also be extracted and freeze dried.

Properties: a sweet and sour, warming herb which has a specific effect on the heart. It improves peripheral circulation and regulates heart rate, blood pressure and coronary blood flow. Hawthorn is relatively non-toxic, but serious heart conditions should be treated by a qualified practitioner.

Heartsease (*Viola tricolor* - wild pansy)

Parts used: herbage, which is dried and used for decoctions, infusions liquid extracts, or powdered and used in skin creams.

Properties: a bitter-sweet, cooling herb that is laxative and diuretic, cleanses toxins, lowers fever, relieves pain and reduces inflammation. It is also expectorant and promotes healing.

Note: saponins in the herb have an irritant effect on the digestive system and large doses can cause vomiting or nausea. There is no problem with standard doses.

Horseradish

Parts used: leaves (which are picked fresh) and root which are used fresh for culinary purposes and in poultices and syrups, or macerated into vinegar and honey for medicinal use.

Properties: a very pungent, stimulant herb that controls bacterial infection and lowers fever by increasing perspiration; it is diuretic, and irritates the tissues, causing improved circulation locally. **Caution: do not take if you have stomach ulcers or thyroid problems; Chris says it gives him indigestion - so approach carefully!**

Hydrangea

Parts used: roots which are dried for decoctions, tinctures and liquid extracts.

Properties: a sweet, pungent herb that soothes irritated tissue; acts as a diuretic and stimulates the kidneys. Good for bladder infection, kidney stones and prostate disorders.

Hyssop (*Hyssopus officinalis*)
Parts used: herbage, which is dried for infusions, syrup, liquid extract and tinctures.
Properties: a bitter, aromatic (smells like camphor) astringent herb that is expectorant, reduces inflammation and lowers fever. It has a tonic effect on the bronchial, urinary, digestive, and nervous systems. **Caution: should not be taken if pregnant.**

Iceland Moss (*Cetraria islandica*)
Parts used: whole plant, which is dried for use in decoctions, liquid extracts, powders, and tinctures.
Properties: a bitter-sweet, nourishing and cooling herb that soothes irritated tissue, reduces respiratory and digestive inflammation and infection, and controls vomiting.

Lavender (*Lavendula officinalis*)
Parts used: flowers, used fresh, distilled for oil, or dried for infusions, spirits, and tinctures.
Properties: an aromatic, tonic herb that helps relieve stress and depression and is beneficial for the skin. Good for headaches, burns, psoriasis, and skin problems.

Lemon Balm (*Melissa officinalis* - Balm)
Parts used: herbage, used fresh (for oil) or dried for infusions, liquid extracts, ointments and tinctures.
Properties: a cooling, sedative herb that lowers fever, improves digestion, relaxes spasms and peripheral blood vessels. Fresh leaves can be placed directly onto insect bites and sores or used as a poultice.
Lemon balm is also used as a culinary herb and is particularly popular as a calming tea.

Lime Flower (*Tilia cordata* - Linden flowers)
Parts used: flowers (from the tree), freshly dried for infusions and tinctures.
Properties: a sedative and antispasmodic, it increases perspiration, reduces fever, irritability and nervous tension. Lime flower tea before bed and/or a lime flower bath at night are good for insomnia.

Linseed (*Linum usitatissimum* - flax, flaxseed)
Parts used: seeds, which are either stored whole, or pressed for oil.
Properties: a mucilaginous herb that soothes irritated tissue, is a laxative and controls coughing.

Liquorice (*Glycyrrhiza glabra*)
Parts used: roots, stolons which are dried for decoctions, liquid extracts, lozenges, and powders.
Properties: a very sweet, soothing herb that is anti-inflammatory and cleanses catarrhal conditions, is a mild laxative that soothes the intestinal tract; detoxifies and protects the liver; and has hormonal effects. **Caution: should not to be taken by pregnant women, patients with high blood pressure, diabetes, glaucoma, severe menstrual problems, kidney disease, or taking digoxin-based medication.** Take a break after seven days.

Lobelia Inflata
Parts used: whole plant which is used fresh or dried for infusions, decoctions, liquid extracts and tinctures.
Properties: an acrid, emetic herb that stimulates respiration, increases perspiration rate, reduces inflammation and is expectorant. This is an excellent herb but we have to restrict our recommendation to an ingredient in a combined tincture or for external use. You will need to consult a herbalist for internal use as a single herb. **Caution: do not use if pregnant or have a heart complaint.**

Marigold (*Calendula officinalis*)
Parts used: flower petals, which are used fresh or dried for infusions, tinctures, creams.
Properties: a bitter-sweet herb that stimulates the gall bladder and liver, clears infections, and soothes digestive inflammations. Also helps to regulate the menstrual cycle. Externally, calendula soothes irritated tissue, promotes healing of burns and wounds and controls bleeding.

Marsh Mallow (*Althaea officinalis*)
Parts used: roots (dried for liquid extracts, syrup, and ointments), leaves (dried for infusions, liquid extracts and ointments).
Properties: a sweet, cool, mucilaginous herb that soothes and moistens irritated surfaces e.g. skin and membranes; reduces inflammation (particularly in the gastrointestinal, respiratory and urinary tracts), and controls bacterial infection.

Meadowsweet (*Filipendula ulmaria* - queen of the meadow)
Parts used: herbage and flowers, which are dried for infusions, tinctures, tablets, liquid extracts.
Properties: an antacid, astringent, aromatic herb that soothes, heals, and relieves pain, and reduces inflammation especially in the digestive tract and in joints. The main ingredients of the plant are salicylic acid compounds. It was from this plant that salicylic acid was first isolated and later synthesized as "asprin".

Melissa - see Lemon Balm.

Milk Thistle (Silybum marianum)
Parts used: whole plant, seeds, are dried for infusions and tinctures or for extraction of silymarin.
Properties: a bitter, tonic herb that regenerates liver cells, stimulates bile flow, is diuretic, and relaxes spasms. Milk Thistle contains unique substances collectively referred to as "silymarin" which protects the liver against toxins.

Motherwort (*Leonurus cardiaca*)
Parts used: herbage (cut when flowering but before the seed is set), which is dried and used for infusions, tinctures and liquid extracts.

Properties: a very bitter herb that is a sedative and a good heart and nerve tonic. It relaxes spasms and is a uterine tonic and regulates menstrual flow.

Mullein (*Verbascum thapsus* - great mullein, Aaron's rod)
Parts used: whole plant, leaves and flowers, which are dried for infusions, liquid extracts, and tinctures. Fresh flowers can also be used for infusions, syrups and medicated oil.
Properties: a cooling, bitter, mucilaginous herb that has expectorant, analgesic, diuretic and antiseptic effects. It acts on swollen glands and is a valuable remedy for the respiratory system. It promotes healing and soothes and lubricates tissues.

Myrrh (*Commiphora myrrha*)
Parts used: oleo-gum resin, which is collected from cut branches, dried and processed for oil, tablets or tinctures.
Properties: a pungent herb that is a stimulant and antiseptic and relieves inflammation and digestive discomfort. It encourages healing, especially of ulcers, gums, skin etc. and is expectorant. **Caution: should not be taken if pregnant.**

Nettle (*Urtica dioica* - stinging nettle)
Parts used: herbage, which is dried for infusions, liquid extracts, ointments, powders and tinctures, also the seeds.
Properties: a very good tonic herb that clears toxins, strengthens kidneys and lungs, is diuretic and controls bleeding. A nourishing and strengthening herb with high levels of chlorophyll and iron and other vital minerals. **Note: raw leaves are highly irritant.**

Oats (*Avena sativa* - groats)
Parts used: grain and stalk. The grain is dehusked, and rolled for use in cereals, liquid extracts and tinctures.

Properties: a sweet, warm, nutritive herb that acts as an excellent tonic to the nerves and endocrine system, especially to the thymus gland. Can be used externally for skin problems.

Parsley (*Petroselinum crispum*)

Parts used: leaves (used fresh, frozen or dried), roots and stems (dried for decoctions and liquid extracts), seeds (dried for infusions and liquid extracts).

Properties: an aromatic herb that is warm, diuretic, clears toxins, particularly watery poisons, and mucous discharges, and stimulates normal activity of the digestion; helps bladder, liver, kidney, lung, stomach and thyroid function. Parsley is a very popular culinary herb and contains various minerals and vitamins such as Vit A and C (more vitamin C than oranges, by weight) iodine, phosphorus, and potassium and contains more iron than most green vegetables.

Passiflora incarnata (maypops, passion flower)

Parts used: herbage (dried for use in infusions, liquid extracts, tablets and tinctures) fruits (for culinary use).

Properties: a bitter, cooling, herb that acts as a gentle sedative; relaxes spasms and relieves pain, and is helpful for anxiety, stress related disorders, nervous insomnia, restlessness and headaches. **Caution: should not be used in high doses in pregnancy.** Passiflora contains certain alkaloids and flavonoids (one of which, called apigenin, is anti-inflammatory and is an anti-spasmodic) which act as non-addictive sedatives that do not cause drowsiness.

Peppermint (*Mentha piperita*)

Parts used: herbage, oil, used fresh or dried for use in concentrated waters, infusions, liquid extracts, powders, spirits. Peppermint tea is a great favourite and the leaves can be added to cool drinks, and salads.

Properties: a bitter, strongly aromatic, decongestant herb that improves digestion (it works mainly on the digestive system, particularly the bowel), and has a mildly anaesthetic effect on the mucous membranes and the gastrointestinal tract. The leaves contain 1 to 3 per cent essential oil which has more than 50 per cent menthol. Menthol is an antiseptic, decongestant, analgesic compound and gives the plant its typical smell and taste.

Prickly Ash (*Zanthoxylum americanum* - Toothache tree)
Parts used: bark and fruits, which are dried for decoctions, tinctures and liquid extracts.
Properties: a spicy, warming, stimulating herb that stimulates circulation, relieves muscle and nerve pain, improves digestion, controls diarrhoea, is anti-rheumatic and anti-infective.

Plantain (*Plantago major* - ribwort)
Parts used: leaves, which contain glycosides, minerals, and tannins.
Properties: an alterative, mildly astringent herb that is beneficial to the glandular system, urinary tract and lungs. It is an effective remedy for poisonous bites and stings and one of the best healers of blood poisoning.

Red Raspberry (*Rubus idaeus*)
Parts used: Bark, leaves, root (dried for use in infusions, liquid extracts, tablets) fruits are used fresh.
Properties: an astringent herb that tones the uterine muscles and is good for many female disorders such as flushes and menstrual cramps, is effective in lessening menstrual flow and for soothing and toning the stomach and bowel; it is also used as a preparation for childbirth and is given to pregnant women in the last three months and during labour (not during early pregnancy) as it promotes a safe and easy delivery and quietens premature labour pains; good for mouth, throat and eye inflammation. Contains calcium, citric acid, iron, magnesium, malic acid, manganese, pectin, phosphorus, potassium, selenium, silicon, sulphur, tannic acid, Vit B1, B3, C, D, and E.

Red Clover (*Trifolium pratense*)
Parts used: flowering tops, which are dried for infusions, liquid extracts, ointments and tinctures.

Properties: a cooling, sweet, alterative herb that relaxes spasms, and has expectorant and diuretic effects. Acts as an antibiotic and blood purifier, is good for bacterial infections, skin disorders, and a weakened immune system. This herb has potent healing properties particularly for skin problems, wasting diseases and is one of the herbs used, in herbal medicine, to fight cancer. Contains minerals such as magnesium, manganese, selenium, and vitamins A, B1, 2, 3, 6, 12, and C.

Rose hips (*Rosa canina* - dog rose)
Parts used: fruits (hips), used fresh or dried, in decoctions, or syrups.
Properties: an acidic, astringent, tonic herb that is rich in vitamins, particularly Vit C, and is good for minor infectious diseases, bladder problems, colds, influenza, diarrhoea. **Note: hips and seeds contain irritant hairs.**

Rosemary (*Rosmarinus officinalis*)
Parts used: leaves.
Properties: a sweet and slightly bitter, warm, restorative herb that stimulates circulation and digestion; helps fight infection, and acts as an astringent and decongestant. Good for mental fatigue, vision impairment, headaches, and depression. It also makes a good scalp and hair tonic.

Sage (*Salvia officinalis* - garden sage)
Parts used: leaves, which are dried for infusions, liquid extracts and tinctures. The leaves, fresh or dried, are very popular for culinary use.
Properties: an antiseptic, astringent herb that is particularly effective for inflammation of the mouth and throat and also for night sweats and generally drying up excess secretions including breast milk. It has a calming effect on the heart, nervous system and brain, and also promotes hair growth. **Caution: not to be given in pregnancy, or to individuals with seizure disorders.**

386

St. John's Wort (*Hypericum perforatum*)
Parts used: herbage, which is dried for use in creams, tinctures, infusions and medicated oils.
Properties: a cooling, astringent herb that calms the nerves, reduces inflammation, promotes healing, and relieves depression. Good for anxiety and nervous tension. Externally for bruises, psoriasis, varicose veins and wounds. It is locally antiseptic and analgesic. **Note: may cause sun sensitivity if fair skinned.**

Saw Palmetto (Serenoa repens)
Parts used: fruits, which are partly dried for elixirs, infusions, liquid extracts and tinctures, or dried and powdered for use in tablets.
Properties: a warming, tonic herb that tones the reproductive area, restores the endocrine system, and reduces swelling and inflammation; acts as a diuretic and urinary disinfectant. It is used effectively for prostate problems and is commonly held to be an aphrodisiac.

Shepherd's Purse (*Capsella bursa-pastoris* - witches' pouches, pick- pocket)
Parts used: whole plant, which is used fresh or dried for infusions, decoctions and liquid extracts. The leaves (which are rich in vitamins) are picked fresh for culinary use.
Properties: an astringent herb that is diuretic, acts as a urinary antiseptic and is styptic (causing contraction of tissues or blood vessels and tending to check bleeding). Used internally and externally to stop bleeding, especially excessive menstruation, nosebleeds and wounds.

Skullcap (*Scutellaria lateriflora* - Virginia skullcap, mad dog skullcap)
Parts used: herbage, which is dried and used for tinctures, infusions, liquid extracts or tablets.
Properties: a bitter, sedative, tonic herb that tones and strengthens the nervous system, relaxes spasms and headaches.

Slippery Elm (*Ulmus fulva* - moose elm, red elm)
Parts used: inner bark, which is dried for powders, tablets, decoctions, ointments, poultices and liquid extracts.
Properties: a moist and very nutritive herb that soothes and restores mucous membranes of lungs and stomach. It promotes healing of tissue, e.g. burns, inflammation, and is effective with ulcers and hyperacidity. Contains Vit K, calcium, phosphorus, bioflavonoids.

Squawvine (*Mitchella repens* - partridge berry, running box)
North American tribes used the herb to ease labour, hence the name.
Parts used: herbage, which is dried for infusions, liquid extracts and tinctures.
Properties: an astringent, slightly bitter, diuretic herb that relaxes the uterus, strengthens uterine contractions, is good for menstrual cramps, and calms the nervous system. **Caution: not given during the first six months of pregnancy.**

Tea Tree (*Melaleuca alternifolia*)
Parts used: leaves and twigs are distilled to make essential oil and used in ointments or in spirits.
Properties: an antiseptic herb that stimulates the immune system. It is very effective against fungal and bacterial infections. Good for disinfecting wounds and healing most skin conditions. **Caution: not recommended for internal use unless supervised. Discontinue or dilute with water or base oil if irritation results from topical use.**

Thyme (*Thymus vulgaris* - common thyme)
Parts used: flowering herbage, which is distilled for oil, or dried for infusions, liquid extracts or elixirs. Thyme is a very popular herb, fresh or dried, for culinary use.
Properties: an aromatic, warming, astringent herb that is strongly antiseptic and anti-fungal, is expectorant, relaxes spasms and controls coughing, and improves digestion. Contains Vitamins C, D and B complex, fluorine, chromium,

iron, silicon, thiamine. **Caution: not to be taken by pregnant women, as it may, in large amounts, act as a uterine stimulant.**

Valerian (*Valeriana officinalis*)
Parts used: rhizomes, roots, which are used fresh or dried for decoctions, infusions, tablets, tinctures or distilled for oil.
Properties: a fairly strong sedative herb that relaxes spasms, calms the nerves, improves circulation by slowing the action of the heart whilst increasing its force, relieves pain and is good for insomnia, it is also healing for stomach ulcers. **Caution: If you have a liver problem consult with a qualified herbalist before taking this herb.**

Vervain (*Verbena officinalis*)
Parts used: herbage, which is dried and used in infusions, decoctions, liquid extracts, tinctures and ointments.
Properties: a bitter, cooling, aromatic, diuretic herb that increases perspiration and lactation, relieves pain, calms the nerves; reduces inflammation. **Caution: it is not recommended during pregnancy although it may assist contractions during labour.**

Walnut leaf (*Juglans regia*)
Parts used: leaves, inner bark, nut. The leaves are dried for infusions and liquid extracts.
Properties: a vermicide (kills worms) and anti-fungal that contains an organic iodine which is very antiseptic and healing.

Watercress (*Nasturtium officinale*)
Parts used: the leaves, which are cut as required and used whole or liquidized. It loses both taste and smell when dried.
Properties: a pungent, bitter, stimulant herb that clears toxins, has diuretic and expectorant effects, and benefits the digestion.

Watercress also has a popular culinary use. The fresh herbage contains the mustard oil glycoside glyconasturtiin. It also contains the locally strong irritant raphonal, and is rich in vitamins, including iron, iodine and calcium. **Caution: due to pollutants in water courses, particularly water flukes, collection from the wild is not recommended. Raphonal can cause a burning sensation in the urinary canals.**

White Willow (*Salix alba*)
Parts used: leaves (fresh or dried for infusions), bark (dried for use in decoctions, liquid extracts, powders, tinctures and tablets).
Properties: a bitter, astringent, cooling herb that lowers fever, reduces inflammation and relieves pain. Willows yield salicylic acid - which provides the basis of asprin. **Caution: should not be taken during pregnancy or by children, unless under the supervision of a herbalist.**

Wild Carrot (*Daucus carota*)
Parts used: whole plant (dried for infusions and liquid extracts) seeds (dried for infusions or distilled for oil).
Properties: an aromatic herb that is a diuretic and urinary antiseptic and the seeds are helpful for flatulence and colic. **Caution: if pregnant, see a herbalist before taking the herb.**

Wild Cherry Bark (*Prunus serotina* - black cherry, wild rum cherry)
Parts used: bark, which is dried for infusions, powders, tinctures, syrups and liquid extracts.
Properties: an astringent, aromatic, warming herb that controls coughing, improves digestion and has anti-bacterial, anti-viral and sedative effects.

Wild Yam (*Dioscorea villosa*)
Parts used: rhizomes, roots, which are used fresh or dried for use in liquid extracts.
Properties: an anti-inflammatory, anti-spasmodic, relaxant herb that is effective with colic, and with catarrhal conditions. It has a potent tonic effect on the uterus and relaxes spasms. It is also known for its property as a progesterone precursor useful in

menopause. For further comments on the menopause/yam/oestrogen/ progesterone connection, see chapter 15.

Witch Hazel (*Hamamelis virginiana*)
Parts used: leaves, twigs, bark, which are dried for liquid extracts, ointments, and tinctures.
Properties: an astringent herb that checks bleeding and mucous discharge, and reduces inflammation, relieves itching. Externally good for haemorrhoids, varicose veins, sprains, bruises, eye and skin inflammation.

Wormwood (*Artemisia absinthium*)
Parts used: herbage whilst in flower, and leaves, picked before flowering (dried for infusions, decoctions, tablets, powders and tinctures).
Properties: a very bitter, diuretic herb that acts as a tonic on the liver, digestive system and nerves; it increases stomach acidity, has anti-inflammatory effects, and expels intestinal worms. (Wormwood foliage is used to drive away moths, bugs and parasites.)
Caution: take in small doses for short term treatment only as it can be habit forming. Not to be taken by children or pregnant women.

Yarrow (*Achillea millefolium* - milfoil, soldier's woundwort)
Parts used: herbage, which is dried for infusions, liquid extracts, lotions and tinctures.
Properties: a bitter, aromatic, astringent tonic herb that increases perspiration and has diuretic effects. It purifies the blood and regulates the functions of the liver. It reduces inflammation, relieves indigestion, is good for fevers and uterine problems, and has a healing effect on mucous membranes. **Caution: Prolonged use may make the skin more sensitive to sunlight.**

Yellow Dock (Rumex crispus - curled dock)

Parts used: roots, which are dried for use in decoctions, liquid extracts and tinctures.

Properties: an astringent, cooling, bitter herb that stimulates the liver and gall bladder, has a laxative effect and cleanses toxins. Acts as a blood cleanser and purifier and improves colon function.

Appendix Five

Plant and Food Sources for Vitamins and Minerals

Vitamins and minerals are vital for the effective maintenance of the physical body. In an ideal world with no toxins and a naturally fed and replenished soil we could, no doubt, extract all we need from the food we eat. Our body is, after all, designed to absorb all it needs from the food that passes through it. Minerals are naturally occurring elements found in the earth which are passed from the soil to the plant and then to us as we eat the plant or, to the herbivore and then to us. With intensive farming, when the same crop is planted year after year and the ground is fed only with man made fertilizers, the soil has nothing to feed it. Eating fresh organic vegetables and meats overcome this problem and make supplements unnecessary. Some locations on the planet are naturally low in some minerals and so if you live in an area which has little selenium in the soil, supplements of that mineral will of course be helpful.

When we eat so called junk foods (aptly named), instant foods, and micro-waved foods which contain very little, if any, nutrients, the body is unable to function efficiently and becomes deficient in essential vitamins and minerals (a recent Swiss study found that eating micro waved food alters body blood chemistry - source: *Nexus* Vol.6 N°2, Feb-Mar 1999).

If you have been on a junk food diet for some time, vitamins and minerals in a supplement form may be necessary to bring the body back into balance. When purchasing supplements be aware that some contain artificial colouring, sugars, starches and preservatives. Advice on the recommended daily allowances (RDAs) may be found on the packaging or from a good book on the subject.

There is, of course, no substitute for a well balanced, organic diet to maintain the body in as peak a condition as our environment allows.

The proper balance of vitamins and minerals is important. Research has shown that an excess of an isolated vitamin or mineral can produce the same symptoms as a deficiency of a vitamin or mineral. Synergy is where two or more vitamins act together to create a stronger vitamin function.

Vitamins

Vitamin A and the Carotenoids (beta- alpha- and gamma-) - found in fish liver and fish liver oils, yellow and orange fruit and vegetables, especially carrots, green vegetables such as broccoli, kale, spinach, dandelion/mustard/turnip greens, Swiss chard, watercress, asparagus, sweet potatoes, yellow squash, pumpkin, papayas, apricots and peaches (fresh or dried), garlic, red peppers, tomatoes. They act as antioxidants helping to protect the cells against cancer and other diseases; needed for healthy skin and mucous membranes, and is particularly helpful with vision and eye problems. It is important in the formation of bones and teeth and helps protect the body against infection of the kidneys, bladder and lungs. Protein cannot be utilised by the body without Vitamin A. Beta-carotene is thought to aid in cancer prevention by scavenging, or neutralizing, free radicals.

Vitamin B Complex - help to maintain the health of the nerves, circulation, skin, eyes, hair, liver, and mouth, healthy muscle tone in the digestive tract and proper brain function. The B vitamins act together as a team.

Vitamin B1 (thiamin) found in wheatgerm and wholegrain cereals, especially brown rice, millet, oatmeal, rice bran, egg yolks, fish, kelp, pulses, broad beans, peas, pork, poultry, liver, cashew nuts, peanuts, sesame seeds, potatoes, broccoli, asparagus, brussel sprouts, watercress, brewers yeast/yeast extract, plums, dried prunes, raisins. Thiamin acts as an antioxidant; is needed for muscle tone of the intestines, stomach and heart; enhances circulation and assists in blood formation.

Vitamin B2 (Riboflavin) - found in cheese, egg yolks, pulses, meat, milk, yogurt, poultry, whole grains, spinach, leafy greens, dandelion greens, watercress, asparagus, avocado, brussel sprouts, kelp, nuts, mushrooms, molasses, currants. Necessary for red blood cell formation, antibody production, healthy skin, clear eyes, a strong nervous system and uninterrupted sleep.

Vitamin B3 (Niacin, Nicotinic Acid) - found in brewers yeast/yeast extracts, broccoli, carrots, potatoes, tomatoes, dandelion greens, globe artichokes, eggs, fish, pork, beef liver, nuts - especially peanuts, cheese, milk, peas and beans, some cereals including rice but not maize, corn flower, dried fruit. Important for good brain and nerve function, healthy skin, healthy adrenal glands, a balanced digestion and the proper energy production of food in the body. Niacin improves circulation and is a memory enhancer.

Vitamin B5 (Pantothenic Acid) - found in most foods but especially - beans, egg yolk, legumes, liver, oranges, nuts, peanuts, wheatgerm and wholegrain cereals, fresh vegetables, saltwater fish, mushrooms. It is required by all cells in the body and is concentrated in the organs; needed for normal functioning of the gastro-intestinal tract; plays a role in the production of adrenal hormones and the formation of antibodies; aids in vitamin utilization and the proper energy production of food in the body.

Vitamin B6 (Pyridoxine) is found in most foods but especially - brewer's yeast, bananas, carrots, spinach, broccoli, peas, sunflower seeds, walnuts, chicken, fish, eggs, pulses, prunes, raisins, soya bean and flour (check that it is not genetically modified), brown rice and other whole grain cereal. It promotes red blood cell formation; the production of antibodies against infection; necessary for the absorption of fats and proteins.

Vitamin Bl2 (cyanocobalamin) are especially high in foods of animal origin, especially liver, meat, kidney; seafood, brewers yeast, egg yolk, milk and dairy products, particularly cheese. Vitamin Bl2 is not found in many vegetables but is available from sea vegetables such as dulse, kelp, nori, and kombu. It is also present in soy products. This vitamin is linked to the production of acetylcholine, a neuro-transmitter that assists memory and learning; is needed within the body to prevent anaemia as it helps in the utilization of iron and aids folic acid in regulating the formation of red blood cells.

Biotin is found in brewer's yeast, meat, milk, nuts, oats, saltwater fish, soybeans and wholegrain. Biotin aids in cell growth; in the metabolism of carbohydrates, fats and proteins and in the utilization of B complex vitamins; promotes healthy nerve tissue and bone marrow; needed for healthy hair and skin.

Choline is found in egg yolks, legumes, meat, milk, wholegrain cereals, soybeans, and lecithin. Choline is needed for the proper transmission of nerve impulses from the brain through the central nervous system, gall bladder regulation, liver function and lecithin formation; it aids in hormone production and aids in fat and cholesterol metabolism.

Folic Acid - found in green leafy vegetables, root vegetables, mushrooms, legumes, lentils, whole grains, whole wheat, brown rice, bran, brewer's yeast, wheatgerm, milk, cheese, chicken, pork, lamb, beef, liver, salmon, tuna, dates, oranges. Folic acid is important for red blood cell production, healthy pregnancy, sound digestion and normal brain functioning. Folic acid works best when combined with Vitamin B12 and Vit C.

Inositol is found in fruits, lecithin, legumes, meat, milk, raisins, unrefined molasses, vegetables and wholegrain. Inositol is needed for hair growth, helps prevent hardening of the arteries and is important in the formation of lecithin and the metabolism of fat and cholesterol.

Para-Aminobenzoic Acid (PABA - one of the basic constituents of folic acid and helps in the assimilation of pantothenic acid) is found in liver, kidney, molasses, whole grain and spinach. This antioxidant helps protect against sunburn and skin cancer; assists in the formation of red blood cells; acts as a coenzyme in the breakdown and utilization of protein, and aids in the maintenance of healthy intestinal flora.

Vitamin C (Ascorbic Acid) is an antioxidant that is required for tissue growth and repair, adrenal gland function, healthy skin, bones, tendons, cartilage, ligaments, blood vessels, gums, teeth; energy production and growth; resistance to infection; wound healing; iron absorption; control of blood cholesterol. Found in - fruits and fruit juices, especially citrus fruits and blackcurrants, and green vegetables (all best eaten raw); rosehips and syrup, potatoes, asparagus, avocado, kale, dandelion/ mustard/turnip and beet greens, spinach, Swiss chard, watercress, green peas, chillies and sweet peppers, onions, brussel sprouts, and tomatoes.

Vitamin D is found in fish-liver oils and oily fish such as kippers, mackerel, sardines, tuna, salmon; liver, sprouted seeds, butter, milk, dandelion greens, sweet potatoes, egg yolk, oatmeal, and malted milk drinks. Vitamin D is also formed by the body in response to the action of sunlight on the skin. Vit D is required for the absorption and utilization of calcium and phosphorus, so remember to take Vit D foods with calcium rich foods to help the body hold onto the calcium. It is an important vitamin in the prevention and treatment of osteoporosis and hypocalcemia, enhances immunity and is necessary for thyroid function and normal blood clotting.

Vitamin E - an important antioxidant that maintains healthy cell membranes (so may retard effects of ageing); healthy blood cells, skin, hair, nerves and muscles; helps guard against cardiovascular disease as it improves circulation, strengthens the capillary walls and helps strengthen connective tissue; boosts the body's resistance to infection. Found in most foods but especially in cold pressed vegetable oils, dark green leafy vegetables, watercress, sweet potatoes, legumes (peas, beans etc.), nuts, seeds, whole grains, particularly brown rice, oatmeal, egg yolks, and kelp.

Vitamin K is essential for bone formation and repair; it is necessary for the synthesis of osteocalcin, the protein in bone tissue on which calcium crystallizes (helpful in the treatment or prevention of osteoporosis); it is needed for the production of prothrombin, which is necessary for blood clotting; promotes healthy liver function; aids in converting glucose into glycogen for storage in the liver. Vit K is naturally synthesized by friendly bacteria in the large intestine but can be found in dark green leafy vegetables, brussel sprouts, cabbage, cauliflower, broccoli, asparagus, potatoes, tomatoes, egg yolks, blackstrap molasses, seaweed (kelp), oatmeal, oats, rye, soybean, wheat-germ and liver.

Bioflavonoids have an antibacterial effect and promote circulation; stimulate bile production; help in the treatment or prevention of cataracts; help balance cholesterol levels. Bioflavonoids act synergistically with Vit C to protect and preserve the structure of capillaries. Although bioflavonoids are not in the strictest sense true vitamins they are sometimes referred to as Vitamin P. They are found in peppers, black-currants, apricots, cherries, citrus fruits, grapes, prunes, rosehips, buckwheat, green peppers, walnuts, and beer.

Coenzyme Q10 (a vitamin-like substance whose actions in the body resemble those of Vit E - an antioxidant) and is found in mackerel, salmon, sardines, beef, peanuts and spinach. Coenzyme Q10 plays a role in the production of energy in every cell of the body. It aids circulation, stimulates the immune system, increases tissue oxygenation, and has vital anti-aging effects. The amount of Q10 declines as the body ages, so it is particularly useful for people over fifty to eat these foods.

Minerals

Boron - found in apples, grapes, pears, nuts, carrots, leafy vegetables and grains. Boron is needed for healthy bones and for the metabolism of calcium, phosphorus and magnesium. Boron helps to prevent postmenopausal osteoporosis and build muscle.

Calcium - found in fish, and especially sardines, pilchards and other fish whose bones are eaten; green leafy vegetables, watercress, parsley, cabbage, dandelion/mustard/turnip greens, broccoli, asparagus, kelp, whey, yogurt, cheese, buttermilk, oats, sesame seeds, almonds, brazil nuts, chickpeas, soybeans, mung beans, broad beans, olives, oats, prunes, blackstrap molasses. The amino acid lysine is needed for calcium absorption and is found in cheese, eggs, fish, milk, lima beans, potatoes, soy products and yeast. Insufficient Vit D intake hinders the absorption of calcium so combine both food groups.

Chromium - found in beer, brown rice, cheese, meat, liver, chicken, wholegrains, brewer's yeast, fresh fruits, nuts, dried beans, eggs, mushrooms, potatoes. Chromium helps maintain stable blood sugar levels through proper insulin utilization; important in the synthesis of cholesterol, fats and protein, and in the function of the skeletal muscles.

Copper - found in nuts especially brazil and almonds, avocado, broccoli, green leafy vegetables, radishes, mushrooms, garlic, oats, barley, beans, lentils, oranges, seafood, blackstrap molasses, raisins, liver. Copper aids in the formation of bone, haemoglobin, and red blood cells; healthy nerves and joints.

Germanium - found in garlic, onions, shiitake mushrooms, and can be found in the herbs aloe vera, comfrey, ginseng and suma. Germanium acts as a carrier of oxygen to the nerves, this helps to fight pain and keep the immune system functioning properly.

Iodine - found in seafood, saltwater fish, kelp, sea salt, asparagus, Swiss chard, turnip greens, garlic, mushrooms, lima beans, sesame seeds, soybeans. Iodine is needed for a healthy thyroid gland and is important for mental and physical development; helps to metabolize excess fat.

Iron - found in fish, liver, meat, poultry, green leafy vegetables, watercress, whole grains, fortified white flour and products, fortified breakfast cereals, rice and wheat bran, nuts - especially almonds, peaches, pears, avocados, blackstrap molasses, brewer's yeast, kelp, lentils, millet, kidney and lima beans, soybeans, dried apricots, prunes and figs, raisins, dates, sesame seeds, and pumpkins. Iron is important for healthy blood function; distribution of oxygen to, and removal of carbon dioxide and other waste products from, body tissues by haemoglobin.

Magnesium - found in most foods especially green leafy vegetables, watercress, seafood, kelp, fish and meat, milk, apples, apricots, bananas, grapefruit, lemons, peaches, figs, avocados, brown rice, millet, wheat and wholegrains, blackeyed peas, lima beans, soybeans, tofu, nuts especially peanuts, sesame seeds, garlic. Magnesium assists in calcium and potassium uptake; plays a part in the formation of bone; is vital for the proper function of muscles, nerves, and metabolic enzymes (enzymes involved in energy production). With Vit B6, magnesium helps to reduce and dissolve calcium phosphate kidney stones.

Molybdenum - found in many foods but especially buckwheat, barley, oats, liver, pulses and dark green leafy vegetables. It promotes normal cell function; iron metabolism; male sexual function; for prevention of dental problems.

Phosphorus - found in most foods especially sesame, sunflower and pumpkin seeds; dried fruit, whole grains, dairy products, fish, eggs, garlic, pulses, nuts, meat, poultry, salmon, asparagus, bran and brewer's yeast. Phosphorus is needed for bones and teeth formation; conversion and storage of energy in all cells; muscle function; function of some enzymes; the intestinal absorption of some foods. Vit D increases the effectiveness of phosphorus. Phosphorus is also found in soft carbonated drinks and excessive consumption can prevent intestinal absorption of calcium, iron, magnesium and zinc.

Potassium - found in fish, fruit, legumes, meat, poultry, vegetables and wholegrain; and particularly in apricots, bananas, dried fruit, dates, figs, raisins, avocados, potatoes, brown rice, wheat bran, brewer's yeast, nuts, and garlic. Potassium is important for a healthy nervous system; the functioning of nerves and muscles; maintenance of the body's balance of fluids, especially water; is important for maintaining the body's acid/alkali balance.

Selenium - found in vegetables, particularly broccoli and onions, salmon, tuna, seafood, kelp, wheatgerm, brown rice and whole grains, brazil nuts, chicken, dairy products, liver, molasses, brewer's yeast and garlic. Selenium is a vital antioxidant, especially when combined with Vit E. Both act synergistically to aid in the production of antibodies and to help maintain a healthy liver and heart. Selenium protects the immune system by preventing the formation of free radicals, which can damage the body; it is needed for pancreatic function and tissue elasticity. Selenium, Zinc and Vit E combined may provide relief from an enlarged prostate.

Silicon - found in leafy green vegetables, whole grains, brown rice, alfalfa, beets, and soybeans. Silicon is necessary for healthy nails, skin, and hair; for the formation of collagen for bones and connective tissue; is needed to maintain flexible arteries; is helpful in counteracting the effects of aluminium on the body; is important in the prevention of osteoporosis; stimulates the immune system and inhibits the aging process in tissues.

Sodium - found in all foods, but especially cured meats, smoked fish and bakery products. Basically, its common salt so make sure that your intake is not excessive as this can cause its own problems. The correct balance of sodium is necessary for maintaining proper water balance and blood ph. It is also needed for stomach, nerve and muscle function.

Sulphur - found in garlic, onions, brussel sprouts, cabbage, kale, turnips, eggs, fish, meat, pulses, dried beans, soybeans and wheatgerm. Sulphur disinfects the blood; helps the body resist bacteria and toxic substances; protects the protoplasm of cells; stimulates bile excretion; is found in haemoglobin and in all body tissue.

Vanadium - found in dill, olives, radishes, vegetable oils, whole grain, meat and fish. This mineral is needed for cellular metabolism; for the formation of bones and teeth; it plays a role in reproduction and growth.

Zinc - found in seafood, particularly oysters, kelp, fish, sardines, lima beans, soybeans, soy lecithin, brewer's yeast, pumpkin and sunflower seeds, pecans, poultry, liver, meat, lamb, mushrooms, egg yolks, wholegrain flour. Zinc is an essential mineral; it promotes a healthy immune system and the healing of wounds; protects the liver from chemical damage; vital for bone formation; helps fight and prevent the formation of free radicals; is important in prostate gland function and the growth of the reproductive organs; it is a constituent of insulin and many vital enzymes; increases the absorption of Vit A. Zinc is needed to maintain proper concentrations of Vit E in the blood. A loss of the senses of taste and smell may be a sign of zinc deficiency.

As you can see from the above, it is important to a have a well balanced diet. Most foods contain a wide variety of vitamins and minerals and are in common daily use. If you take an excess of one mineral or vitamin it may block the body's absorption of another. The body must maintain a proper chemical balance, and as one mineral has an effect on every other, if one is out of balance all mineral levels are affected.

Antioxidants

Although antioxidants can be obtained from food sources such as sprouted grains and fresh fruit and vegetables, it is quite difficult to obtain sufficient from these sources to support the body in its fight against the free radicals which constantly bombard us from our environment and non-organic foods. Antioxidants protect the body's cells from harmful chemicals called free radicals which are known to speed the ageing process, and are linked to the onset of degenerative conditions. We thought we would list the most powerful antioxidants for clarity (in alphabetical order).

The herbs Bilberry and Gingko Biloba (see appendix four); Co-Enzyme Ql0; Grape Seed Extract and Pine Bark (see below); Green Tea; Selenium; Superoxide Dismutase (SOD - see below); Vit A and Beta-carotine; Vit C; Vit E (Selenium enhances Vit E uptake - these two nutrients should be taken together); Zinc.

Grape seed and Pine bark contain bioflavonoids. Bioflavonoids provide the blues, purples, emerald green and red colours of fruit, berries, vegetables, evergreen shrubs and trees, and flowers. A French scientist, Jacques Masquelier, found that they contained active compononents to which he gave the name oligomeric proanthocyanidin complexes (OPCs). He discovered that both grape seed and pine bark extract are potent antioxidants, around 20 times more potent than Vit C, 50 times more potent than Vit E, in terms of antioxidant activity. OPCs also work as a Vit C helper, supporting it in its collagen (the protein in the skin) building role. Masquelier believes that it is the bioflavonoids found in red wine, and not the alcohol, that provide the answer to why the French have one of the lowest rates of heart disease. The active ingredient of the red wine is the grape seed. White wines, where the seed is removed before fermentation, are not as effective.

Superoxide Dismutase (SOD) is an enzyme. SOD revitalises cells and reduces the rate of cell destruction. It neutralizes the most common, and possibly the most dangerous, free radical - superoxide. It also aids in the body's utilization of zinc, copper and manganese. SOD levels decline with age, while free radical production increases. Its potential as an anti-aging treatment is currently being researched. SOD occurs naturally in barley grass, broccoli, brussels sprouts, cabbage, wheatgrass, and most green plants. SOD is also available as a supplement.

Appendix Six

Alternative Therapists

During the course of this book, we have made mention of several alternative therapies. We have not mentioned all of the therapies that are available as we do not have direct experience of what these therapies have to offer. Where we have suggested therapies during the text, we either have our own experience of their effectiveness or have had good reports from those who have experienced them.

There are a growing number of alternative treatments becoming available, all of which have some benefit and will appeal to people on an individual basis. Set out below is a description of many of these therapies and their purposes. We have marked with a * those therapies which we have personal knowledge of and would recommend.

Acupuncture *

Acupuncture is a therapy which was first used by the Chinese, several hundred years ago. The energies of the chakras are distributed around the body by a number of energy "conduits" called meridians. These meridians were also first mapped by the Sumerians.

There are sixteen meridians altogether, fourteen are named for the organs to which they relate and two run vertically within the body on the spine and the middle of the front of the body. The fourteen meridians follow quite convoluted routes through the body but basically run vertically up and down the body, arms and legs. The meridians are called: the heart, small intestine, bladder, kidney, gall bladder, liver, lungs, colon, stomach and spleen. There are two other organs which are unfamiliar to western medicine and these are the pericardium, which controls circulation and sexual activity, and the triple warmer which controls the endocrine system and is the body's thermostat. The two central meridians are called the Ren (conception) and runs up the front of the body and the Du (governor) which runs up the spine.

The Chinese call the flow of energy within the body Qi (pronounced chi). The Qi is divided into two opposed but balancing forces called Yin - the female force and Yang - the male force. Yin is passive and tranquil and represents darkness, coldness, moisture and swelling. Yang is aggressive and stimulating and represents light, heat, dryness and contraction.

The Chinese view is that illness comes about because of an imbalance between the Yin and Yang within the body which is represented by blockages within the meridians. What acupuncturists aim to achieve is a re-balancing of the Yin and Yang to bring about healing. This they achieve by placing needles at appropriate points along the meridians to help unblock the energy. The needles do not hurt. Originally, the Chinese used 365 acupuncture points, but over the centuries, the number has increased to over 2 000. This does not mean that acupuncturists place this number of needles into the body at one time, but choose, usually, no more than fifteen. The therapist will ask a number of questions and measure various pulses etc. to arrive at an accurate diagnosis and select the appropriate acupuncture points to stimulate.

It usually takes about six sessions to bring about a change in a health condition.

Within the field of acupuncture, there are other, allied therapies which some acupuncturists will employ.

Acupressure is thought to be a forerunner of acupuncture and includes other therapies such as Shin Tao, Jin Shin Do and Shiatsu.

All of these treatments are a combination of massage and pressure. The pressure is applied to the acupuncture points but no needle is used. The practitioners begin by forming a diagnosis in the same way as described for acupuncture. The appropriate regions are then massaged and pressure applied to the acupuncture points. No oil is used in the massage and the patient remains fully clothed.

Alexander Technique *

This is a therapy developed by FM Alexander earlier this century. This is a very simple approach to relieving health problems which does not involve any drugs or heavy manipulation of the body. The process involves learning how to re-use your body and muscles correctly. It teaches how to stand, sit and lie, to walk and to use muscles correctly. Children use their bodies in very natural ways, as they grow older, they develop a number of bad habits which affect the body's posture and pressure can be put onto regions or organs causing stresses and discomfort. The Alexander Technique teachers help to correct these posture problems and a variety of ailments can be successfully treated.

Ailments which can be treated in this way include: exhaustion, depression, anxiety, tension headaches, high blood pressure, respiratory disorders, peptic ulcers, irritable bowel syndrome, collitis, rheumatoid arthritis, osteoarthritis, lower back pain, sciatica and asthma. The teacher first assesses your muscular problems and through a series of very gentle muscle manipulations and movement exercises, helps you to retrain your body into the correct posture. This technique can also be very good at boosting your self confidence. Alexander Technique therapists normally require a number of consultations.

Autogenic Training

This is a technique developed by a Dr Johannes Schultz in the 1920's and involves six exercises to help you relax and let go of tensions. There have been a number of medical papers written on this technique which seem to show a number of benefits. There are books available on this technique where you can learn the six exercises for yourself or there are trained practitioners.

Ayurvedic Medicine

This form of treatment is originally derived from the Sumerian practices of Ayurveda (The Science of Life). Ayurvedic practitioners are totally holistic in their approach to healing and incorporate many different concepts in their treatments which can range from surgery to meditation. Their main approach is preventative. These are mainly Indian practitioners with a growing number of western doctors and therapists being trained in these approaches.

The underlying basis for this doctrine are three basic forces: Vata, the wind, is constantly on the move and controls the central nervous system; Pitta, the sun, is a source of energy and controls the digestive system and all biochemical processes; Kapha, the moon, governs the movement of fluids within the body maintaining balance in tissues and cell growth. Ill health is seen as imbalances within these three forces.

An ayurvedic practitioner will ask a large number of questions about your life and how you live it, attitudes towards your life, etc.. From your answers they will arrive at a diagnosis and treat you with remedies from a variety of sources. Remedies fall into three main categories: medicinal remedies, these include herbs, minerals, homeopathic remedies or even western drugs; dietary regimes, the needs of an individual patient are assessed and a food regime given; practical aids, these include massage, enemas, steam baths, meditations and yoga etc..

Bach Flower Remedies **

These are fully described in chapter twelve and appendix two.

Flower and Tree Essences

In addition to the Bach, there are a growing number of flower and tree essences becoming available. Each of these essences have their functions and are designed to work with particular conditions, either physical or emotional. As our energies change for the better, these forms of remedies are increasing in their relevance and potency. The easiest way of describing these remedies is to say that they work and work extremely well for all sorts of conditions. We have listed the addresses of several of these essence suppliers in appendix seven so we would suggest that you speak to them directly to discuss your particular problem or requirements.

The Bates Method

This is a means of improving eyesight which was developed by Dr William Bates. These are a series of seven basic exercises which are designed to correct a variety of vision problems but cannot be used for conditions such as glaucoma or cataracts. In addition to the exercises, patients are given dietary advice, nutritional supplements and homeopathic remedies. The basic philosophy is that eyesight problems are not a symptom of growing old but can be corrected by using these methods. We understand they can be very successful.

Biochemic Tissue Salts **

These are fully described in chapter twelve and appendix three.

Biofeedback Training

These are a series of exercises and self help programmes to help you to relax and consciously alter some of the mechanisms within the body. These are techniques which can help people with high blood pressure, migraine, tension headaches, anxiety attacks and many stress related conditions.

It is called biofeedback because the patient is monitored by a machine which measures physical and mental states. You are able to see the machine and its readings and the therapist helps you to understand what the readings mean. By using certain exercises, it is possible to consciously alter what is happening within your body and, consequently, the machine readings. Once you have learned to recognise the signs of stress or tension within the body, you can use the exercises to calm yourself down, lowering blood pressure etc., at any time. There have been a number of medical studies carried out on these exercises and most say the technique is very helpful for these conditions.

Cognitive Therapy

This is a concept developed by an American psychologist, Aaron Beck. It is a form of psychotherapy which is taught either individually or in groups. The basic concept behind this treatment is that if people have a low opinion of themselves, they will behave in a way which reflects this and other people will respond to this behaviour in a way which will reinforce this low opinion. By helping people to see that they have many good points, they can be helped to be more self confident. These techniques can be very effective.

Counselling

Although counselling is a form of psychotherapy, it comes in many forms. Just talking to a friend about your problems can be a form of counselling. For some people, a friendly chat does not go far enough and the help of a trained counsellor may be necessary.

Counsellors are people who are trained to listen and to ask the right questions in response to what they hear. They can, therefore, help you to understand the root causes of your problem.

Counselling takes many forms and has a variety of names.

Gestalt Therapy
This is a form of counselling which begins to help you to recognise patterns of behaviour within your life. Gestalt is a German word which means "an organised whole". This form of counselling helps you to understand how your patterns of behaviour arose and how to overcome the learning processes which led to those patterns arising. The therapy was developed by Fritz Perls who described the aims of the therapy as helping people to understand themselves and not to judge themselves by others: "I do my thing, and you do your thing. I am not in this world to live up to your expectations and you are not in this world to live up to mine. You are you and I am I" is the underlying philosophy behind this kind of counselling.

Hypnotherapy
Hypnosis has a very chequered history, at least as far as the medical profession is concerned. The whole concept was developed by Franz Anton Mesmer (hence the old term of mesmerism) at the end of the 1700s. What a hypnotist attempts to do is to relax their patients to a point where they are in a state close to sleep. As the patient relaxes, the body's physical structures begin to let go and the sub-conscious begins to take over. This is the region that hypnotherapists try to work with, somewhere between the conscious and the sub-conscious mind. Locked away in the sub-conscious are all of our memories and all of our experiences. By accessing these regions of the mind, it is possible to unlock some of the underlying causes for health problems and the possibility of releasing them. It works extremely well for some people and not so well for others. If it works, it can provide many of the answers to the root causes for illness and the patient can begin to let go of those causes.

Cranial Osteopathy *

This branch of osteopathy (see also osteopathy and CranioSacral therapy below) was developed in the 1920s by William Garner Sutherland who noticed that pressures on various parts of the skull produced differing effects in other parts of the body. What he discovered was that the plates of the skull moved very minutely. Up until then it had been assumed that once past childhood, the bones of the skull were fixed in position. If these plates were readjusted to a more comfortable position, many illnesses within the body disappeared.

This kind of work involves the osteopath "feeling" the skull and the way in which the various plates sit one against another. If there is a displacement of a skull plate, very gentle pressure is applied to push the out of place plate back into its correct position. Many childhood conditions can be treated in this way, especially conditions such as hyperactivity. As the child is born, the skull becomes squeezed by the birth canal. This squeezing can displace one or some of the skull's plates putting pressure on various nerves throughout the body. Gently manipulating the plates into their correct position can result in some "miraculous" healings and changes of personality. This treatment can be extremely effective for a number of conditions, particularly with children.

CranioSacral Therapy *

The origins of this therapy go back to the 1920s where it was developed by Dr William Sutherland. The cranial work has been described above. However Dr Sutherland's work has been carried on by a number of doctors and osetopaths and in the 1970s, one of these practitioners, Dr Upledger, noticed that when working on the skulls of his patients, he could sense a pulse running the length of the spine. By monitoring the pulse, he was able to find and clear blockages within the spine itself with some remarkable results.

412

The therapy involves the practitioner monitoring and working with the spinal pulse to determine areas where blockages have locked into place. By applying extremely gentle pressure, many of these blocks can be removed. This treatment is one of the most effective we have come across for helping to relieve stresses within the body. It can also help to remove energy blockages, wobbles, etc. within the chakras.

Highly recommended.

Crystal Healing *

The use of crystals for healing purposes has been around for many thousands of years. In some ways, the use of crystals can be very subtle, whilst in others, they can be very powerful and effective. Crystals are naturally occurring minerals which have the capability of holding and focusing energies of particular frequencies. Crystals come in all shapes and sizes and colours, each of which has a particular property and frequency of energy.

If you think of the chakras. Each chakra has an energy frequency and that frequency shows itself as a particular colour. We only see colours because they resonate at a particular frequency of energy. The same is true for crystals. The composition of crystals can be extremely complex and so we are not about to give a full description. However, they work by generating and holding energies within their structure. We can make use of those energies to help us to heal our health problems.

Generally, there are two ways of using crystals. The first is to arrange suitable crystals around the body and sit or lay within their energy field. The second is to carry a particular crystal around with you in a pocket or a handbag. The body's meridians will take up that energy and use it to help heal a particular health problem.

As a note about choosing suitable crystals. There are many places where crystals can be bought. Crystals are naturally occurring minerals and all things naturally occurring have variations. Crystals are also mined so the way in which they are extracted from the ground will have an effect upon the way in which they hold and release energy, so bear this in mind when you choose a crystal. Always buy a crystal in as raw a state as possible, and as close a condition as possible as to how they were when they were taken from the ground. The more they have been polished or shaped, the less they will hold energy. They look very pretty when they have been highly polished but these should be generally avoided. Size is not necessarily an indicator of energy potential. The authors are able to see energies and when they have looked for a crystal, very often the small one at the back which everyone has ignored has the greatest energy. The best way to choose a crystal, silly as it sounds, is to hold it in your hand and mentally "ask" if it is the right one for you, if it answers, buy it, if it doesn't "speak" to you, carry on trying other crystals until one does. People who buy the largest crystals usually have more money than knowledge as they tend to not understand their energies. People who work with crystals tend to buy the ones with the "right" energy, whatever their size.

We were intending to include crystal healing as one of the main treatments used in the second half of this book as it can be extremely effective. However, crystals are naturally occurring and are, therefore, a finite resource. The more people buy crystals in large quantities, the more have to be mined from the earth with consequences for all of us. If you decide to explore the possibilities offered by crystal healing, consult with a crystal healer who will be able to match crystals to your health requirements. If you then decide to buy your own crystals, follow the advice given above and limit the number you buy.

Dowsing *

Most people's experience of dowsing, if they have any at all, is with someone using a hazel rod to find underground water. Whilst it is extremely effective at finding water courses, dowsing can also be used as a means of diagnosing medical problems and potential remedies.

Dowsers come in many guises and it is an art which virtually anyone can learn. For medical purposes, most dowsers use a crystal or a shaped, wooden pendulum suspended on a thread or a chain. There are many schools of thought as to which is the best material to form a pendulum from and what should suspend it, ultimately, these choices are totally individual.

The way in which dowsing works is that the dowser focuses on the pendulum, as they focus they let go of some of the physical constraints on the senses and they begin to access their higher selves. After a number of years of practice, many dowsers find that they do not need any kind of intermediate device, but can access this higher element without any artificial aid.

Dowsing works for many areas of our lives which we would like answers to. It can be very accurate in diagnosing health problems.

Faith Healing **

Faith healing is more usually called healing these days. The origin of the faith label is, largely, misunderstood. It is usually assumed that the patient has to have faith in the effectiveness of the healing in order for the healing to work. This is not the case. The faith is that of the healer in that they can make a difference.

Healing works by the transference of energy from one person, the healer, into the body of another, the patient, in order to correct a health problem. This whole process works because, as explained in the first half of this book, all illnesses are brought

415

about by an imbalance being created within the body's energy structures, namely, the chakras. The energy provided by the healer will help to re-balance the affected chakra, or chakras, and healing takes place.

A recent study carried out by a doctors' surgery in Devon into healing shows how effective it can be. The study was carried out in accordance with all of the requirements of the medical profession. The doctor asked a number of patients on his lists if they would take part in the study. Fifty six agreed and these were divided into two groups. All of these patients had been treated by the doctors for at least six months and they all had conditions which were not responding to orthodox medical treatment. One group of the study patients were to receive only healing and the other group were to continue with their orthodox medicines. The trial ran for two years with each of the healing patients receiving ten healing sessions. At the end of the two years, the twenty eight patients on orthodox medicine reported that they were either no better or were worse than when the trial started. Of the twenty eight patients who received healing, one reported that there was no change in their condition and the other twenty seven claimed that they were cured. Whilst one study of this type is hardly conclusive, there are many thousands of people every year who receive healing and the vast majority report that they have had a major improvement in their condition or they claim to have been cured.

Healing does not work for everyone. In our own psychic surgery healing practice, we do not expect to heal everyone who consults us. However, we do have a success rate of about 95%. By success rate we mean a situation where there has been a minimum of 75% improvement in the client's symptoms. This does not make us miracle workers. We work with the body and the chakras to help our clients understand the root causes of their illness. We heal the symptoms and help our clients to identify and work on the root causes. This is where our success comes from, the identification of the root cause for an illness.

The chakras, as a means of diagnosis, are totally accurate and foolproof.

Healing works and can be effective for virtually all ailments.

In recent years, healing has been given new names in order to divorce it from the term of faith healing and the associations which people have with this term. There are several, but most people will be most familiar with *Therapeutic Touch Therapy*. This is a very much watered down version of healing but still very effective.

Another form of healing is called *Absent Healing*. This is where the healer is at a distance from the patient. This form of healing has been practised for many centuries and is usually practised by prayer. Many religions practise prayer for healing (sometimes called charismatic healing) and it can be very effective.

If you wish to find out more about healing, see *"The Healing Book"* by the authors.

Flotation Therapy

This is a concept developed by Drs John Lilly and Jay Shurley and has been in use for about twenty years. The idea is that you lie in a tank of water (the water is about ten inches, 25cm, deep) which is at body temperature and filled with Epsom and other salts. The tank is covered and you lie in either total or near darkness. The tank is also shielded to cut out outside sounds. As you lie in this world devoid of all sensory distractions, the brain slows down and the muscles totally relax. If you are able to relax in a dark space, this therapy is supposed to totally relax the body and mind which, in health terms, can only do good.

Herbal Remedies **

This is fully described in chapter twelve and appendix four.

Homeopathy **

This is fully described in chapter twelve.

HRT - Alternative Approaches

The dangers and problems associated with chemical treatments for menopause symptoms have been discussed in several sections throughout this book. We cannot stress too highly the serious problems that can arise from this kind of chemical treatment or the surgery that sometimes accompanies it. However, there are a growing number of alternative practitioners who are able to advise on natural treatments for this time in a woman's life. These include herbalists, nutritionists, and a growing number of therapists specialised in treatments for these kinds of problems.

The menopause is not the "disease" that the medical profession and pharmaceutical companies' advertising would like to make us think it is. How many thousands of years were women going through the menopause before we invented drugs? These alternative practitioners can help to put this life change into perspective and advise on natural remedies to help ease the body through this natural and empowering change.

Iridology *

This has been described in chapter thirteen.

Kinesiology **

Although this has been briefly described in chapter thirteen as a diagnostic aid, there is much more to this therapy. Most people know this therapy by the description of the way in which problems are diagnosed, muscle testing. Practitioners believe that the condition of the meridians can be determined by the way in which muscles respond to gentle manipulation. Diagnosis is carried out by "asking" particular muscles what state the body is in. The diagnostic technique is also used, with great accuracy, to determine any food allergies or sensitivities. Kinesiologists can also help with treatment of symptoms by a variety of means. These include very gentle massage of the muscles to stimulate the free flow of lymph fluids, acupressure and dietary advice.

Very effective diagnostic aid and treatment.

Massotherapists *
This is a term that has recently come into usage to describe the group of therapists that provide massage. Forms of massage can range from very gentle stimulating treatment to deep tissue work. Massage is the oldest recorded form of treatment with records going back at least three thousand years and has been used by virtually all cultures for therapeutic purposes. There are a variety of therapies available that range from Aromatherapy to Physiotherapy all of which have particular strengths and uses.

Aromatherapy *
This form of massage uses the healing properties of herbs, flowers and tree essences in a concentrated form. These are the essential oils of a plant. Each essential oil has its own properties and works on the body in very subtle ways. The oils work both by their smell and by the essence being absorbed through the skin into the body's tissues. A huge variety of essential oils are now available each of which can benefit in different ways. Essential oils are not put directly onto the skin as this could cause allergic reactions or mild burning, instead a few drops of the essential oils are added to a carrier oil (such as grape or almond etc.) and the mixed oils are then used to massage the skin.

419

The essential oils are also used in burners or potpourri to fragrance rooms. Two oils in particular are useful to have in the medicine cabinet, these are lavender and tea tree. Both of these are safe enough to use directly onto the skin and are natural antiseptics. A few drops of lavender can be put onto minor burns and insect stings etc. with great effect. Tea tree is a much more powerful antiseptic and can be used very much in the same way as disinfectants are.

Feldenkrais Method

This is a therapy which uses gentle manipulation to retrain muscles to move in more efficient ways helping the posture and muscles in general. Although not strictly a massage type therapy it is included here as a therapy which works with the muscles and involves a certain degree of massage.

Hellerwork

This is a treatment very similar in aims to that of Feldenkrais.

Rolfing

This is a form of deep tissue manipulation developed by Dr Ida Rolf. Dr Rolf believed that body posture gave rise to many health problems. She developed a series of manipulations which she called "structural reintegration".

Meditation **

This is fully described in appendix one.

Naturopathy *

These are therapists who take a totally holistic approach to health problems and treat the person not the illness. Their approach encompasses virtually all therapies but particularly osteopathy (many naturopaths are also qualified osteopaths), dietary advice, etc. etc.. All illnesses and people of all ages can be treated by these therapists. Their basic approach is that illness is caused by an imbalance within the body and that the body wants to heal itself. They recommend treatments to their patients which can help to bring back the body's natural healing processes with, sometimes, quite remarkable results.

We understand that it is very difficult to find a naturopath in America. They have been so successful in treating illness that doctors and drug companies have found ways of preventing them from practising.

Neuro Linguistic Programming (NLP) *

NLP first came about as a teaching process. A person skilled in a particular field was studied and the processes used were recorded in minute detail. Anyone wishing to learn these skills were taken through the recorded process until the new skill was learned. This process was found to be so successful that it began to be used to "unlearn" non-desirable character traits. These include conditions such as phobias, irrational fears, compulsive behaviour, etc.. NLP practitioners work by taking their clients gently through their fears etc. and helping them to gently break the patterns that led them into their problem in the first place. It can be extremely effective.

Nutritionists *

Nutritionists are therapists who will help you to understand the affects which the food you eat has upon your body and your health. During the second half of this book we have tried to point out the benefits of certain foods, nutritionists will go considerably further than this and provide you with specific food groups and dietary supplements which suit your specific dietary needs. Many health symptoms can be treated by a simple change of food. It works, but be prepared to work at it.

Osteopaths

As detailed in chapter three, the skeleton is the basic framework of the body. If our lives put us into periods of high stress or we have an injury, the skeleton and associated muscles can be badly affected. Osteopaths are practitioners who are trained to manipulate the bones and muscles back into their correct positions. Their work involves placing the body into positions where displaced bones can be manipulated back into place and the muscle structures then corrected to ensure that the bones stay there. They will also give you a series of exercises which are specifically designed to strengthen the muscles and give back movement and posture. In our experience the work of an osteopath can be extremely effective at correcting many bone and muscle problems, however, if you have to visit an osteopath to have the same bones corrected on more than three occasions, the manipulations themselves can cause damage by wearing the bones and stretching connecting tissues.

In America, many osteopaths now work as doctors and carry out very little manipulative work. We received a report which shows that American osteopaths have prescribed more drugs than doctors in recent years.

Polarity Therapy

This is a therapy which uses a combination of different approaches to health treatment. It is based upon the concept that the body has an energy flow throughout the meridians and by a combination of acupressure, massage, diet and exercise, the energy flow can be rebalanced and corrected. It was developed by a Dr Randolph Stone who was a chiropractor, naturopath and osteopath. He also studied acupuncture, ayurvedic medicine and yoga. So, it is a combination of a number of approaches and doctrines which sounds as though it should be effective for a number of symptoms, but we have no direct experience of the treatments.

Reflexology **
This is fully described in chapter twelve.

In addition to reflexology, there is a new therapy which incorporates many of the principles of reflexology. This is called Metamorphic Technique and was developed by a British naturopath, Robert St John, in the 1960s. Basically, the technique involves using the reflex points on the feet and acupuncture points on the spine and head to remove blockages that are of a more long term or mental type. In other words, breaking patterns of illness or behaviour which can go back as far as childhood. It is intended to be a way of unlocking patterns and to help the patient begin building new ones. It sounds promising, but we have no direct experience of the therapy.

T'ai-chi Ch'uan
This is an exercise developed in China which is designed to balance the body's energy flow through the meridians. The exercise is a series of movements that flow one to another in a sequence which will help to clear the mind and relax and energise the body. There are two forms: the long form and the short form. The short form has about forty movements without repetitions and takes between ten and fifteen minutes to complete. Many experts consider the short form to be not as beneficial as the long form as it does not complete the full cycle of movements for full body harmony. The long form involves more than one hundred movements, some of which are repeated and takes up to forty minutes to complete. The movements are very elegant and measured and represent the cycles of life. By slowly moving through these cycles, the body reaches harmony, balance and relaxation. To practice t'ai-chi ch'uan, you will need to find an experienced teacher as it is not possible to teach yourself. The movements involved require the spine, pelvis, etc. being in correct alignments and you will need someone to help correct any mistakes you might make. We have not experienced the exercises for ourselves but have watched people practising

and there can be an extremely good flow of energy through the body.

Yoga

Yoga is another Sanskrit word adopted by India. The word means "union", in this case, union of the mind and body. In India, yoga is a form of religion which brings together a number of aspects of the body, mind and spirit. These are Raja (control of the mind), Jnana (intellect and understanding), Karma (moral action), Bakti (the devotional aspect) and Hatha (physical movement). In the west, it is mainly the Hatha element which is taught.

Hatha yoga is a series of exercises which gently stretch and exercise the body to improve posture and to relax the body and mind. It can also help with injuries by freeing muscle movement. Although yoga can be practised by virtually anyone, you will need to find a good teacher to ensure that you do not overstrain yourself. People who regularly practice yoga report that they feel relaxed, supple and mentally alert.

Conclusion

This has been a brief list of some of the many alternative therapies which are available. All of these therapies have benefits, some more so than others. Many have been studied and their effectiveness measured. As more and more people turn away from orthodox, allopathic, medicine and towards an alternative, holistic, approach, the more the medical profession becomes threatened. This is resulting in an increase in the legislation governing alternative therapies. Whilst tighter controls of those who work with other people can only be a good thing, the motives behind much of this legislation is a little worrying. As alternative therapists do not prescribe any drugs, most therapists are actually against any kind of drug treatment, so the drug companies are adding their considerable resources to campaigns that attempt to discredit or prevent alternative therapists from working.

If you decide to explore a more alternative approach to your health problems, we have included a list of some of the governing bodies and professional associations in Britain and other countries.

However, the best way of finding an alternative practitioner of your chosen therapy is by personal recommendation from friends, family or colleagues. Many local libraries carry lists or advertisements for local therapists. Most health food stores and restaurants also carry advertisements for practitioners and therapists in your local area.

Alternative therapies have been in existence for many thousands of years and are the roots from which modern western medicine grew. As the western drug culture increasingly fails to find answers for modern health problems, the alternative approach is having increasing success. Somewhere or other, there must be a balance, a patch of common ground, where doctors and alternative practitioners can work together.

This is our wish.

We also wish you success in your search for the answers to your health problems and your journey back to your soul.

Chris Thomas and Diane Baker.
March 1999.

Appendix Seven
Useful Addresses

Acupuncture
British Medical Acupuncture Society
Newton House, Newton Lane, Lower Whitley, Warrington,
Cheshire WA4 4IA.

American Academy of Medical Acupuncture
5820 Wiltshire Boulevard, Suite 500, Los Angeles, California
9003

Acupuncture Research Institute
Spring Valley Health Center, 3880 S. Jones Boulevard, Suite
214, Las Vegas, Nevada 89103.

Acupuncture College of Australia
520 Harris Street, Ultimo, Sydney, New South Wales.

Brisbane College of Traditional Acupuncture
2nd Floor, Century House, 316 Adelaide Street, Brisbane 3000,
Queensland.

Northern American Academy for Acupuncture Research
Box 28, Wheatly, Ontario, NOP 2PO.

Acupressure
Shen Tao Foundation
Middle Piccadilly Natural Health Centre, Holwell, Sherborne,
Dorset DT9 5LW.

Shiatsu Society
19 Langside Park, Kilbarchan, Strathclyde PA10 2EP.

The American Foundation of Traditional Chinese Medicine
505 Beach Street, San Francisco, California 94133.

Alexander Technique
Society of Teachers of Alexander Technique
10 London House, 266 Fulham Road, London SW10 9EL.

Autogenic Training
Positive Health Centre, 101 Harley Street, London W1N 1DF.

Ayurvedic Medicine
The Association of Ayurvedic Practitioners
7 Ravenscroft Avenue, London NW11 0SA.

Bach Flower Remedies
The Dr Edward Bach Centre
Mount Vernon, Sotwell, Wallingford, Oxfordshire OX10 0PZ.

Ellon (Bach USA) Inc
PO Box 320, Woodmere, New York, New York 11598.

Flower Essence Society
PO Box 1769, Nevada City, California 95959.

Martin and Pleasance Wholesale Pty Ltd
PO Box 4, Collingwood, Victoria 3066, Australia.

Nonesuch Botanicals Pty Ltd
PO Box 68, Mount Evelyn, Victoria 3796, Australia.

Holland Pharma
Postbus 37, 7240 AA Lochen, Holland.

Camette
Murervej 16, 6700 Esbjerg, Denmark.

Mechthild Scheffer HP, Bach Centre - German Office,
Eppendorfer Landstrasse 32, 2000 Hamburg 20, Germany.

Other Flower Essences and Tree Essences
Silvercord Essences
Turnpike Cottage, Chawleigh, Chulmleigh, Devon EX18 7EU.

Green Man
2 Kerswell Cottages, Exminster, Exeter, Devon EX6 8AY.

Circle of Light
70 Alexandra Road, Ashingdon, Essex SS9 1AD

Aquarius
Threpwood Hill Cottage, Birtley, Hexham, Northumberland
NE8 3HL.

Bates Method
Bates Association of Great Britain
PO Box 25, Shoreham by Sea, BN34 6ZF.

Biofeedback
The Institute for Comparative Medicine
21 Portland Street, London W1N 3AF.

Biofeedback Certification Institute of America
10200 West 44th Avenue, Suite 304, Wheat Ridge, Colorado
80033.

Cognitive Therapy
British Psychological Society
St Andrews House, 48 Princess Road East, Leicester LE1 7DR.

Counselling
The British Association for Counselling
37a Sheep Street, Rugby, Warwickshire CV21 3BX.

Gestalt Centre London
64 Warwick Road, St Albans, Hertfordshire AL1 4DL.

British Society for Medical and Dental Hypnotherapy
151 Oteley Road, Leeds LS16 6HN.

American Society of Clinical Hypnotherapists
2250 East Devon Avenue, Suite 336, Des Plaines, Illinois
60018.

Milton H Erikson Society for Psychotherapy and Hypnotherapy
PO Box 1390, Madison Square Station, New York, New York
10159.

Cranial Osteopathy
The Cranial Osteopath Association
478 Baker Street, Enfield, Middlesex EN1 3QS.

Cranial Academy
8606 Allinsonville Road, Suite 130, Indianapolis, Indiana
46250.

CranioSacral Therapy
The Upledger Institute UK
52 Main Street, Perth PH2 7HB.

The Upledger Institute
11211 Prosperity Farms Road, Palm Beach Gardens, Florida
33410.

Crystal Healing
The Affiliation of Crystal Healing Organisations
PO Box 344, Manchester M60 2EZ.

International College of Mineral Therapy
State Bank Building, 2nd Floor, 60 Young Street, Victoria,
Australia.

Dowsing
British Society of Dowsers
Sycamore Cottage, Tamley Lane, Hastingleigh, Ashford,
Kent TN26 5HW.

Healing
The World Federation of Healing
8 Earl Road, Penarth, West Glamorgan CF64 3UN.

2 Little Tribe Street, South Melbourne, Victoria 3205,
Australia.

Lerchengrasse 15/5, 1080 Vienna, Austria.

Town House, 64-331 Military Trail, West Hill, Scarborough,
Ontario, M1E 4E3, Canada.

Hermann-Roth-Str. 12D, 82065 Baiersbrunn, Germany.

Agios Lavrentios, Pillion 38500 Volos, Hellas, Greece.

PO Box 3444, Petach Tikva, Kfar Sirkin, Tel Aviv 61033, Israel.

1-26-13 Kamakurayama, Kamakura City 248, Japan.

PO Box 2152, Pietermaritzberg, 3200 Natal, New Zealand.

Myrgatany 7, SE 36073, Lenhovda, Sweden.

Bruckenstr, 6, 3005, Bern, Switzerland.

PO Box 377, Princeton, New Jersey-08542, USA.

National Federation of Spiritual Healers
Old Manor Farm Studio, Church Street, Sunbury-on-Thames,
Middlesex TW16 6RG.

Confederation of Healing Organisations
Suite J, Second Floor, The Red and White House, 113 High
Street, Berkhampstead, Hertfordshire HP4 2DJ.

Herbalists
Herbs, Hands, Healing
The Cabins, Station Warehouse, Station Road, Pulham Market,
Norfolk IP21 4XF.

National Institute of Medical Herbalists
56 Longbrook Street, Exeter, Devon.

International Register of Consultant Herbalists and
Homeopaths
32 King Edward Road, Swansea SA1 4LL

American Herbalist Guild
PO Box 746555, Avada, CO 80006-6555.

Herb Research Foundation
1007 Pearl Street, Suite 200, Boulder, CO 80302.

North Eastern Herbal Association
PO Box 146, Marshall, VT 05658

Herbal Suppliers

Organicly produced herbs, tinctures and preparations can be supplied by:
Hambleden Herbs, Court Farm, Milverton, Somerset TA4 1NF.
tel: (01803) 401104.

Herbs, Hands, Healing., The Cabins, Station Warehouse, Station Road, Pulham Market, Norfolk IP21 4XF.
tel/fax: (01379) 608201.

Homeopaths

Society of Homeopaths
2 Artisan Road, Northampton NN1 4HU

UK Homeopathic Medical Association
Administration Office, 6 Livingstone Road, Gravesend, Kent DA12 5DZ.

National Center for Homeopathy
801 North Fairfax Street, Suite 306, Alexandria, VA 22314.

Pan American Homeopathic Medical Congress
Francisco del Paso y Troncoso Edifico 166, EntradaD Unidad Kennedy, Mexico 9, DF.

HRT - Alternative Advice Sources

Annie Gedye, the HRT advisor for this book, tel: UK (01752) 337859
E mail: annie@anahata.free-online

Light Unlimited Productions, Locked Bag 8000 - MDC, Kew, Victoria 3101, Australia. (run by Sherrill Sellman).
tel: +61 (0)3 9249 9591
E mail: golight@ozemail.com.au

Natural Hormone Health Counselling and Referral Service
Australia tel: 1902 211 191

The Menopause Helpline
0181 938 3777

Women's Nutritional Advisory Service
(01273) 487366

Natural Progesterone Information Service
PO Box 24, Buxton SK17 9FB

Serenity
Rieds Pharmacy, St Helier, Jersey, Channel Islands

Iridology

Guild of Naturopathic Iridologists
94 Grosvenor Road, London SW1V 3LF

British School of Iridologists
PO Box 205, Cambridge CB3 7YF

Kinesiology

The Kinesiology Federation
PO Box 83, Sheffield S7 2YN

Association of Systematic Kinesiologists
39 Browns Road, Surbiton, Surrey KT3 8ST.

Massotherapists
American Massage Therapy Association
820 Davis Street, Suite 100, Evanstown, IL 60201-4444.

Aromatherapy
International Society of Professional Aromatherapists
ISPA House, 82 Ashby Road, Hinckley, Leicestershire LE10 1SN.

The Register of Qualified Aromatherapists
PO Box 3431, Danbury, Chelmsford, Essex CM3 4HA.

International Federation of Aromatherapists
4 Eastman Road, West Dulwich, London SE21 8HA.

National Association for Holistic Aromatherapy
PO Box 17622, Boulder, CO 80308-7622.

Feldenkrais
The Feldenkrais Guild Uk
188 Old Street, London EC1V 9BP.

The Feldenkrais Guild
PO Box 489, Albany, Oregon 97321.

Hellerwork
Roger Golten, The Peak, Hyatt Carlton Tower, Cadogan Place, London SW1 9PY.

Rolfing
The Institute of Structural Bodywork
The Peak, Hyatt Carlton Tower, Cadogan Place, London SW1 9PY.

434

Rolf Institute
205 Canyon Boulevard, Boulder, CO 80302.

Naturopathy
General Council and Register of Naturopaths
Frazer House, 6 Netherall Gardens, London NW3 5RR.

American Association of Naturopathic Physicians
2366 Eastlake Avenue East, Suite 322, Seattle, Washington
98102.

Neuro Linguistic Programming (NLP)
The Proudfoot School of Hypnosis.
Eastfield Business Park, "Blinking Sike", Scarborough, North
Yorkshire YO11 3YT. tel: (01723) 585960.

McKenna Brean Ltd.
Aberdeen Studios, 22-24 Highbury Grove, London N5 2EA.
tel: 0171 704 6604.

Nutritionists
Society for the Promotion of Nutritional Therapy
PO Box 47, Heathfield, East Sussex TN21 8ZX.

The Institute for Optimum Nutrition
Blades Court, Deodar Road, London SW15 2NU.

Osteopaths
Natural Therapeutic Osteopathic Society and Register
14 Marford Road, Wheathampstead, Hertfordshire AL4 8AS.

The General Council and Register of Osteopaths
56 London Street, Reading, Berkshire RG1 4SQ.

American Academy of Osteopathy
3500 DePaul Boulevard, Suite 1080, Indianapolis, IN 46268-1136.

Polarity
The Federation of Polarity Training
7 Nunnery Close, Cheltenham, Gloucestershire GL51 0TU.

The International School of Polarity Therapy
12-14 Dowell Street, Honiton, Devon EX14 8LT.

Reflexology
British Reflexology Association
Monks Orchard, Whitbourne, Worcester WR6 5RB.

Reflexologists Society
28 Holnfield Avenue, Leicester LE2 2BF.

T ai-chi Ch uan
The School of T'ai-chi Ch'uan
5 Tavistock Place, London WC1H 9SS.

Yoga
Yoga Biomedical Trust
PO Box 140, Cambridge CB4 3SY.

This is a list of all of the associations etc. that we could find. These are addresses and telephone numbers that existed at the time we put this book together. Addresses change, so it is best to check for yourself.

If you wish to find a local therapist, many libraries, health food shops, health food and vegetarian restaurants etc. carry advertisements for many alternative therapists. There are also a range of magazines which carry articles and advertisements for alternative therapists. These include: Kindred Spirit, Caduceus, Here's Health etc.. There are also an increasing number of articles appearing in daily newspapers and magazines.

Organic Produce

There are a growing number of producers of organic produce in most countries, many of whom are quite small in their scale of production. To find out the ones nearest to you, you can contact the following organisations who can supply you with a list of local growers and suppliers.

In Britain
The Soil Association
Bristol House, 40-56 Victoria Street, Bristol BS1 6BY.
tel: 0117 929 0061

There is also The Organic Directory,
Published by Green Books, Foxhole, Dartington, Totnes,
Devon TQ9 6EB.

In Europe
International Federation of Organic Agricultural Movements
(IFOAM)
Based in Theley in Germany telephone (0049) 685 35190.

In America
Eden Acres Inc.
12100 Lima Center Road, Clinton, Michigan 49236.
tel: 517 456-4288.

Details of Grapefruit seed extract from:

Higher Nature
Burwash Common
East Sussex
TN19 7LX

Appendix Eight

Suggested Reading

There are literally hundreds of books, magazines, websites etc. which can provide information about therapies, health, diet, drug companies, medical reports etc., many of which we have read for the research for the second half of this book. There is so much information which we have not been able to include due to lack of space. Also, the main message that we are trying to promote with this book is that all illnesses originate within and is within the power of everybody to heal themselves without recourse to drugs or surgery and so we did not want to become embroiled in too much discussion over other issues. The information provided in chapter twenty one is only the tip of the iceberg as far as our research is concerned. We are providing only a short list of books etc. to try to give you some idea of where to begin to look. These are books and publications which we have found useful in our research.

What Doctors Don't Tell You
by Lynne McTaggart.
Published by Thorsens
ISBN 0 7225 3024 2
Lynne McTaggart edits a monthly newsletter of the same name, which includes reports on new drugs, medical treatments, etc.. This book is a compilation of reports over several years. Even we didn't think the medical profession was this bad! - it gets worse the more you read.
Knowledge is power. Even if you choose to stay with western medicine, this book will give you an insight into the best questions to ask and just how much good a treatment can do for you.

For further information consult their website: www.wddty.co.uk
For subscription details for the monthly newsletter call 0800
146054

Genetic Engineering
by Dr Mae-Wan Ho
Published by Gateway Books
ISBN 1 85860 051 0
Dr Ho is a biologist and an expert in genetic engineering
techniques and is the GM advisor to the Third World Network.
Working within the field, she is able to explain the horrors of
what is going on from the inside. The book is a little dry in
places as it includes a great deal of necessary technical detail,
but stay with it as it will change the way you view your food
and how it is produced. A chilling read!

Hormone Heresy: What Women MUST Know About Their
Hormones
by Sherrill Sellman
Published by GetWell International
ISBN 0-9587252-0-9
Ms Sellman is an authority on alternative treatments for
hormone therapies for women. She lives and practices in
Victoria in Australia.
This book is full of information and research on hormones and
what not to take. It also contains a great deal of help and
advice on alternative approaches. A book that is an absolute
must for all women (and men) to understand their bodies and
the role that artificial hormones have played in so many health
problems.

Bach Flower Therapy: The Complete Approach
Mechthild Scheffer
Published by Thorsens
ISBN 0 7225 1121 3
This book explores all avenues of The Bach Flower Remedies
and is an invaluable guide to their uses and applications.
Highly recommended.

440

Magazines which carry articles on health issues, alternative therapies, medical exposes etc. include the following, all of which have been useful in our research. They are all available from newsagents.

Caduceus
Caduceus is a journal exploring transformation and healing for person, community and planet. It draws on leading international thinkers and activists, and those initiating locally, to address the convergence of issues "at the edge" such as healing, genetic engineering, dying, birth, anger, love, new feminine and new masculine, emerging spiritual paths, new energy, and new consciousness.
Subscription details: Caduceus, 38 Russell Terrace, Leamington Spa, Warwickshire CV31 1HE. tel: 01926 451897. fax: 01926 885565.
email caduceus@oryx.demon.co.uk

Kindred Spirit.
Subscription details: Kindred Spirit, Foxhole, Dartington, Totnes, Devon TQ9 6EB. fax: 01803 866591.

Nexus
Nexus magazine covers health alternatives, suppressed science, Earth's hidden history, conspiracies, UFO's and the unexplained. It is a link to the work and research of individuals who are pushing at the frontiers of knowledge.
Subscription details: Nexus Magazine, 55 Queens Road, East Grinstead, West Sussex RH19 1BG. tel: (01342) 322854. fax: (01342) 324574.

Here's Health.
Subscription details: Here's Health, Tower Publishing Services, Tower House, Sovereign Park, Lathkill Street, Market Harborough, Leicestershire LE16 9EF. tel: 01853 435339.

Other books we used as reference sources:

Prescription for Nutritional Healing
by James F Balch, MD and Phyllis A Balch, CNC

The Royal Horticultural Society of Herbs and Their Uses
Deni Brown
Published by Dorling Kindersley

There is also a growing volume of information on the Internet. As the net is not regulated, the truth is usually told but watch out for vested interests such as web sites from drug companies.

Menopause News - San Francisco
email: mnews@well.com

Mineral and health information - Dr Joel Wallach
http: //www.american-nutrition.com/

Aspartame
http: //www.livelinks.com/sumeria/npoi1.html
Natural medical products, articles etc.

Other books by the authors, all published by Capall Bann
The Journey Home
by Chris Thomas
ISBN 186163041 - 7
This book looks at the recent changes in global energy patterns and the underlying reasons for many of our problems and the world situation.

The Healing Book
by Chris Thomas and Diane Baker
ISBN 186163053 - 0
The authors are working non-intrusive psychic surgeons who teach healing to beginners and established healers. This book is their teaching course for beginners who wish to learn to heal others or animals. The second half of the book details more

advanced methods of energy manipulation for existing healers. The book also includes an explanation of how the healing energies work and where the energy comes from.

The Fool's First Steps:- The True Nature of Reality
by Chris Thomas
published by Capall Bann
ISBN 186163 072 7
This book looks at the real history of humanity from Atlantis to the present and describes the process of human change and development. It also contains a glimpse into the near future for the planet and all of its life.

Planet Earth - The Universe's Experiment
Chris Thomas
ISBN 186163 224X
As we approach the completion of our climb back to reality, we are awakening the ghosts of this knowledge. Lemuria, Atlantis, the thirteen races have all played their part in "The Human Plan", all are now working to assist us to our chosen goal - full consciousness. But, time is short and unless we complete our journey soon, the Earth will be lost to us. Virtually all our experience and history is at odds with the archaeological and scientific versions of our past, only the Akashic tells the real history. What is told here is the Akashic's story.

In addition to their healer teaching classes, Chris and Di also give talks and workshops on the planet's changing energies and the Earth's "mysteries" together with the role we have all played in shaping the new human consciousness.

The authors can be contacted at:
PO Box 49
Llandysul
SA44 4YU
Wales

or Email us at Chrisanddi@psychicsurgery.freeserve.co.uk

Questionaire

1. How long ago did the problem start?

2. How old were you?

3 List all of your symptoms. List everything that you are having a problem with, no matter how trivial it may seem. List any medical diagnosis or diagnosis from any other source.

4. If this has been a long term problem, please list your full medical history, including details of any treatment you have received.

5. Include your full name and address.

6. Include your payment of £20 (twenty pounds) in sterling. Cheques or money orders etc should be made payable to Diane Baker.

7. Post to the PO Box address given above. We will reply as quickly as possible, but please allow 28 days.

8. If you are intending to use this questionaire, maybe you need to go back and reread the relevant sections (or the whole book!) and save yourself £20! But, if you are really stuck, we will be more than happy to help.

We are legally not allowed to express an opinion on any medical diagnosis you may have already obtained nor speculate upon your health condition if you have not sought a medical diagnosis. We wish to stress that the answer we will forward back to you is an opinion based upon a chakra root cause and should not be seen as a substitute for a medical diagnosis. What we will endeavour to give is guidance upon the root cause issue which brought about your chakra imbalance in the first place and make suggestions (homework) on methods of approach on how to deal with correcting that imbalance.

An Update On Our Changing World

We are currently in the middle of a massive change of consciousness. A change so immense that it is difficult to describe with any degree of accuracy or describe our full state at the end of this change. Many have called it 'Ascension' but that is to imply that we are 'ascending' to somewhere else. What we are actually achieving is the reintegration of the total soul into the physical body. Therefore, we are not 'ascending' out of the body but 'ascending' to greater heights within the body.

This change is well under way and the most visible signs of the changes taking place within peoples' bodies are the colours of the chakras become totally different. Ultimately, the chakras all become a transparent energy. That is, spinning vortices of pure energy at such a high frequency that they move beyond colour. It is easier to understand what we mean by transparent if you can imagine a warm summers day when the sun is shining and as the heat rises back from the ground, the air seems to 'shimmer'. This is what the chakras now look like for many people, transparent, shimmering, sparkling, pure energy. Where we have suggested using a meditation in this book, we would suggest that you use the meditation that follows instead. This new meditation energises the chakras up to their maximum and will work for whatever level of change is occurring within your own chakras. The meditation will also work for the final stages of this change which some are already beginning to achieve.

The final stages are when the whole of the spine becomes one energy. In other words, the separate points of the chakras merge into the energies flowing within the spine. The energies then become a graduated 'column' of energy with the lowest frequencies where the first chakra was with the highest where the crown chakra was. Once this stage is reached, the only stage left is the final one where the rest of the consciousness, the rest of the soul, the 'Higher Self' is fully absorbed into the body.

This final merging of the soul will take place very soon. The final date for this integration to occur has been brought forwards, for many reasons, from the end of 2011 to the end of 2005.

Many are already poised to make this final change and many more will soon be joining them. The first small number of people to undergo the final stages, and are now complete, did so on the 2nd of June 2003. Nobody is excluded from this integration process, all it takes is the will so to do.

So good luck and with our best wishes.

Chris Thomas and Diane Baker
January 2004

446

Chakra Meditation For the New Colours of Life

Close your eyes and begin to relax. Relax your shoulders and your back, feel the tensions draining out and all of the muscels relaxing The idea of this meditation is to fully energise and balance all of the chakras. By working in the way described in this meditation, there is no need to "shut down " afterwards as your energy fields will be virtually impenetrable to outside influences. Remember that the chakras take the form of a vortex. This is a little like an ice cream cone with the point attached to the spine with the "bell" of the cone opening outwards, away from the body.

Start by using your usual method of reaching a state of relaxation. Once you have relaxed and are in a meditative state, begin to form a point of concentration about one foot (30cm) above the top of your head.

Once you feel your concentration has formed a small ball, bring this point of concentration all of the way down the spine to the first (root) chakra. When you have reached the very bottom of your coccyx, form the cone pointing directly downwards with the point attached to the bottom of the coccyx. The colour is a transparent 'heat haze' shimmer, just pure energy. Try to imagine as clear a shimmer as possible and spinning very fast. When you have achieved this, move the point of concentration up to the second chakra.

The second (sacral) chakra is located just where the spine meets the pelvis. The point of the vortex is attached to the spine with the 'cones' opening equally front and back. The vortex is transparent. Imagine as clear a shimmer as possible and spinning very fast. When you have achieved this, move up to the third chakra.

The third (solar plexus) chakra is located about one inch (2.5cm) above the tummy button and the point of the vortex is attached to the spine with the 'cones' opening outwards equally front and back. This is also a transparent shimmer. Imagine as clear a shimmer as possible and spinning very fast. When you have achieved this, move on to the fourth chakra.

The fourth (heart) chakra is located at the heart with the point of the vortex attached to the spine and the 'cones' opening equally front and back. The vortex has no colour, just a heat haze shimmer. Imagine as clear a shimmer as possible and spin it very fast. When you have achieved this, move on to the fifth chakra.

The fifth (throat) chakra is located mid way between the adams apple and the chin. This is also a transparent heat haze shimmer. When you have a fast spin and total transparency, move on to the sixth chakra.

The sixth (third eye) chakra is located on a line with the spine just above the bridge of the nose. The cones of the vortices open equally front and back and the colour is the same transparent heat haze shimmer as all of the other chakras. When finished, move on to the seventh chakra.

The seventh (crown) chakra is located on the top of the head on a line˘ with the spine. The point of the vortex is on the top of the he˘ad with the cone opening directly upwards. This chakra is also a heat haze shimmer. When you have made this spin very fast, bring this clear, pure energy down to the sixth chakra, adding the crown energy into the vortices. Do this for each chakra in turn all of the way down the spine to the first chakra. Once you have added the shimmer of the seventh to the first chakra, all of the chakras will be fully balanced and energised.

Finally, move your point of concentration back to above the top of the head and slowly bring yourself back to the present.

Index

286, 295-296, 317, 319-321,
329-330, 334, 354-355, 358,
367-370, 372-373, 375-381,
385-387, 391-393, 395-400,
402-403, 407, 410
blood pressure, 53-54, 264-
268, 329-330, 369, 375-379,
381, 407, 410
blood sugar, 55, 94, 255, 295-
296, 376, 399
bone, 10, 20-21, 35, 38, 43-49,
53, 65-66, 103-104, 107,
113-114, 130, 134, 144, 165,
167, 204, 206, 213-217, 239-
240, 319, 321, 355, 396,
398, 400, 402, 422
bone marrow, 53, 104, 107,
113-114, 396
bowel, 41, 99-101, 133, 235,
259-261, 293-294, 376, 384-
385, 407
brain, 25, 41-42, 73, 93, 104,
109, 130, 134, 137-140, 142-
143, 147, 152-154, 156-157,
191, 193, 280, 282, 296-297,
317, 319, 328-329, 386, 394-
397, 417
bronchial channels, 23, 124-
125
BSE, 311
bulbourethral gland, 65
buttocks, 20

calcium, 43-46, 130, 212-216,
222, 228-229, 232, 239-241,
244, 256, 270, 300, 312,
319, 354-355, 366, 376, 385,
388, 390, 397-401
cancer, 51, 70, 79-80, 96-98,

120-123, 132, 158, 160-161,
174-175, 251, 270, 298-299,
313, 317-318, 321-322, 325,
334, 375-376, 386, 394, 397
cartilage, 10, 35, 46, 127, 204,
216, 220, 397
cells, 3, 12, 43, 51, 53, 61-62,
64, 74, 84, 90-95, 99, 104-
105, 107, 111, 113-115, 120-
121, 125, 127, 129-130, 139,
141, 144, 153-154, 156, 159-
161, 219, 240, 247, 268,
283, 302, 314, 316-317, 334,
352-353, 355, 357, 359-360,
382, 394-398, 400-404
cellulite, 91
central nervous system, 25,
30, 41, 137-140, 280, 285,
311, 396, 408
cervix, 21, 60-61, 69, 71
chemotherapy, 160, 313, 375
childbirth, 35, 38, 40, 385
chocolate, 55, 228, 292, 296
cholesterol, 109, 267, 318, 320-
323, 376
cirrhosis, 84, 249
clitoris, 61
coccyx, 14, 20, 191, 193, 354
colon, 99-100, 191, 193, 218,
222, 256, 260, 277, 294,
369, 376, 392, 405
conception, 11, 29, 406
constipation, 22, 100, 227,
232, 249, 259-261, 293-294,
356, 359-360, 372, 375
contraceptive, 51, 235
craniosacral, 38, 256, 412, 429
Crohn's disease, 100
crone, 72-73

A selection of titles From Capall Bann - Full Catalogue available

The Healing Book   by Chris Thomas & Diane Baker

This book is for those who wish to heal, starting at the beginning of the healing process with simple, easily followed exercises which can begin to unlock the healing potential which is inherent in all of us. Nobody needs to feel left out of these abilities. We are all healers, all that we need to do is to stop telling ourselves that we are not. Whatever level of experience you have of healing, this book explains in simple uncomplicated language that does not use mysticism or any form of ritual, how to understand the "Chakras" and the way in which our daily lives influence them, to relate medical conditions to the chakras and to learn methods which will bring the chakras back into balance, both for yourself and for others. These methods apply equally to humans and to animals. If you do not have any experience of giving healing, but would like to learn, this book can set you on that path. If you already work as a healer, in whatever capacity, and would like to explore your greater potential, this book is also for you. The authors have a combined experience of over twenty five years of providing healing and have taught very many people to unlock their own healing potential. This book is not only about learning to heal from the beginning, but also explores some of the energy manipulation techniques used by the authors in their daily practise as "Psychic Surgeons".   ISBN 186163 053 0   £8.95

The Fool's First Steps   by Chris Thomas

Are you asking Questions? Transforming? Wanting to know the purpose of it all? Do the old answers no longer work?   The true purposes of Avebury and Stonehenge and the knowledge contained there, stellar gateways, the origins of crop circles, changing Earth energies, the true nature of angels... Personal transformations happening now on a grand scale, mental, emotional and physical and realising the spiritual origins of the human race... If this book were a novel it would make fascinating reading, but as the explanations again and again strike a true chord, it makes compulsive and unforgettable reading which will help you change how you view life.   ISBN 186163 072 7   £9.95

The Journey Home   by Chris Thomas

Who are we? Why are we here? Are we alone? What relationship does Earth and its multitude of lifeforms have to themselves and to the universe. The answers to many of these questions have long been available, but over the centuries they have become hidden by personal interests and clouded by repetition and dogma. As we undergo a vast shift in consciousness, the underlying reasons for our existence have to be rediscovered and put into their proper perspective. This book brings these issues into a sharper focus and sheds light into some of the darker corners. Gone are the dark days of Karmic re-cycling and suffering; we have reached the time of the birth of a new human existence so far removed from human experience that most have not yet recognised its coming.   ISBN 186163 041 7   £7.95

The Sequel to Everything - The Case Histories by Chris Thomas and Diane Baker

The authors had many requests for a collection of real case histories to help people understand how the symptoms can be read and how to make more sense of the body and soul's messages. All that is required is an alteration in focus and understanding of the workings of the body and the way in which the soul, the unconscious and the body are inextricably linked together. The book describes the ways in which the symptoms of an illness can be tracked back to its root cause and the "homework" given to help deal with these root cause issues. Illness is not a punishment of any kind, from any source, nor is it a 'test', or an obstacle to be struggled against. Illness is a message from our own soul trying to tell us that we have taken a step in the wrong direction. All that we need to do to heal any illness is to relearn how to read the body's messages and take some simple corrective actions. It is this simple.   ISBN186163 1375   £11.95

FREE DETAILED CATALOGUE

Capall Bann is owned and run by people actively involved in many of the areas in which we publish. A detailed illustrated catalogue is available on request, SAE or International Postal Coupon appreciated. **Titles can be ordered direct from Capall Bann, post free in the UK** (cheque or PO with order) or from good bookshops and specialist outlets.

Contact us for details on the latest releases. Over 300 titles include:

Crystal Clear - A Guide to Quartz Crystal, Jennifer Dent
Crystal Doorways, Simon & Sue Lilly
Face of the Deep - Healing Body & Soul, Penny Allen
Fool's First Steps, (The) Chris Thomas
From Past to Future Life, Dr Roger Webber
Gardening For Wildlife Ron Wilson
Healing Homes, Jennifer Dent
Healing Journeys, Paul Williamson
Healing Stones, Sue Philips
Herb Craft - Shamanic & Ritual Use of Herbs, Lavender & Franklin
Intuitive Journey, Ann Walker
Journey Home, The, Chris Thomas
Magic of Herbs - A Complete Home Herbal, Rhiannon Ryall
Magical Guardians - Exploring the Spirit and Nature of Trees, Philip Heselton
Medicine For The Coming Age, Lisa Sand MD
Medium Rare - Reminiscences of a Clairvoyant, Muriel Renard
Mind Massage - 60 Creative Visualisations, Marlene Maundrill
Personal Power, Anna Franklin
Practical Meditation, Steve Hounsome
Reality - How It Works & Why It Mostly Doesn't, Rik Dent
Romany Tapestry, Michael Houghton
Vortex - The End of History, Mary Russell
Wondrous Land - The Faery Faith of Ireland by Dr Kay Mullin
Menopausal Woman on the Run, Jaki da Costa

FREE detailed catalogue and FREE 'Inspiration' magazine